ASPECTS OF ORKNEY 4

THE PEOPLE OF ORKNEY

This series has been developed in order to provide detailed and thorough texts on a range of aspects of the life, history and environment of the Orkney Islands. Each book is designed to make specialist knowledge available to the general reader.

Editor —Howie Firth
Consultant Editor —William P. L. Thomson

1. Kelp-making in Orkney   William P. L. Thomson

2. The Birds of Orkney   Chris Booth, Mildred Cuthbert and
                                                  Peter Reynolds

3. This Great Harbour — Scapa Flow   W. S. Hewison

4. The People of Orkney   R. J. Berry and H. N. Firth (eds.)

Subjects to be covered in forthcoming volumes will include the history of aviation in Orkney, old Orkney industries, and old Orkney songs. Up-to-date details are available from the publishers.

Series design — Bryce Wilson

ASPECTS OF ORKNEY 4

THE PEOPLE OF ORKNEY

edited by

R. J. BERRY and H. N. FIRTH

1986
THE ORKNEY PRESS

Published by The Orkney Press Ltd., 12 Craigiefield Park, St Ola, Kirkwall,
Orkney

ISBN 0 907618 08 1

Printed by The Kirkwall Press, "The Orcadian" Office, Victoria Street, Kirkwall,
Orkney
Bound by James Gowans Ltd., Glasgow

The publishers wish to thank Orkney Islands Council and the Highlands and
Islands Development Board for financial assistance towards the publication of
this volume, and the Publication Fund of Aberdeen University's Extra-Mural
Department for provision of a loan

Contents

Foreword

1 The People of Orkney   *R. J. Berry*   7

2 From the First Inhabitants to the Viking Settlement
                                 John W. Hedges   19

3 Biological Characteristics
          Don Brothwell, Don Tills and Veronica Muir   54

4 Genetic Affinities   *Derek F. Roberts*   89

5 Relationships of the Orcadians: the View from
   Faroe   *Robin Harvey, Diana Suter and Don Tills*   107

6 Length of Life in Orkney   *Evelyn J. Bowers*   118

7 Traditions and Customs   *Howie Firth*   137

8 Pre-Viking Contacts between Orkney and Scandinavia
                                    Peter Foote   175

9 Scandinavian and Celtic Contacts in the Earldom of
   Orkney   *Bo Almqvist*   187

10 Pict, Norse, Celt and Lowland Scot
                          William P. L. Thomson   209

11 The Lairds and Eighteenth-Century Orkney
                                R. P. Fereday   225

12 Lairds and Historians   *R. P. Fereday*   246

13 Who are the Orcadians?   *Ronald Miller*   268

Appendices   275

Notes and References   299

List of Figures   329

List of Photographs   331

List of Tables   337

Index   339

There are fifty islands, more or less, in the archipelago, and some are no bigger than a field with a fringe of red seaweed, but the Mainland, the greatest of them, is twenty-five miles from Greenigoe Taing in Deerness to the Earl's Palace of Birsay. They tell different stories, of saint and viking, of seafowl and shaven priest and Pict and trader, but all have a common tale of misery and destitution after they passed from Norseman and Churchman to the Scottish Crown.

Eric Linklater, *The Man on my Back*

Foreword

This book brings together a series of disciplines in an effort to identify some essential characteristics of the people of Orkney. To shine light from several different angles to get better illumination is nothing new in the islands: the life of Robert Rendall, poet and scientist, would be a concrete example of the process. His *Mollusca Orcadensia* is the standard work on Orkney sea-shells; his *Orkney Shore* blends together abstract mathematical ideas of the design of the spiral in a shell with detail of the flotsam and jetsam of a Birsay fisherman's woodpile; and extracts from his poems have been chosen quite separately by the authors of the first and last chapters of this present book to sum essential aspects of the Orkney character.

Orkney Shore sets out lucidly the elements of the Orkney landscape in which the story of the people of Orkney is set—"the long familiar curve of the far horizon seen from a Birsay cliff-top, the green links of the north banks at Westray, stitched with yellow trefoil, a solitary man hoeing turnips in a field, a black reef of rocks sticking up out of the sea, a mere patch of seapinks"—and the shore itself.

The shore was integral to the old Orkney way of life. Crofts were sited near the shore, sometimes by a burn-mouth, and so fitted into the landscape as to become natural features of the foreshore. The boat-noust or landing rock was never far away. Hillside slopes may have drawn the eye 'when the peats were on', but the shore was a permanent element in local life. Sea-fishing, taking of lobsters, gathering dulse and whelks and mussels, bait-gathering for cod-fishing, carting sand and seaweed for the land, or shingle for road-making, the bleaching of flax, kelp making, quarrying flagstone for house roofs or for paving, beachcombing for driftwood—there was no end to the resources of the shore for the maintenance of that old way of life. Little wonder that the Orkney system of land tenure styles possession as being "from the lowest stone in the ebb to the highest stone on the hill". For a mode of life that was more or less self-subsisting, everything that nature could provide, from hill or shore, was needed.

In such surroundings, Robert Rendall said, there were many people who "without giving heed to the why and how of it live lives of ordered simplicity in surroundings of natural beauty, content with their daily lot".

These, for the most part, live and work within sight of the shore. They are familiar with tides and seasons. They work out-of-doors under an open sky—plough, do fencing, feed hens, repair outhouses, walk among their fields, attend the cattle. Work is the salt of country living: without it everything becomes insipid.

In an island group where resources have always been finite, craftsmanship, too, would long have been an important characteristic of the people of Orkney—the skill that makes a piece of driftwood into a spade-handle or a fiddle, scrap metal into gears for an engine, or perspex into polished ground lenses. To hold a community together through a long winter, self-enhancing behaviour had to be discouraged, hence Orcadian reluctance to push forward and Orcadian embarrassment at displays of emotional behaviour. "No' bad" and "ower weel" are the normal extremes of superlatives, while philosophy in face of the worst that fate may bring is exemplified by that keen observer of the Orkney scene, R. T. Johnston, in his cheerful tale of the loss from the mythical parish of Stenwick of one Ezekiel Drever:

His wife did not re-marry, but she found some solace for her loss in the purchase of a parrot, which proved much more loquacious, and better company, than her husband had ever been. Indeed, Mrs Drever was heard to remark that she was sorry she had not bought the parrot instead of getting married in the first place.

Analysing the Iatmul people of the Indonesian island of Bali, the anthropologist Gregory Bateson noted that they had deeply-entrenched blocks against emotional intensity in public life. Such a display would trigger off further emotion, he noted, in the same way as other forms of reactive behaviour, such as boasting, disrupt a society that had to hold together. Behaviour patterns to prevent this would have been of survival value for early man, but

West Shore, Stromness

The Harray Loch

Yesnaby

Sandwick, South Ronaldsay

Making Orkney Cheese: Mrs Jamesina Laird of Hozen, Dounby

Drying cuithes: James Wilson, Stromness

perhaps they now only remain in areas isolated by geography. Amongst the people of the arid Kalahari desert, for instance, a number of specific rituals are carried out to discourage individual conceit. A successful hunter must not come back and boast about a kill. The correct procedure is to sit down in silence by the fire and wait until someone asks what he saw that day, whereupon the correct reply is along the lines of "Ah, I'm no good at hunting, I saw nothing at all . . . maybe just a tiny one." "Then," explained one of the people of the tribe, "I smile to myself because I know he has killed something big." The bigger the kill, the more it is played down.

That behaviour pattern is well-established in Orkney—a musician, casually playing an unfamiliar tune during a break prior to supper, can be persuaded by a similar process to admit, though not in so many words, to composing it—and in a divided modern world it is a pleasant thought to think that such attitudes cross boundaries of language or race. Orcadians of the last two centuries encountered many archaic peoples in Canada, Australia and New Zealand, and it is certainly noticeable how far they integrated, learning languages and new ways of living. In the Arctic, for instance, John Rae, who surveyed over 1700 miles of new land and coastline and discovered the fate of Franklin and his ships, used the techniques of the native people to travel by snowshoe and canoe, building snow houses and wearing local clothing and living off the land. Although there is a suspicion that General George Armstrong Custer of the U.S. Army may have been of Orcadian descent, there is also the record of Governor William Tomison of the Hudson's Bay Company, who in the winter of 1781-2 tended the Indians of his area during a smallpox epidemic, throughout which he and his men shared their food and stockade with them. "The white men worked to the point of exhaustion," writes William Towrie Cutt in *The New Orkney Book,* "cutting down trees, fishing, attending the sick, bringing in the dead and the dying, making coffins and burying the dead."

Today the opportunities overseas and in the Merchant Navy have dwindled, and it is becoming dangerously easy for Orcadians to allow themselves to be trapped in a cosy mediocrity. The outward energy is still there, though, as can be seen from the expansion of Orkney's fishing fleet, and the vision of the Sea School in Stromness provides skill and confidence to the fishery development. Vision is urgently needed in other aspects of modern life, however, particularly in agriculture and education. Acceptance of the pressure towards farm amalgamations has damaged the structure of scattered small farms that was the backbone of Orkney society, and though new ideas for the smaller unit are beginning to emerge, for some islands the future is coming perilously close to the landscape of cattle-ranches and whitemaas that we were warned about in the 1960s by the late John D. Mackay, Sanday schoolmaster, man of letters, and one of the most perceptive men of a highly perceptive generation. That was the generation that produced the late Lord Birsay, Chairman of the Scottish Land Court and the Scottish National Dictionary, a tireless worker for many causes and arguably the finest public speaker of our time; the late Ernest Marwick, scholar and writer, who gave of his utmost to encourage others and to preserve the best of the past for their future; and John Mackay himself, who made a world of ideas come alive for a whole generation, and whose letters to the local press had a radical imagination and observant wit that are sadly missed in modern Orkney.

Now a new generation must look outwards at the world outside the islands and examine their own society to see clearly what are the essential characteristics that give it, and them, identity. This book contains a great deal of information on the very basic question of identity, and it also contains sufficient references to open up a host of paths of research, both within Orkney and beyond. The various chapters began in the main as papers put forward at the Kirkwall conference on "Who are the Orcadians?" held in September 1982, organised by Professor R. J. Berry with financial assistance from the Nuffield Foundation, and opened by the Convener of the Orkney Islands Council, Mr Edwin Eunson. Lord Birsay himself and Professor Gordon Donaldson were among the chairmen of conference sessions, and over the succeeding four years the ideas put forward there have gradually developed into the present form as the authors have worked to highlight both the areas of agreement and also those areas where debate continues. One of the most exciting aspects of this whole subject is the fact that there is so much still to do: this book in many areas defines the questions—the answers are there to be sought.

In order to bring the work to the stage of publication many people have provided help in many ways and though it would be impossible to mention each individually I would like to express our warmest thanks to them all; in particular there is the great effort that has been put in by the artists Angela Townsend and Anne Leith Brundle who have turned data and notes into clear illustrations and diagrams, and the help of so many people in the search for photographs. We felt that in a book on this theme, the people of Orkney should be present in strength, and out of the many photographs which we should have liked to include made a varied selection. We were not able to contact all the subjects, but felt in each case where this happened that the picture and the person were so suitable as representatives that we could not leave them out. In fact, we can freely admit, despite the objective aim of the whole book, to showing a degree of sentiment in the choice of photographs and our main regret is that we did not have room for many more.

As always, William Thomson, the consultant editor of this series, has provided a great deal of valuable advice and encouragement, working patiently through numerous manuscripts, and his help is greatly appreciated.

When thinking over the qualities that give the Orkney shore its essential character, Robert Rendall wondered whether it might be the distinctive light observed by Edwin Muir and set down on canvas by Stanley Cursiter. If this book encourages some of the next generation of Orcadians to want to see more clearly themselves and their surroundings, then the authors and editors will be more than satisfied with the results of their efforts.

Howie Firth

Everywhere in Orkney there is the sense of age, the dark backward and abysm. The islands have been inhabited for a very long time, from before the day of the plough.

The Norsemen came 1,200 years ago to a place that was already populous with fishermen, herdsmen, farmers; a clever ingenious folk who built "brochs" along sea coasts and lochs to defend themselves against sea-raiders, or perhaps to dominate a subject population . . .

But the broch-builders were themselves invaders. The silent vanished races stretch back beyond them, laid in barrows and howes under the green waves of time.

George Mackay Brown, *An Orkney Tapestry*

They came up along the coast, slowly, from the Mediterranean, bringing a remnant of the culture of their warm southlands to this colder and bleaker scene; they advanced across Europe and spread northwards; they came West-over-sea from Scandinavia to a less snow-bound land; they arrived from Ireland to bring us Christianity; they came across the Firth from Scotland, hounded by religious persecution or for sheep-stealing; they were brought home from the nor'-west of Canada by returning fur-trappers and whalers; they were wrecked on our rocks by waves that tall ships and galleons could not withstand; or they came from the south to purloin our land in the name of the Crown. Orkney absorbed them, and that is why there is no such person as a typical Orcadian. This one may observe from a Kirkwall street corner any day outwith the tourist season; just stand and watch the racial types go by, all of them talking in their Orcadian mither-tongue.

Bessie Skea, *A Countrywoman's Diary*

A fine mixter-maxter!

George Mackay Brown, *What is an Orcadian?*

CHAPTER 1

The People of Orkney

R. J. Berry

At the 1981 Census there were 19,056 people in Orkney, 611 of them visitors. Of the 18,425 residents, 16,638 are recorded as having been born in Scotland. Most of these will have been born within the islands, and hence fairly regarded as Orcadians.

But is being born within the county (or Islands Council area) a proper definition of an Orcadian? Is the correct qualification for being an Orcadian to be born in Orkney, or to have parents, or grandparents, who were born there? Or what? Is there such a thing as a *real* Orcadian?

Orkney's position at the crossroads of northern sea-routes has repeatedly been significant through the centuries. Bo Almqvist, indeed, (Chapter 9) speaks of Orkney in Viking times as playing a role in the North Sea "similar to that played by Venice and other mighty Italian republics in the Mediterranean". Certainly the chances of geography coupled with the advantages of soil fertility have brought in successive influxes of new people over the past six thousand years or so, so an Orcadian of today can look back to a eclectic constellation of possible antecedents. What Orcadians have in common is expressed by Ronald Miller in the last chapter of this book, where he describes an Orcadian as someone who has lived long enough in the islands to have been shaped with their peculiar genius. He asserts for Orkney a similar truth to that set out for Norway by A. W. Brøgger: "from the very moment the first people came to Norway, they had to become Norwegians, because of the natural conditions of the country."[1]

The influence of Orkney is something which impresses itself on all who spend time there. Robert Rendall called it "necromancy":

I sing the virtue
    of country living,
Of long days spent
    without misgiving,
In calm fulfilment
    of rustic labours
Among good friends
    and kindly neighbours.

I sing of Nature's
    necromancy,
The beauty and wonder
    that wake the fancy,
When after winter's
    cheerless rigour
Gay summer flowers
    the earth transfigure.

I sing of sea-swept
    burial places,
Shore-graves where native
    legend traces
Time's finger, and glimpses
    as in vision
Our ancient Orkney
    sea tradition.[2]

However, even magic needs substance to work its wonder: it is
all very well to plaud the environment of the islands which has
made its own from George Mackay Brown's "fine mixter-
maxter",[3] but who are the ingredients which added up to 18,425
on Census Day 1981? Are there still Pictish genes in Orkney? Is
Orkney still a Viking-land? Who are the Orcadians?

Traditional understanding

One of the most hotly-disputed phases in Orkney's history is
the arrival of the Norsemen, and whether they came as peaceful
settlers or plundering raiders; the debate between the 'war' and
'peace' protagonists has continued throughout this century, both
in Orkney itself and further afield. Complicating this is a well-
entrenched belief that when the Vikings crossed the North Sea at
the end of the eighth century they came to a virtually empty
land. John Gunn, in the 'old' *Orkney Book* which was for long a
standard work on many an Orkney bookshelf, had no doubts:

> If there had been a native population, and if these had
> been expelled or exterminated by the invaders, we should
> surely have been told of it by the Saga writers, who would
> have delighted in telling such a tale. It has accordingly been
> supposed that at the time of the Norse settlement the
> islands were uninhabited save by the hermits of the Culdee
> Church. When or how the former Pictish inhabitants
> disappeared, it is impossible to say. Possibly some early
> Viking raids, of which no history remains, had resulted in
> the slaughter of many and the flight of the rest to the less

exposed lands south of the Pictland or Pentland Firth. Whatever the reason may be, the chapter of [Orkney] history which opens with the Norse settlement is in no way a continuation of anything which goes before, but begins a new story.[4]

Gunn was in no way atypical. The Shetland antiquarian Gilbert Goudie writing at much the same time, believed that the Picts "and their Christianity alike" appear to have vanished before the arrival of the Scandinavians, whilst a generation later D. P. Capper claimed that "the Pictish inhabitants, numerous as they must have been, had been wiped cleanly off the page of history in some unexplained fashion . . . an entire people disappears in silence."[5]

The fullest expression of this point of view is by Brøgger:

> The Norsemen did not destroy a numerous Celtic population in the Shetlands and Orkneys. They did not wage a war of extermination against such a population or drive it into the sea and seize its possessions, its farms, and its civilization. It seems clear that a race which possessed the great brochs for defence and real fleets of ships, would not have allowed itself to be destroyed by the Norsemen even if the craftsmanship of the latter in the shaping of weapons was superior and their art in shipbuilding of a very high order . . . Perhaps the broch-people, small in numbers, a warlike aristocracy, had gradually drifted away from the islands into the Scottish mainland, leaving the poorer classes of Celts in possession . . . The Norse settlers came sailing to a land in which there were few people. On all sides they saw traces of old houses and farms, ruins and foundations of houses and outhouses. The greatest impression they received was that created by the sight of old brochs. All their imagination was fired. Did they not step ashore into a veritable museum?[6]

However, not all agreed, and the 'war' school has a long tradition behind it. The twelfth-century *Historia Norvegiae* states that in the days of Harald Fairhair, King of Norway, pirates of the family of Rognvald of Møre "destroyed" Orkney, then called Pictland, and took the islands for themselves. The same history states that the islands were inhabited by two kinds of people, *Peti* (Picts) and *Papae* (Christian priests).[7] As to the "destruction" of the Picts, Hugh Marwick argued that the Vikings would have been fully aware of the market value of the natives as slaves, and suggested that they would have been not so

much exterminated as expropriated: "From the distaff side,
indeed, in all likelihood, there was in the succeeding population
of the isles a very considerable strain of ancient Pictish blood."[8]
As to the *Papae,* Marwick believed there was strong evidence
that Christianity had survived the Norse settlement. He pointed
to such names as Papa Westray and Papa Stronsay where Papey
(isle of the *Priests*) was the old saga name. He noted how the
sanctity of such islands continued into Norse times, with for
example the body of the slain Earl Rognvald Brusason being
carried to Papa Westray for burial in 1046. He also recorded the
frequency amongst early farm-names of Kirbister—Kirk-bister,
or farm with a church.[9] Even a name like Egilsay, he observed,
could be interpreted not only as the island of a Norseman Egil,
but also, as the Norwegian P. A. Munch had suggested, as
deriving from a Celtic name for a church—*eaglais* or *ecles* (from
Latin *ecclesia*).[10]

One of the best books for many years on this and many other
aspects of Orkney's past has been the collection of essays edited
by F. T. Wainwright and published in 1962 under the title *The
Northern Isles.* Reviewing the arguments over the Norse
settlement, Wainwright himself supported the case for the
continuity of Christianity through the period, noting that as well
as the place-name evidence there were also signs that early Norse
settlers were beginning to bury their dead in Christian
churchyards. "The Picts and their Christianity were not swept
out of the Northern Isles" was his conclusion.[11] However, with
few other survivals apart from Christianity that could definitely
be demonstrated, Wainwright concluded that, although not
vanishing or exterminated, the Picts were "overwhelmed by and
submerged beneath the sheer weight of the Scandinavian
settlement".[12]

> During the historical Pictish period (AD 300-850) the
> inhabitants of Orkney and Shetland became part of the
> historical Pictish kingdom and were included within the all-
> embracing collective name *Picti.* Long before the Scandi-
> navians arrived they were being subject to intrusive Scottish
> influences from the Gaelic west, represented most clearly in
> missionary activity and the ogam inscriptions, and com-
> memorated in the *Papae* (ON *Papar*) of history and place-
> names . . .
>
> It is not suprising that the sagas do not mention the
> Picts. The sagas are concerned chiefly with the deeds of
> great men and the feuds of great families, and they were
> composed at a time when, in England at least, the Picts

House at Skara Brae

Knap of Howar, Papa Westray

Maeshowe

The Tomb of the Eagles, Isbister

were less than a memory and no more than a fable. There is no reason why the Picts should appear in the sagas, and their failure to do so cannot be used as evidence that they did not exist or were too few to merit notice . . . Whether or not the Picts lost all their lands, as is suggested by the Historia Norvegiae, it is virtually certain that they were depressed to an altogether inferior status, and that they were completely dominated by the numerically and politically superior newcomers. The Scandinavian settlement was the result of a mass-migration, and its impact on the Picts must have been overwhelming.[13]

Periods and labels

The Scandinavian settlement of Orkney was a major event, perhaps the most important event in the human history of the islands after they were first colonized. It has often been seen as a hiatus, and it is easy to understand why that should be so, since we know a great deal about the Scandinavians but much less about the Picts or whoever the pre-Norse Orcadians were. If we are unsure of their language, for example, whether it was related to Gaelic or to Welsh or something completely different altogether, it is difficult to know what to look for in trying to prove survival or extinction. The place-name evidence is a good example of this sort of doubt. The doyen of place-name researchers, Jakob Jakobsen, initially believed that no pre-Scandinavian place-names survived in Orkney or Shetland but then he changed his mind and produced a list of over forty Celtic elements still in use. Hugh Marwick strengthened the position by listing nearly thirty Celtic place-name elements in Orkney, but Wainwright argued that the bulk of these were of Gaelic form which could have come from mainland Scotland *after* the Norse era and not before it.[14]

Wainwright's verdict, which is more of a "Not Proven" than a total rejection of Marwick and Jokobsen's lists, has stood for a quarter of a century but is re-examined in Chapter 7 of this book in which Howie Firth argues that Orkney tradition and folklore show less similarities to those of Norway than would be expected if there was a complete population and cultural replacement. He argues that there is a Celtic sub-stratum attributable to an Iron Age society in Orkney before the arrival of the Norse and which can be traced back to the culture and beliefs of the broch-builders.

William Thomson in Chapter 10, while sounding a cautionary note on the place-name question, summarises arguments for a

B

degree of continuity in the system of land division. It seems likely that the Pictish land-unit of the *davach* was directly taken over as the early Norse *urisland,* which formed the basis of the taxation system. This was proposed by Captain Thomas as long ago as 1884; and the idea was developed by Storer Clouston and Hugh Marwick. William Thomson notes that although the whole question of the origin of the *urisland* must still be regarded as uncertain the balance of opinion is that it dates from the pre-Norse period. He observes that if a system of district organisation could survive the coming of the Vikings, it points, not necessarily to peaceful colonisation, but at least to a takeover in circumstances which permitted the survival of Pictish institutions.

The chapters by Peter Foote and Bo Almqvist, (Chapters 8 and 9), are wide-ranging in their analysis of Norse institutions and review of evidence for possible Celtic influences. As they emphasise, the problems are many and acceptable solutions hard to find. Even when a possible Celtic influence is identified, we have still to establish whether it was early or late, and also whence it came, whether in the Northern Isles themselves or from across the Irish Sea or elsewhere. Nevertheless, they have some interesting examples of cross-cultural contacts involving Orkney, and in terms of our search for the make-up of the Orkney population help to confirm the move away from the old idea of a complete extermination of the Norse population.

In the years since the publication of *The Northern Isles,* we have also had the advantage of a number of archaeological excavations on sites whose occupations span the Pictish-Norse transition, in particular several in the Birsay area. For example Anna Ritchie found the lower levels at Buckquoy were Pictish and the upper ones Norse, but with a continuity in artefacts and life-style that implies "considerable integration between native Picts and incoming Norsemen" during the initial settlement period of the latter.[13]

The case for continuity is taken up in this book by John Hedges, who as founder director of North of Scotland Archaeological Services has been responsible for a series of investigations which give new insight into the Neolithic period, the Bronze Age, and the Iron Age. John Hedges is particularly well qualified to give a complete overview of Orkney prehistory and, as he follows particular artefacts and techniques through the centuries, he repeatedly shows a pattern of continuity and integration, both in the Viking period and in the earlier major incoming—the people of the brochs—which he believes to be the only other significant immigration after the original Neolithic colonisation of Orkney.

The reason why the continuity of Orkney life from Pict to Viking times needs particular emphasis is that virtually every Orkney history divides the occupation of the islands into three or four periods: the early settlers, often linking these with the Picts (up to about 800 AD); the Viking period; and the period of Scottish influence, beginning with the impignoration of 1468 followed by the Act of Parliament of 1471 when James III "annexed and united the earldom of Orkney and the lordship of Shetland to the Crown, not to be given away in times to come to any person or persons except to one of the king's sons got of lawful bed". The coming of the Vikings is described in great detail, usually relying on the doubtful historicity of the saga accounts. (It is worth recalling that the *Orkneyinga Saga* is not equivalent to the Icelandic *Landnámabók*; it is an Earls' Saga treating of individual people and their relationships in life or death with little concern for history or geography.) The effect is that each phase of history tends to be regarded as a separate unit, with a beginning and an end. Although it is clearly necessary to identify the dominant influences of different eras, too often the giving of names to a period isolates it from the ongoing interactions of history, and thus distorts our understanding of the whole process. This distortion tends to be magnified by the attention that is given to the Pict-Viking divide.

One reason for the degree of attention to this particular period emerges from Ray Fereday's survey of Orkney historians (Chapter 12) in which he notes that they tended to keep clear of the relatively recent past with the risks of alienating the local lairds with unflattering descriptions of their ancestors; instead they focused more safely on the more remote past. When this is recognised, we are better able to get into proportion the assessments by past historians of key periods such as the Pict-Viking transition, as well as gaining a perspective on the hitherto much-neglected 18th century in Orkney.

Quite apart from its intrinsic interest and its influence on our own times, the study of the life and habits of the families of Orkney lairds is also significant as an example of the role of an incoming minority 'aristocracy' in relation to the ordinary people of Orkney, who were there before them and who remained there after them—and indeed, helped by the impact of death duties on large estates, have ended up by taking over the lairds' land and houses! The arrival of the Norse was no doubt on a much bigger scale, but the model of politically dominant ruling groups that come and go, while the underlying pattern of agricultural life continues, is a useful one for interpreting Orkney's history.

We can now indeed see Orkney history as an ongoing story

with high and low points, triumphs and tragedies, incomers and out-migrants, but with no absolute interruptions. A present-day Orcadian is a person moulded by something like 6000 years of life in the islands. This book is about the moulding process.

Finding out about the Orcadians

Wideford Hill chambered cairn was excavated by George Petrie in 1849. This pioneer work has been followed by an ever-increasing sophistication of archaeological investigation. The classic studies of Gordon Childe at Skara Brae[16] have been continued by many others, and from the variety of human bones found we can look directly at some of the features of Orcadians of long ago.

Don Brothwell of the Institute of Archaeology in London spans the divide between archaeologist and anthropologist: he has studied the skeletons of past Orcadians in his excavations at Deerness, and he has measured and characterized living Orcadians. He and his colleagues describe many of the physical traits (and diseases) of the population, including differences between different islands, and discuss the significance of these various features for the study of Orcadian antecedents (Chapter 3).

Three other chapters are concerned with the physical characteristics and relationships of the people of Orkney. Evelyn Bowers (Chapter 6) discusses human life-span in Orkney and some of the factors that determine it; Derek Roberts (Chapter 4) compares Orkney with the Scottish and Scandinavian populations, to see which of these the islanders most resemble; and Robin Harvey and his colleagues (Chapter 5) develop this theme with particular reference to the Faroe Islanders, who are generally acknowledged to have a much closer genetic relationship to Scandinavia than to Orkney.

For a long time it has been clear that no single person can unravel the full story of human history, even in such a microcosm as Orkney. As Wainwright put it, after bringing together specialists from archaeology, philology and history to tackle *The Problem of the Picts* (1955),

> . . . the need for co-operation and co-ordination is most urgent. The archaeologist may feel himself competent to deal alone with the remote ages of prehistory, and the historian may affect to disdain assistance in the study of a modern period, but [overall] . . . no single scholar would claim to be self-sufficient. Specialists of different dis-

ciplines, bringing different methods to the varied assort-
ment of evidence, must pool their resources and tackle
together the problems that none of them alone can solve.[17]

That is exactly what this book seeks to do. The past and
present Orkney populations have been studied by a host of
scholars, but their results have never before been brought
together. There have been a number of general books about
Orkney, with works such as those by Hugh Marwick (1951), Eric
Linklater (1965), John Shearer, William Groundwater, John D.
Mackay (1966), Patrick Bailey (1971), and Ronald Miller (1976)
all adding particular insights to Orkney's past.[18] (Ronald Miller
himself, who was born and lives in Orkney and was until his
retirement Professor of Geography at Glasgow University, is a
highly appropriate person to sum up our attempts to answer this
whole question "Who are the Orcadians?", q.v. Chapter 13.)

Historians have been particularly active in documenting the
past four or five centuries in Orkney, and William Thomson and
Ray Fereday, who themselves have made notable contributions,
give full references in their chapters. There has also been the
major ethnographic work of Alexander Fenton, *The Northern
Isles: Orkney and Shetland,*[19] as well as a great deal of new
information from archaeologists such as Colin Renfrew (see John
Hedges' chapter for a comprehensive list of references). The last
major review of the Orcadian "mixter-maxter" was a collection
of essays edited by Wainwright in 1962. Since that time, a vast
amount of information has been collected, not only in the
traditional fields of archaeology, philology, and history, but also
in complementary disciplines of anthropology, sociology, and
general biological background. Without in any way claiming to
be all-inclusive or to produce answers to all the questions about
the Orcadians, this book is aimed towards a better understanding
of the past, and as a help for scholars to appreciate the wealth of
Orkney past and present.

Retrospect and prospect

The clear emphasis from the essays in this book is the
continuity of Orkney history from about 4000 BC onwards.
During this time major immigration episodes can be recognised:

1. The original settlers had two distinct backgrounds,
   coming from what the archaeologists call the Grooved
   Ware and Unstan Ware 'cultures' (exemplified by Skara
   Brae and by the Knap of Howar on Papa Westray

respectively.) However, as John Hedges explains in the next chapter, these two groups were largely contemporary and had more in common than they had differences.

2. Around 700 BC the Iron Age came to Orkney, as shown by the occurrence of round houses, which later evolved into brochs. Archaeologically, it is often difficult to distinguish overt invasion from imported influence, but the fairly sudden appearance together of iron, horses, rotary querns, round houses, and long-headed combs implies a new wave of immigrants. These seem to be the people we call the Picts. Perhaps in time the archaeologists and anthropologists will be able to tell us more about these shadows. The *Historia Norvegiae* says that they "little exceeded pigmies in stature; they did marvels in the morning and the evening in building towns, but at midday they entirely lost their strength, and lurked through fear in little underground houses. . . Whence the people came there we are entirely ignorant. . ."[20] We are not so ignorant about them nowadays. Anthony Jackson has shown that even the apparently baffling symbol stones can be tackled systematically, and it is clear that not all that the *Historia Norvegiae* says about them should be taken literally (Bo Almqvist in Chapter 9 has an interesting point to make about an interpretation of one part of this account). But Pictish times are still very mysterious. They may be nothing more than a simple revealing of an 'aboriginal' culture through intensification of contacts; notwithstanding, we still have a long way to go in attempting to understand this period.

3. Before 800 AD—whether before or after is still subject to argument—Scandinavians began to make their presence felt in Orkney, culminating in a massive population movement into Orkney at the end of the eighth century when they arrived in overwhelming numbers; the question of how overwhelming these numbers were is discussed by several of the authors of this book.

4. During medieval times and building up to a peak in the 16th and 17th centuries, there was a considerable influx of Lowland Scots, especially clergy and followers of earls who had a Scots base or origin. We still have little idea of the numbers who contributed genetically to the population.

5. Finally, we have recent immigration—soldiers and sailors in two world wars, but even more recently a large influx

of (mainly) English people who have halted and reversed the population decline which has been continuing in Orkney for more than a century.

For the past twenty years, migrants have been moving into Orkney who have had no previous links or interests in the islands. Egilsay now (1986) has only one native-born Orcadian in a population numbering 24, and a number of the other islands (especially the North Isles) now have as many incomers as native Orcadians. Diana Forsythe has studied the effect of this in one of the islands, which she calls Stormay.[21]

Stormay had a population in 1981 of 186, of which 77 (41%) were incomers, all except nine of these from outside Orkney. This produced a degree of distancing between members of the community which did not exist previously.

Despite the incomers' expressed desire to preserve the Stormay way of life, their very presence is helping to destroy it. Although individually the incomers are generally pleasant and well meaning additions to the island community, they are also contributing to a cultural revolution in which ethnic, regional and national differences are being eroded away, to be replaced by a more standardized and homogenous way of life. In 1981, incomers were still a minority on Stormay, albeit a vocal and powerful minority. But the receiving population on Stormay is relatively old, whilst continuing in-migration from Scotland and England brings in a steady steam of young adults in their prime child-bearing years. In the face of this in-migration, its influence augmented by national radio, television and standardised education, the number of people who actually use and identify with Stormay speech and customs will inevitably diminish . . . There is tragedy in this situation for both islanders and incomers. The Stormay folk have welcomed the migrants as bringing new life and new ideas to their depopulated and ageing community, but they already have reason to regret their generosity. The energy the incomers bring to the island is committed to a vision of the future in which local people have no active part. They have sought to attain this vision by moving to a remote island to partake of the mystique of country life. But these migrants are not countrymen, nor do they really wish to become so; instead they seek a stage on which to act out an urban conception of what rural life should be like. The coming of urban refugees may revitalise the community in

a demographic sense, but it will also transform it beyond
recognition, for most incomers have little understanding of
the distinctiveness and value of Orkney's cultural heritage
as different from their own. In the long run, the conflicts
that have accompanied the incomers' move to the island
probably will be resolved through the submergence of the
way of life of the receiving community—a high price to pay
for the personal fulfilment of a few.[22]

It is difficult not to be depressed by this analysis, or to
disagree with Forsythe's conclusion:

> Through history the Orcadian way of life has continually
> changed and developed. Successive waves of in-migrants
> have helped to shape the course of island life, contributing
> to the mixture of Pictish, Norse, Scottish, and English
> elements that make up the heritage of Orcadians today.
> Over time, Orkney has managed to retain an identity
> related to but consciously separate from those of Norway
> and mainland Britain. Now, once again, outsiders are
> coming into the archipelago, not as conquerors this time
> but as refugees from the cities of the south. Like those of
> earlier eras, this latest wave of migration will lead to a new
> cultural synthesis. However because of the nature of this
> particular in-migration, it is doubtful that the new synthesis
> will retain very much that is distinctively Orcadian.[23]

We must accept that there is a problem and a challenge here.
The rate of depopulation, particularly in the outer isles, has
increased so greatly in recent years that there is a need for new
people to help to maintain viable communities, and Orkney over
the years has traditionally benefited by new ideas and welcomed
them. The challenge now is to find ways of benefiting by the
present situation while yet retaining the "synthesis . . . that is
distinctively Orcadian".

Will you who read the thirteen chapters and 300 pages of this
collection of essays be able to say definitely who are the
Orcadians? Almost certainly not, if you are honest. True, you
should now be able to avoid some of the inaccuracies of your
predecessors, but even the vast amount of new data herein can
only give a partial answer. Nevertheless this book is worthwhile
on three counts:

1. The rich yet circumscribed nature of Orkney makes a
   synthesis of its history and influence much more possible
   than that of larger areas. The density of archaeological
   sites, the wealth of historical material, and the discrete
   nature of the island communities allow a much fuller

collection and analysis of data than for virtually
anywhere else in the United Kingdom and probably in the
world.

2. Because the picture of the making of the Orcadians can
   be drawn so fully (despite its gaps and uncertainties), it
   provides a model of how different disciplines can throw
   light on each other. This book is the product of a group
   of individuals meeting together for two days and
   remaining in contact for four years afterwards. But much
   more needs to be done in bringing together the results of
   the different disciplines. Notwithstanding, these essays
   represent the present state of knowledge of the Orcadians.
   It would be misleading to force a cohesion on what, after
   all, is a mixter-maxter of a situation.

3. At the risk of being trite, it is relevant to recall that the
   proper study of mankind is man. The more we know
   about the whole environment of our species, the better
   can we appreciate what produces sickness and health, in
   the widest sense of those terms. For example, Orkney has
   the highest prevalence in the world of multiple sclerosis.
   There has been much argument about the causes of this
   disease, and diet, geology, inherited factors, trauma,
   infection, climate, have all been blamed by different
   authorities. Almost certainly, many of these interact to
   produce clinical symptoms. Puzzles like this which affect
   people everywhere can be investigated best in places like
   Orkney because of the possibility of untangling so many
   factors there.

Continuity is a word I have repeatedly applied to Orkney
history. What does it mean in the context? Derek Roberts in
Chapter 4, comparing Orkney with other places, refers to the
Orcadians as an "extreme relic". By this he does not mean that
the Orkney population has remained untouched and static over
the centuries, but only that it retains many of the traits it had in
past centuries. This conservatism in the face of so much coming
and going is an expression of the magical influence that I
referred to at the beginning of this chapter: despite being at the
crossroads of seaways for so long, there is still such a person as
a real Orcadian. But can the "fine mixter-maxter" survive the
homogenizing effect of easy communications, canned culture,
confusions about the meaning of the quality of life (which is
always perceived as being somewhere else)? This is the crucial
question which may help us to understand something of the
process that has made the Orcadians.

CHAPTER 2

From the First Inhabitants to the Viking Settlement

John W. Hedges

SETTLEMENTS AND GRAVES

The Neolithic period (c. 4000-2000 BC)

As far as we know, Orkney was never inhabited by man prior to the Neolithic settlement, a mere 6,000 years ago. As will be seen, peoples with two distinct backgrounds were involved — known as the Grooved Ware and Unstan Ware 'cultures' — but they appear to have been largely contemporary and had more in common than they had differences.[1] Settlements of the former group have been investigated at Skara Brae[2] in Sandwick and Rinyo in Rousay, while work is ongoing at the Links of Noltland in Westray.[3] The only Unstan Ware settlement known is the Knap of Howar[2] on Papa Westray.[4] The preservation at Skara Brae and Knap of Howar is remarkable and the sample as a whole is unparalleled in Britain.

Skara Brae was actually a village which was built and rebuilt over 600 years. Most of the houses we see today belong to the later phase, and then — as now — they would have appeared subterranean as they were built into previous midden deposits and had more piled around them. What is particularly striking is the coherence of the plan, with individual dwellings leading off shared covered passageways (Fig. 1). The dwelling rooms are remarkably similar in size and shape and in the layout of their well-preserved stone furnishings. There was a central fireplace, up to four stone box-beds, perhaps a dresser, small stone boxes in the floor, and ambries and cupboards in the walls (Plate 5a). In the earlier phase the box-beds were let into the wall. All these buildings duplicate each other and are apparently the dwellings of family units. How many would have been occupied at any one

Fig. 1—Skara Brae

time is difficult to say, but the settlement probably housed something like half a dozen families during its second phase.

The two buildings to be seen at the Knap of Howar are different in plan and conception; they are rectangular and divided into rooms by transverse partitions (Plate 5b). One feature in common with Skara Brae is that the buildings were recessed into earlier midden; some of this material had additionally been used to pack the walls.

If the preservation of these Neolithic settlements is remarkable, so too is that of some of the coeval chambered tombs. There are two main types, 'Maeshowe' (or 'Maes Howe') and 'stalled,' and it is largely the pottery found in them which tells us that the former may be linked with the Grooved Ware 'culture' and the latter with the Unstan Ware. Both consist of surface chambers surrounded and surmounted by thick built casings, which are generally of masonry. The Maeshowe type chambers are entered by a relatively long, low passage which opens into a central room; off this are several small side cells (Fig. 2). The passage in stalled tombs, which enters from the end or side, leads into an elongated chamber which is notionally divided off by paired orthostats projecting from the side walls — like the stalls in a byre. There were sometimes shelves at the end of the stalled chambers.

Maeshowe[2] itself, which is in Stenness, has been described as

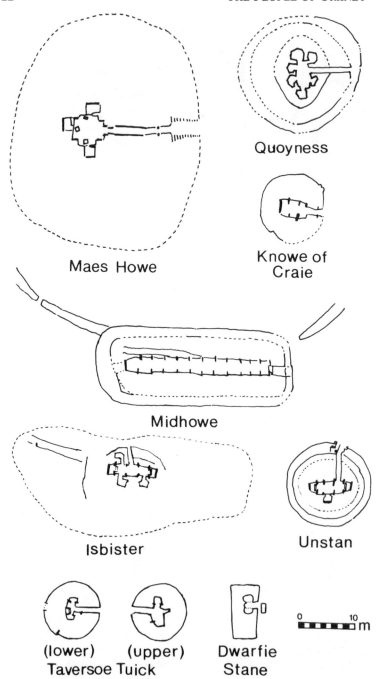

Fig. 2—Plans of selected Orcadian chambered tombs

'one of the greatest architectural achievements of the prehistoric people of Scotland'[5] (Plate 6a). Less grand tombs of the Maeshowe type can be seen at Quoyness[2] in Sanday, Cuween Hill[2] in Firth, Wideford Hill[2] by Kirkwall, and on the Holm of Papa Westray,[2] but the one from which we have most information is Quanterness by Kirkwall.[6] Similarly, a number of stalled tombs are officially open to the public — Blackhammer, Knowe of Yarso, and Midhowe, all on Rousay, and Unstan in Stenness — but it is Isbister[7] in South Ronaldsay which has given us greatest insight (Plate 6b). Unstan and Isbister are actually hybrids of the two tomb types described above, having both stalls and side cells. There are other variants such as the so-called Bookan-type tombs, of which Taversoe Tuick[2] on Rousay is a two-storeyed example, and there is additionally the Dwarfie Stane[2] on Hoy which is a quite anomalous rock-cut tomb.

Since Audrey Henshall's[9] scholarly compilation on the chambered tombs, the excavations at Quanterness and Isbister have taken us further in our understanding. It would seem that the dead of communities were first reduced to skeletons — perhaps by being left exposed to the elements — and then a selection of the bones was taken into the chamber; subsequently the bones were sorted. Food offerings, broken burnt pottery, bone pins and flints were also taken into the chamber.[10] One thing apparent from the Isbister investigations is that this class of monument is seriously underinvestigated; the chambers have been concentrated on, and the fact that the tombs may be just part of much larger ceremonial complexes has been largely ignored.

Two ceremonial complexes belonging to the later part of the Neolithic which would be difficult to overlook are the Ring of Brodgar[2] and the Stones of Stenness[2] which lie north and south of the Brig of Brodgar on the narrow strip of land between the lochs of Stenness and Harray. When looking at these stone circles it must be remembered that they are actually henge monuments: impressive as they now are, they would be even more striking if the 3m-deep rock-cut ditches which surround each were emptied. The Ring of Brodgar would have originally had 60 stones in the circle, and there were two opposed causeways across the ditch (Plate 7a). The Stones of Stenness originally numbered twelve and there was one causeway; in the centre was found a square setting of stones containing fragments of cremated bone, charcoal and sherds of Grooved Ware pottery.[11] Although some have been removed, several single standing stones exist in the Brodgar area; these and others found in the islands probably also date to the later Neolithic.

The Bronze Age (c. 2000-700 BC)

Until very recently nothing was known about Bronze Age settlement in Orkney (or, by and large, elsewhere in the north and west of Scotland). This situation was greatly improved when it was discovered that the so-called 'burnt mounds' which are abundant in Orkney belonged to at least the Middle and Late part of this period.[12] More recent work in Shetland has indicated that they may have occurred in the Early Bronze Age too.[13]

At the sites of Liddle[7] in South Ronaldsay and Beaquoy in Harray it has been shown that the 'burnt mound' element was only the rubbish which had been piled around the building which generated it (Plate 7b). The reason why what would otherwise have been midden was so voluminous and consisted almost exclusively of burnt stone and ash is indicated by the large hearths and troughs which typified the buildings: it would appear that during this period field stones were heated and used to boil

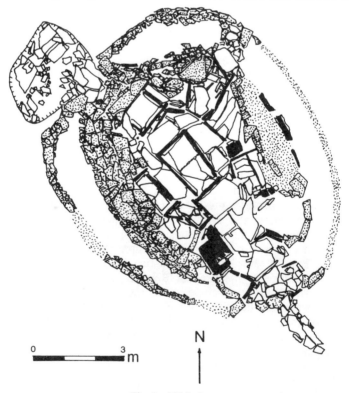

0 _____ 3
▬▬▬▬▬ m

N
↑

Fig. 3—Liddle house

food in large quantities of water. The cooking facilities dominate the building at Liddle (Fig. 3), but it appears to have been a dwelling too, with two putative beds, a bench, and a number of compartments around the inside. In apparent contrast to the Neolithic period, the habitations of the Bronze Age were dispersed, did not hug the coast, and followed the course of small streams inland.

It would be false to give the impression that the burial practices of the Bronze Age are well understood. A glance through the records shows that a large number of burials and burial monuments have been reported which could well be Bronze Age in date, but we know little about them and they generally lack the pottery and datable finds which have eased the situation elsewhere.

Comparison with other areas is by no means a total solution since the situation in Orkney is evidently complex and, to some extent, independent. There is, for instance, no doubt that the influence of the Beaker Folk (who probably introduced metallurgy to Britain) was felt in Orkney, since Beaker sherds have on rare occasions been recovered from otherwise typically Neolithic settlements and tombs,[14] but no classic Beaker crouched burials have been located, and the presence of sherds of the typical pottery and barbed and tanged arrowheads in tombs (as well as a date for Isbister) makes it possible that the few people involved adopted local practices. In the Early Bronze Age it is likely, however, that communal egalitarian burial was partly succeeded by the placing of the bodies or cremated remains of individuals under mounds of earth. The Knowes of Trotty in Harray, for example, include a bell barrow which contained gold discs and an amber spacer-plate necklace,[15] and these give us a link with the south of England. There are a lot of round barrows in Orkney — there is a particularly fine and dense group in the Brodgar area — but we must be careful: barrows are known to have been used in other periods, and it is doubtful whether every burial of the Early Bronze Age was deemed to warrant one. In the Middle and Late Bronze Age we again see the continued influence on Orkney burial customs of ideas from beyond the Pentland Firth: the site of Quoyscottie in Harray with its small barrows and associated cemetery of cremations in holes in the ground[15] is very reminiscent of contemporary practice in the south of England.[16] Similar funerary monuments have been found, for instance, at Quandale on Rousay and at Queenafjold in Birsay.[17]

The Iron Age (c. 700 BC - c. 300 AD)

The image of the gaunt isolated broch tower has dominated our thinking on the occupation of the islands in the Iron Age to the extent that the type of monument and the period have come to be regarded as almost synonymous.[18] Recent excavations and reassessment of earlier information have, however, revealed a more tangled web.[19]

It would seem that the concept of the round house was introduced into Orkney at the beginning of the Iron Age. Examples of an early date are known from Bu at Stromness, Quanterness by Kirkwall, and Pierowall Quarry on Westray;[20] another, undated, was found on the Calf of Eday.[21] These early round houses were scattered across a landscape which they probably shared with habitations built in the traditional way. At Bu, for example, comparatively crude dwellings were dug into the ruins of the round house soon after its evacuation; comparable buildings are known from Howmae on North Ronaldsay.[22] One of the structures at Bu was similar to the type of earth-house found in Orkney at sites such as Grain[2] by Kirkwall (Fig. 4) and Rennibister[2] in Firth: some of these earth-

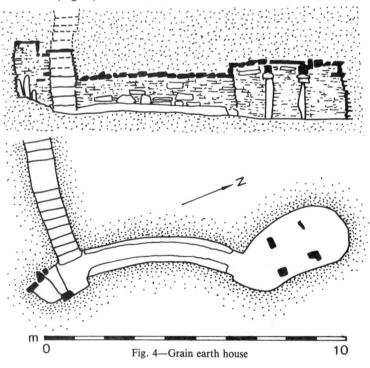

m
0   Fig. 4—Grain earth house   10

The Ring of Brodgar

Bronze Age house, Liddle

Interior, Bu Broch

Broch of Gurness from the air

houses are also of Iron Age date and have had surface occupation above them.

Two aspects of the Bu round house are particularly interesting: one is that its size, 5.2m thick defensive wall, and entrance make it indistinguishable from the lower part of a broch tower; secondly, its interior layout is of a distinct type (Fig. 5; Plate 8a) with a central hearth, cooking tank and service area surrounded by three large cupboards (accessible from the service area) and a series of interconnecting rooms. At Bu the service area contained kitchen equipment, there was the debris from storage in pottery vessels in the cupboards, and the peripheral rooms had the remains of litter or bedding in them.

Bu shows that the broch tower was the ultimate evolution of the style of building which had been introduced, fully fledged, into the islands. On the basis of finds of Roman objects, broch towers have traditionally been considered to date to the 1st and 2nd centuries AD, but there is no hard evidence that the brochs did not evolve before the Romans were in Scotland. When the

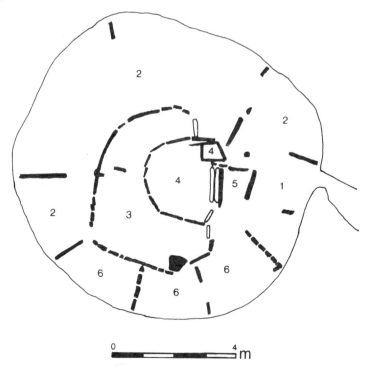

Fig. 5—Interior of Bu Broch. 1 Vestibule; 2 Peripheral Rooms; 3 Kitchen Service Area; 4 Hearth and Cooking Tank; 5 Cupboard; 6 Storage Compartments

Vikings arrived in the late first millennium a number of brochs in Orkney were sufficiently recognisable for them to be called *borgs* (defences) — which is where our name for them comes from.

The currency of the broch towers may, therefore, be longer than has been supposed, and there is no reason to believe that they represent the only type of settlement of the period they belong to. The common conception of broch towers is that they were some sort of masonry shell in which refuge was taken and that when they fell into disuse they were dismantled, shanty building being erected both inside them and around their base. Recent excavations and a review of the evidence show this view to be rather doubtful. Many of the interior plans have a striking resemblance to that at Bu (sometimes being divided, for two families), and there are clear indications of there having been at least one upper storey, perhaps an annular one. Moreover, the surrounding buildings are contemporary with the tower, and this is almost certainly true also of the defensive ramparts and ditches which often surround the whole. What we have here are defended villages which may have housed up to 250 people. The concentration of settlement contrasts with that of the earlier part of the Iron Age, but the great similarity between the early round houses and the broch towers themselves suggests that the latter evolved from the former. The differences between the broch towers and the buildings of their surrounding villages may be related to cultural affinities and social organisation; it is a subject that would repay future study. Good examples of Iron Age defended villages containing broch towers may be seen at Gurness[2] in Evie (Plate 8b) and at Midhowe[2] on Rousay. Another has recently been excavated at Howe by Stromness;[23] and Lingro in St Ola, worked on in the late 19th century, is in the process of being published.[24]

Another type of monument, which is being studied by Raymond Lamb, is the treb dyke. The remains of these boundaries which methodically divide the Orkney landscape are sometimes as much as 18m wide and 1.8m high, and it is possible that they belong to the Early Iron Age.[25]

Burials belonging to the Early Iron Age have been elusive throughout Britain, and Orkney is no exception. I feel that it would require only a minimum of directed effort to make great headway over this problem. Every year, for example, farmers plough the covers off short cists which contain nothing but a pile of cremated bone. The distribution of these cists suggests that they are to be found in cemeteries,[26] and it may well be that they belong to the Iron Age.

The Picts (c. 300-800 AD)

Suddenly we get a name for the people we are dealing with — the Picts. The Picts are first mentioned in a document of AD 297 (though there can be little doubt that they existed before that), and their kingdom came to an end when it was united with that of the Scots in 843.[27] There are a few other literary references and there is very limited place-name evidence (e.g. the Pentland or Pictland Firth). It is the presence of the still unintelligible ogam inscriptions and mystical symbol stones which confirm Orkney's allegiances — at least in the 7th and 8th centuries.[28] Though it is as mysterious as the others, the symbol stone from the Brough of Birsay has the added interest of showing three warriors with their weapons (Fig. 6); this is the earliest datable pictorial representation of a person in Orkney.

Fig. 6—The Pictish symbol stone
from the Brough of Birsay

Where the Picts lived and where they were buried has always been an enigma,[29] but this is another area in which our understanding has been considerably advanced by recent work in Orkney. The conceptual breakthrough was provided by Anna Ritchie when she formed the opinion that any site in an appropriate area and within the known period could, with justification, be considered Pictish; the finding of a spindle whorl with an ogam inscription at her site of Buckquoy in Birsay supported this approach.[30] Other settlements of the second half of the Pictish period have also been found at Saevar Howe in Birsay and at Gurness in Evie,[31] but occupation of great duration, which possibly extends back into the earlier part of the period, has also been investigated at Howe in Stromness.[32]

There is no evidence, yet, of villages as such, and it would seem that dispersed settlement has been reverted to. The style of building, too, has roots in the traditions which predate the round-house/broch idea; the interiors of the rooms are alcoved, and different ones have been referred to as 'figure-of-eight,' 'clover-leaf,' and even 'jelly-baby-shaped' (Fig. 7). One very interesting feature is that buildings tended to be recessed into the ground or the rubble from an earlier structure. It may prove to be the case that some of the promontory forts in Orkney are Pictish;[33] this would add a strand of complexity to our view of settlement of the time.

Christianity was probably brought to the Picts in the late 6th or early 7th century,[34] although evidences for this are slight.

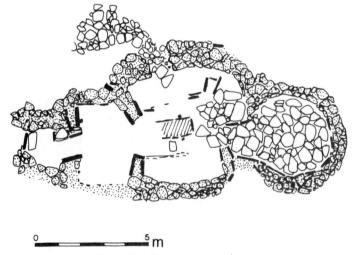

0 _____ 5 m

Fig. 7—The Pictish house at Buckquoy

There are supposed to be traces of an Early Christian monastery on the Brough of Birsay,[35] and Raymond Lamb, on the basis of field observation, has posited others elsewhere.[36] The acceptance of Christianity would have meant that the dead were buried in graves (or long cists), without any goods, and in cemeteries; there is an example of such a cemetery on the Brough of Birsay. What the prevailing burial rite was in the earlier part of the Pictish period is not known, but cremation is one possibility; one of several short cists found overlying the Broch of Oxtro had a symbol stone incorporated in it.[37]

The Vikings (c. 800-1014 AD)

The term 'Viking' is a byword for a plundering warrior, but, apart from five silver hoards,[38] the evidence in Orkney points more to migration (chiefly from Norway). This took place just before or after AD 800 and was of a scale such as to overwhelm the inhabitants 'politically, socially, culturally and linguistically'[39] (though Christianity may have survived). Nonetheless, excavations at Saevar Howe and Buckquoy in Birsay have shown that, although Pictish farmsteads were built over with ones with Norse features, earlier artefact types continued in use (ones distinctive of the Vikings in their homeland being rare), and land use continued unchanged.[40] The archaeological record, as far as it has been exploited, indicates integration rather than continued violent conflict.

One way in which Viking influence does seem to have dominated is in the whole style of building. There is a real transition to rectangular structures with what were probably quite low walls made of two skins with a core; sometimes the outer skin was made of turf and stone, or just turf alone. The internal layout of the buildings and occasional post-holes suggest that the roof was supported on two rows of wooden posts which ran down the length. During this period houses as such tended to have two rooms, one of which had a long central hearth and benches along the sides. At this time outbuildings were separate, although later they were to be joined.[41] Examples of such buildings may be seen on the Brough of Birsay (Plate 9a); what we now regard as the traditional Orkney house stems from these models.

Surprisingly few burials of the 9th and 10th centuries are known, and they display alarming variety; Chris Morris has catalogued the types as burial within existing mounds, burial under new mounds, boat burial, burial under stone cairns, in stone-lined oval graves, in stone-lined rectangular cists, and in

simple dug graves.[42] Key cemeteries have been examined at
Pierowall on Westray and at Westness on Rousay, while isolated
burials are known from Buckquoy and the Brough Road in
Birsay and from Gurness in Evie.[43] Both men and women tended
to be buried with some of their ornaments and effects (Fig. 8), a
practice which ceased with the reintroduction of Christianity at
the very end of the 10th century or the beginning of the 11th.

THE IMPEDIMENTA OF LIFE

In the period under examination there was greater continuity
in the style of life and the impedimenta that went with it than
there was change; technological developments had less of an
impact on Orkney than they did elsewhere. This caused severe
problems for archaeologists who were for a while unable to tell
the artefacts of one period from those of another: in recent years
independent dating by radiocarbon assay has to some extent
resolved this impasse. In this situation artefacts have to be
discussed in broad groupings, with comment, where necessary,
on horizons of change. Matters are not helped by the fact that
most artefacts from Orkney were recovered in the course of
relatively primitive excavations, often on multi-period sites, and

1,2,3 Remains of skeleton   4 necklet
5,6 brooches   7 sickle   8 knife

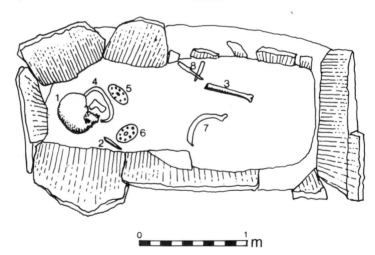

Fig. 8—A Viking grave at the Broch of Gurness

their true date is unknown. It must be borne in mind that the artefacts surviving only reflect a fragment of all the activities undertaken — and we do not understand what they were all for.

Farming and hunting

As we shall see, most of our evidence for this comes from environmental remains, and the light that artefacts can cast on these activities is slight. The polished stone axes of the Neolithic period (Fig. 19) must be taken into consideration, for these objects were developed to clear the primary forests of Europe so that the land could be cultivated. Orkney was probably not heavily forested, but some clearance would have been necessary. The fact that only one axe and two moulds are known for the Bronze Age may not be fortuitous. Among the artefacts, stone ploughshares are the most positive sign of agriculture (Fig. 9) and, although these must usually have been abandoned in the fields when broken, stratified examples are known from the early Neolithic (at Isbister), through the Bronze Age (at Liddle and Quoyscottie) to the Early Iron Age (at Bu). At the Bu site, there was a working area where these and related implements were found with chipping debris. The other distinct stone tool type involved was a thin rectangular blade of stone (Fig. 9); these

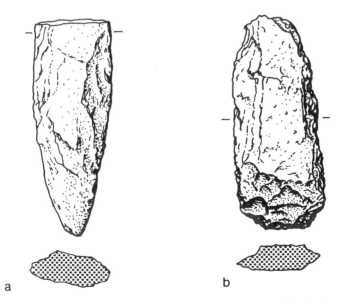

a   b

Fig. 9—Ard share fron Neolithic/Early Bronze Age Isbister (a) and an Early Iron Age 'mattock' from Bu (b). (scale 1:4)

may have been hafted and used as mattocks to break down the clods to a tilth. Identical implements, again, can be traced back to the early Neolithic. We can see here that even in the Iron Age iron was not being used for obvious purposes; similarly very little bronze seems to have been actually used in the Bronze Age. When these stone implements were superseded by metal ones is difficult to say, but they only rarely feature among finds from 'broch sites'. None have been reported from stratified deposits of the first millennium AD.

A great deal of hunting and gathering can be done without any sort of implement, while other aids will have disappeared or been lost away from where they can be recovered or securely dated. Flint and chert are rare in Orkney but leaf-shaped arrowheads were made from these materials in the Neolithic period, being replaced by barbed and tanged ones in the Early Bronze Age (Fig. 10). What such projectiles were tipped with in the Iron Age is unknown. For many implements we can only guess at their function, but fine bone points have been dubbed 'winkle (buckie) pickers' and blades of whalebone, seemingly from the Iron Age, have, perhaps imaginatively, been called 'blubber mattocks.' Certainly oil from marine mammals would have been needed for the cruisie-like stone lamps which have been recovered.

Food preparation

The dietary staple must have been grain, albeit intermixed with weed seeds. At first this was ground with a mortar and pestle or

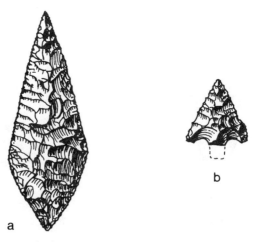

Fig. 10—Leaf-shaped (a) and barbed and tanged (b) arrowheads from Unstan.
(1:1)

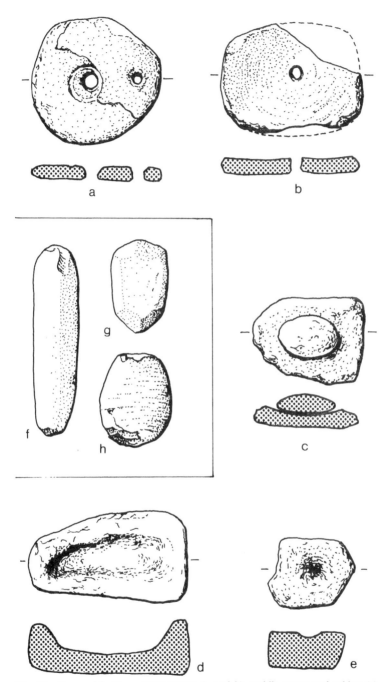

Fig. 11—Top and bottom rotary querns (a and b), saddle quern and rubber (c), trough quern (d), mortar (e), pestle, grinder and pounder (f-h). All from the Broch of Gurness. (a-e 1:15; f-h 1:4)

by rubbing it with one stone along another which was dipped in the middle (hence its name, saddle quern) (Fig. 11). At some time in the Iron Age, certainly after Bu Broch, the rotary quern was introduced (Fig. 11). Here an upper circular stone was rotated on a similar lower one while grain was fed down a central hole; although it became mechanised this principle continued in use in Orkney and indeed is still used to a limited extent. Quernstones need to have their grinding faces periodically roughened, and this could well be the function of some of the innumerable beach pebbles found on sites of all periods (Fig. 11). Others of these pebbles could have been grinders and pounders used with different sorts of devices designed to reduce hard foodstuffs to powder; mortars, for instance, continued in use and there were trough querns in the Iron Age — both reminiscent of 'knocking stanes.'

Meat would have had to be skinned and jointed. Up to the Iron Age this may have been achieved with tools of flint and chert or split stone (only daggers have been found for the Bronze Age). Thereafter iron knives were probably used, handles being found as early as Bu and several blades being known from the Pictish period onward.

The principal function of pots would have been for storage or cooking, and even the hand-made low-fired ones found throughout the period (Fig. 12) could have been heated in embers or had hot stones dropped into them. Thin circles of stone were probably used to seal the tops up to at least the end of the Iron Age (Fig. 12). It is very interesting, technologically, that neither the potter's wheel nor the kiln seems to have had any impact on Orkney. It is also interesting that during two periods — the Bronze Age and the Viking — the art of potting was neglected. There are, of course, other materials from which vessels can be made, and there are alternative methods of cooking. Judging from the amount of debris, the most popular means in the Bronze Age was to drop hot stones into a trough of water; this may have been a local equivalent to the cauldrons used elsewhere. This method remained popular into the Iron Age, although by Pictish times it seems to have fallen out of favour. In the Viking period the main vessels used were of steatite (soapstone); this material does not occur naturally in Orkney and must have been imported from Shetland or Scandinavia. Possible fragments of an iron cauldron have been recovered at Saevar Howe.

It is not possible to exhaust the subject of prehistoric cooking here but spit roasting is another possibility: from the high period of the brochs and throughout the Pictish period sockets are

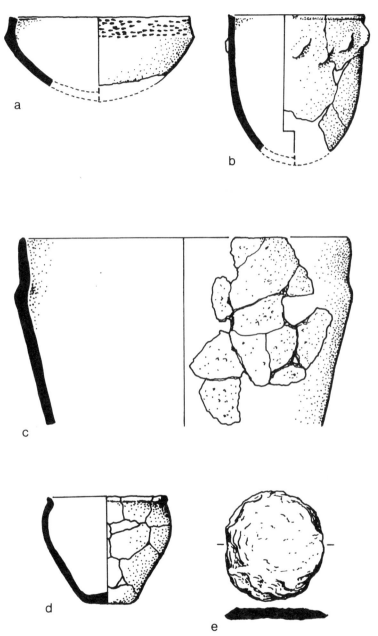

Fig. 12—Neolithic pots from Isbister (a and b), an Early Iron Age one from
Bu (c), a Pictish one from Howe (d), and a pot lid from Gurness (e). (1:5)

commonly found on either side of hearths, although these may have housed a superstructure from which pots were suspended. There are all sorts of aspects of the culinary arts about which we may never gain full knowledge; one of the most obvious is the preservation of foodstuffs (which would have been seasonal) by e.g. salting and drying.

Manfacturing

Tools were used to make things, and they in turn had to be made. Bones (and wood) could be split and shaped with stone blades and pumice (grooved pieces of which are known for all periods), but from the Iron Age there are items which could only have been made with the use of saws, gravers, and even some sort of auger. Earlier, bone tools would have been very important in knapping flint and chert. The main tool for shaping stone implements and furnishings was probably the hammerstone, which can be picked up on most beaches in every shape and size desirable. Metalwork, both bronze and iron, was only introduced slowly and in limited areas. Judging from the fact that the moulds found are of steatite it may be the case that it was not so much the indigenous population of the Bronze Age that were responsible for casting objects as itinerant metalworkers from elsewhere. The first domestic evidence of metalwork comes from Bu Broch where two crucibles were found which bore traces of copper (Fig. 13). Copper is available in Orkney, as is lead, but it is possible that imported items were being re-smelted and cast. Moulds, largely for trinkets, have been found so far in contexts from the high Broch period up to the end of the Pictish (Fig. 13). Iron too is found in Orkney and there was not only slag in the infill of Bu Broch but also a furnace found at Midhowe.

It is very difficult to detect the manufacture of perishable items such as leather, woodwork and textiles through the artefactual assemblage, but one large group of implements which are probably relevant are the numerous bone 'awls', 'gouges,' etc. The occurrence of these diminishes with time and they are comparatively rare in later Pictish and Viking contexts, when the use of iron had probably been fully integrated. Although finds of spindle whorls and needles (Fig. 14) only start in Orkney with the Iron Age, it is likely that people spun (and wore clothes of textiles) in the Bronze Age, at least. Evidence of actual looms is scarce though it is possible that some holed stones of Early Iron Age date were weights used to tighten the warp on one model. Groups of such weights, in clay, were found on the floors of two of the Viking houses at Saevar Howe (Fig. 14).

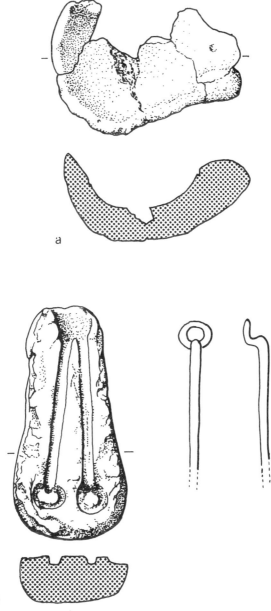

Fig. 13—Early Iron Age crucible from Bu (a) (3:4) and mould for casting Pictish ring-headed pins from Gurness (b) (1:1)

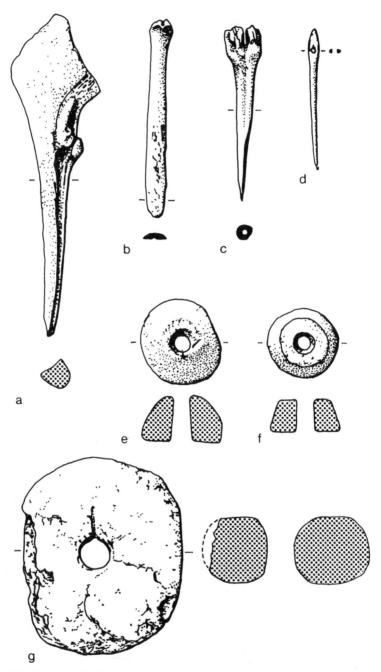

Fig. 14—Bone implements and a needle from the Broch of Gurness (a-d) and spindle whorls and a loom weight from Pictish/Viking Saevar Howe (e-g), (1:2)

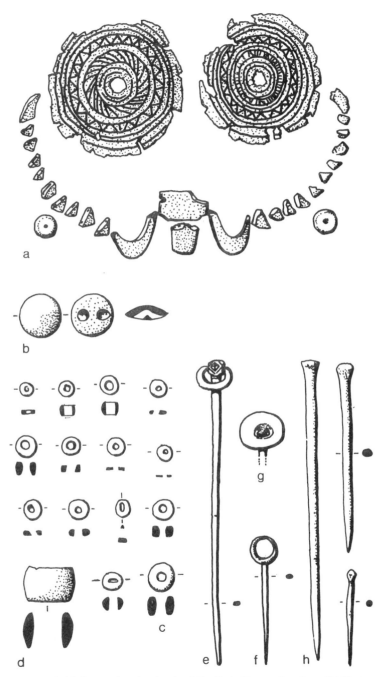

Fig. 15—Gold discs and amber beads of the Early Bronze Age from the Knowes of Trotty (a), jet button, ring and bone beads from Neolithic/Early Bronze Age Isbister (b-d), bronze Viking and Pictish ring-headed pins and an Early Iron age globular-headed one from the Broch of Gurness (e-g), and three bone pins from Pictish/Viking Saevar Howe (h). (1:2)

Personal adornment and recreation

Necklaces seem to have been in vogue in the Neolithic. Gordon Childe painted an imaginative picture of a woman losing her beads as she ran along the passageway at Skara Brae as it was being inundated by sand. Similar beads of bone, shell and antler have been found together with a polished dog's tooth in the tomb fill at Isbister (Fig. 15), while there were 35 slate beads and a pumice pendant in the blocking of the upper passage at Taversoe Tuick. A group of limpet shells with their apices removed (possibly by natural causes) had been taken into the chamber at Isbister, and this may well indicate that Neolithic jewellery was also made of less manufactured (and recognisable) things than beads. Other relevant finds are a jet button and ring from Isbister (Fig. 15); the latter would have fitted a finger, as would a bone one from Quanterness.

In general, the British Isles are very rich in jewellery of particularly the earlier part of the Bronze Age. There are gold and copper neck-rings or diadems, lunulae, torcs, bracelets, rings and pins as well as spacer-plate necklaces of amber and jet and toggles of jet and of bone. However, such articles do not seem to have been at all common in Orkney, although a cist in one of the Knowes of Trotty, Harray, which contained a cremation, yielded an amber spacer-plate necklace and four gold dics (of unknown use) (Fig. 15).

Many of the earlier bone points could have been used as dress

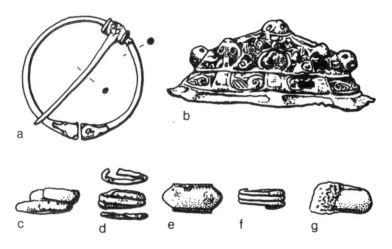

Fig. 16—Bronze penannular brooch (a), tortoise brooch (b), and rings (c-g) from the Broch of Gurness. (1:2)

pins, but from the Iron Age on these become very developed. One class commonly found on 'broch sites' consists of a hemisphere of bone — usually sea mammal ivory — from the bottom of which projected an iron shank (Fig. 15). Another, probably referable exclusively to Pictish times, was of bronze with a fixed ring head. In the Viking period there is a more substantial type with a moving ring head (Fig. 15). Decorated bone pins, some very small, are found in Pictish times and afterwards; very occasionally the top is carved to resemble an animal's head (Fig. 15). Another dress article was brooches, Pictish ones generally being a circle of metal (usually bronze) with a pin hinged across it (Fig. 16). The Vikings had these too, sometimes in silver, but their commonest type are named after

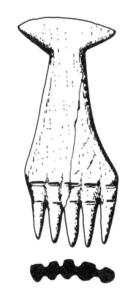

a

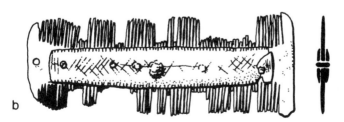

b

Fig. 17—An Early Iron Age long-handled comb from Bu (a) and a composite one from Pictish/Viking Saevar Howe (b). (1:2)

D

the tortoise shells they resemble, and were worn in pairs on the shoulders (Fig. 16). Viking hoards have also yielded armlets, necklets and rings; two severed hands were found at Gurness with rings still on the fingers (Fig. 16) and there are circles of bronze from the same site which are probably ear-rings. When it became available, from the Iron Age onward, coloured glass was popular, pieces often being re-smelted, and it was used to manufacture bracelets and beads.

Gordon Childe suggested that shallow stone dishes at Skara Brae, which contained pigments, may have been used as cosmetic palettes. Certainly other investigators noted blue, red, white and yellow pigment at 'broch sites', and we cannot rule out the possibility that they were used as some sort of make-up. It must be remembered that the name *Picti* actually implies that the

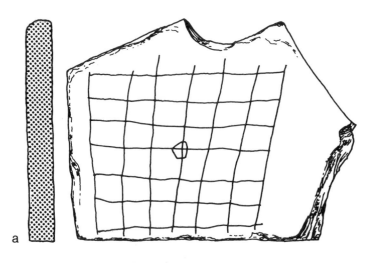

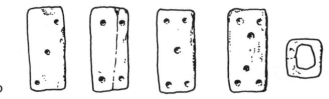

Fig. 18—Stone gaming board from Pictish/Viking Buckquoy (a) (1:3) and a bone die from Gurness (b) (1:2)

people painted themselves. We have some slight insight into other aspects of personal grooming with razors, single examples of which have been found for both the Middle and Late Bronze Age periods. A change which is particularly interesting is that from the long-handled, relatively coarse combs of the Early Iron Age to the fine composite ones which seem to appear in the Pictish period (Fig. 17).

Most leisure pursuits will have left little recognisable trace but Childe found what he supposed were dice at Skara Brae and indisputable ones are known from the Iron Age; actual boards for games have been found from the Pictish period onward (Fig. 18).

The tools of war

Although Neolithic people are not now considered to have been as peaceful as they once were,[44] there is little in the record in Orkney that could have been used for offence, except arrowheads, polished stone mace-heads and, possibly, axe heads (Fig. 19). No serious wounds have ever been noted among skeletal material from the chambered tombs. Similarly in the Bronze Age we only have arrowheads and a few daggers and spearheads (Fig. 19). Even in the Early Iron Age when there are the massive broch towers with defended villages (not to mention earth-houses, which some see as defensive), real hard evidence of weaponry is slight — though bad excavation and conservation techniques will not have helped. The most positive indications consist of pommels and guards of bone which were probably from swords (Fig. 19); two spearheads were reported from the Broch of Ayre in Burray and a spear butt and moulds for the same were found at Burrian in Harray and in Gurness respectively.[45] Several other items recovered may or may not relate to the period. As has been mentioned, some promontory forts may be Pictish and the symbol stone from the Brough of Birsay shows three warriors with swords, spears and shields (Fig. 6); again, however, no weapons have actually been found. The case might have been otherwise if it had been usual to inter the dead with grave goods, and in the pagan part of the Viking period we suddenly get a reasonable amount of information from this source. Men at Pierowall in Westray, for example, were buried with swords, daggers, axes, spears and shields, while in one grave of the 9th century cemetery at Westness in Rousay there was a sheaf of arrows.

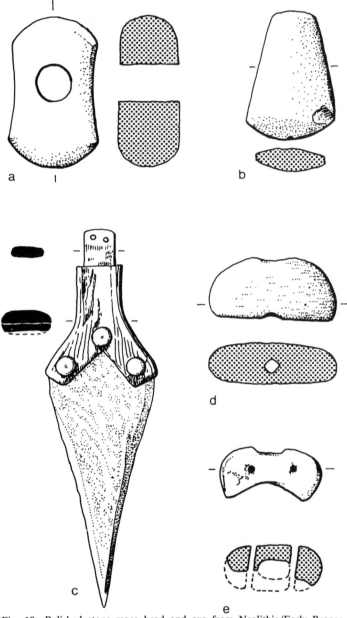

Fig. 19—Polished stone mace head and axe from Neolithic/Early Bronze Age
Isbister (a and b), Early Bronze Age dagger from Flanders Moss, Wasbister (c),
and a sword pommel (d) and guard (e) from the brochs of Lingro and Gurness.
(1:2)

THE ENVIRONMENT AND ITS EXPLOITATION

In the beginning . . .

What was Orkney like at the time of the first settlement, and how did it change under the influence of man and the climate? Most of our evidence comes from the analysis of pollen in peat deposits and sediments, but there are other sources which can be drawn on. The major pollen sequences we have are from Yesnaby and the Loons in the West Mainland, Glims Moss in Harray, the Loch of Skaill in Sandwick, Lesliedale Moss by Kirkwall, and Liddle Farm and Liddle Bog in South Ronaldsay.[46]

Although it would have varied from place to place, it is generally agreed that the Orkney vegetation would have been similar to the only surviving stand of native woodland at Berriedale on Hoy. There would have been an open cover of scrub trees — mainly of birch, willow and hazel, with a rich ground flora of tall herbs and ferns. The presence of the pollen of grasses and of herbs such as plantain suggests that there was some grazing. Arboreal pollen in the deposits may have been blown in, but actual trees have been found, particularly birch and willow, as well as hazel nuts. Forests are known with trees up to 0.6m in diameter, preserved under the sea which inundated them, as at the Bay of Skaill in Sandwick and Otterswick Bay in Sanday.[47]

Less is known about the fauna since bones dissolve in peat deposits and those from archaeological sites are often intrusive. It seems inherently unlikely that domestic mammals would have been in Orkney before man — but deer may have swum over. Whether less useful animals were present before man — otters, foxes, toads, frogs, voles, and so on — is a matter of conjecture. Birds, of course, would not have found the Pentland Firth a barrier, and the flora and fauna of the littoral zone and the mammals and fish of the sea would have been established.

Climatic studies, generally, tell us that the climate was temperate, being at its most favourable in the period c. 5000-4000 BC. The average temperature then would have been higher than now by a degree or two centigrade. The maritime location of the islands would have been responsible then, as now, for the buffering of land temperature and for exposure (with salt-laden winds), but these are things which would have varied in degree. When man first came, conditions would have been as good as they have ever been in Orkney.

With the exception of Hoy, the islands are mainly low-lying with much of the land being below 75m and with only a few hills

over 150m: the underlying flagstones with their natural content
of lime, augmented by glacial deposits, provided a good soil
base. Orkney would have been well suited to agriculture.

The initial impact of man

Around 4000-3000 BC man came with his cattle, sheep, goats,
pigs, dogs and seed corn, and with the ready made knowledge of
how to exploit the environment both by cropping its natural
resources and by husbandry and agriculture. We must be wary of
using information from the chambered tombs, since the food in
them was selected,[48] but there is pertinent evidence from both the
old and the new excavations at Knap of Howar and Skara
Brae.[49]
Preserved remains and impressions show that both barley and
wheat were grown, although this does not rule out the collection
(and cultivation) of other types of seeds such as those of sorrel.
Carbonised seed from the tomb floor at Isbister is particularly
interesting since grain there is contaminated with a lot of seeds
of edible weeds. Pollen evidence from near Isbister hints that in
the Neolithic there was temporary clearance of land, with plots
being exhausted and new ones opened.
Most meat came from sheep and cattle, which were kept in
almost equal numbers — meaning that beef was the main source
of protein; there may have been goats but their bones are
difficult to distinguish from those of sheep. Cattle were smaller
than Neolithic ones elsewhere, as were the sheep (which were not
dissimilar to those found now on North Ronaldsay). Pigs were
kept but were few in number. Most animals were killed when
young; this must have been partly because of the difficulty of
providing fodder for them in the winter, but we must also give
consideration to the possibility that some were slaughtered so
that their mother's milk could be used by man. It is difficult to
say whether there were horses in Neolithic Orkney. The few
bones said to have come from chambered tombs may well have
either been intrusive or incorrectly identified; there is no evidence
from habitation sites.
There was little to hunt in Orkney, except deer (if they were
not herded), and the contribution this made to the economy was
slight. Birds, particularly marine ones, were caught — probably
on cliffs — and some of these could have provided oil as well as
meat. Marine molluscs were gathered, particularly limpets but
also winkles, cockles, razor-shells and oysters, but some of these
may have been intended for fishing bait rather than human
consumption. However, watertight boxes in the floors of houses

at Skara Brae may have been used to keep shellfish in overnight so that they cleansed themselves of grit. Not only inshore fish were caught; Neolithic man clearly exploited deep water two to five miles from the shore, with lines and boats, where large saithe, cod and similar fish were taken. Seal and whale bones may show nothing more than the use of carrion, but they indicate man exploited his environment to the full; crab shells, for instance, were found at Isbister.

The impact on the environment of Orkney both of agriculture and the stock introduced is very clearly reflected in the pollen record. The scrub forests disappeared early, and the remaining tall herb and fern vegetation was quickly replaced with pasture. This, together with a climatic deterioration (which would have involved lower temperatures, more rain and increased wind speeds), led to the formation of blanket peat from 1500-1000 BC onward, particularly on higher ground.

Man in the changed environment

It will be seen from the foregoing that in the Early Bronze Age Orkney was a landscape of rapidly declining richness. This is very well reflected in the apparent poverty of settlement of the Middle and Late Bronze Age and may account for their being so scattered and inland. We have little hard evidence for this period but such as there is suggests that the mode of exploiting the environment continued unchanged; but living would have been more difficult.

It may be that in the Iron Age advances had been made in the efficiency of agriculture, no doubt helped by technological innovations and a slight improvement in climate. It is difficult to imagine how the land could otherwise have supported the villages around the (quite numerous) brochs; indeed recent calculations by Noel Fojut[50] have suggested that the production of grain could not have been far behind what it was in later, historical, times. One important factor may have been the introduction of the horse; lack of horse bones is particularly noticeable at the round house of Quanterness and at Bu, while by contrast at Saevar Howe and Buckquoy they formed a significant proportion of late Pictish/Viking stock (over 5%). There is nothing definite to say when this species was first introduced, but a number of horse bones have been reported from 'broch sites'.[51]

We unfortunately have few environmental remains from the Iron Age since most of the sites were investigated some time ago (and the Howe is, as yet, unpublished). At Bu, however, the economy seems to have been unchanged from Neolithic times, except, perhaps, that cattle outnumbered sheep and the role of the pig was more significant than formerly. It is perhaps unwise to take too much notice of slight changes in the percentage representation of species since it may either be fortuitous or reflect strictly local variation. At the later Pictish and Viking settlement of Buckquoy, for instance, there were 50% cattle to 30% sheep, while at contemporary Saevar Howe there were something like three sheep to every cow; in both cases, as at Bu, the contribution of the pig was significant.

What is truly remarkable is how little the exploitation of the environment seems to have changed in Orkney from the earliest Neolithic through to the Viking period some 5,000 years later; indeed, comparatively recent farming practice may not have been significantly dissimilar. Introductions of the hen (at least by later Pictish times), the domestic goose (by Viking times), and of oats and flax (again by Viking times) pale in to insignificance beside the solid foundation of food production. Even the breeds of the animals seem not to have changed greatly, although further research may shed greater light on this. In prehistory, as in historic times, Orkney stock was noticeably smaller than that elsewhere.

CULTURAL AFFINITIES AND SOCIAL ORGANISATION

Cultural affinities

We have seen in the previous three sections that there was a basic continuity throughout the prehistory of Orkney; house forms had their similarities, types of artefact continued in use for millennia, and the desired outcome of the exploitation of the environment remained constant, though it may have been impeded by some circumstances and aided by others. This is not to claim that there was no change; the point to emphasise, however, is the continuity and strong common thread that ran through the centuries. We have pinpointed certain changes and, although the question must be asked how they came about, the answer is not at all easy to provide. It would be foolish to say that there were no population movements in prehistory when we know that these took place in historical times: it would be equally foolish, however, to equate every change with population movement since ideas can travel without being borne by hordes of people and, after all, some of the innovations we see in prehistory may have stemmed from Orkney. Reliable information on population movement is only likely to come from physical anthropology and related disciplines — although it

Broch of Birsay from the air

St Magnus Church, Egilsay

Yarpha, Orphir

Cutting the crop, Rendall

Quoys, Graemsay, with Hoy High lighthouse in the background

The Flaws family, who operate the Rousay, Egilsay and Wyre ferry service

would largely be archaeologically derived material that would be the basis for study.

The material culture of the Neolithic suggests that some of the settlers — those with Unstan pottery — crossed the Pentland Firth from Caithness, which seems only reasonable. The Grooved Ware element is, however, more problematic, but some stone carved art is very similar to that found in Ireland,[52] and these people may have come up the west coast of Britain — though not necessarily in one step. After they had come, links with the outside must have continued, for at the end of the Neolithic we get the henges and stone circles. This state of affairs clearly continued through the Bronze Age since we have the introduction of beakers, Wessex-style goldwork, spacer-plate necklaces, bronze itself, barrows, and, ultimately, a version of an urnfield.

Previously expressed caution notwithstanding, I am inclined to think that there was an immigration of people on a significant scale which started around 700 BC. The poor climate in the period before that probably meant that the islands were underpopulated and it is at this later time, around 700 BC, that we get the introduction of the round house — which was quite out of keeping with anything there had been in Orkney before — and ultimately of iron and, probably, horses, both of which must have revolutionised agriculture. But immigration does not necessarily mean that the aboriginal population is annihilated or ousted, and in the earlier part of the Iron Age we see the traditional building style existing alongside the new. In this respect tradition may have outlived innovation, for the houses of the Pictish period owe nothing to the round house concept. Again, throughout the Iron Age and the Pictish periods there are indications of links with the outside and there is nothing surprising in this. We know from protohistorical sources that people travelled (and the occupants of Early Christian monasteries must not be forgotten), but it was with the Vikings that what was probably the third big immigration took place. As we have seen, the effect was, in some respects, overwhelming and it has left its mark to the present day, but, again, we see the continuity of life under it all.

Social organisation

Archaeology has a rather dry reputation, but recent advances in our ability to gain evidence and to interpret it have put a bit more life into our conception of the people of the past. Until recently, for example, our mainstay for the Neolithic was to say that there were two peoples, but it is now perfectly clear that they inhabited the islands at more or less the same time and that they had a great deal more in common that they had differences.[53] How, or why, they maintained their distinctiveness in the limited spheres in which it existed, and how they coexisted, are matters of interest. The size, distribution and contents of the tombs suggest that people lived in territorially-based communities, like Skara Brae, and that originally the structure of society was not strongly hierarchical. Comparison of Isbister with other tombs gave us great insight into this, in that the types of food which were deemed suitable as offerings varied from community to community, and there is evidence for groups having had totemic symbols such as eagles, dogs or songbirds. These features would have served to reinforce group identities, but they were part of a pattern which was common to Orkney as a whole — as was the idea of having a tomb on one's territory in which the ancestors of the group were housed. There were modifications in the social organisation towards the end of the Neolithic, since we see monuments being built which were clearly beyond the resources of a single community and which imply some centralisation of power — examples are Maeshowe tomb and the henges of Brodgar and Stenness. This stratification probably continued into the Bronze Age with — in contrast to the Neolithic — the more important elements of society being buried in distinctive ways with rich grave goods.

We must be wary of thinking of Orkney as being the end of the line for colonisers or culture, for it seems it could have been very central on several occasions in the prehistoric period. In the Middle and Late Bronze Ages, however, no doubt due to the poor climate and the slump in the productivity of the land, it, and the rest of the north of Scotland, became a cultural backwater. Individual houses were scattered across the landscape and there is little evidence that their occupants did much more than eke out an existence. There is nothing to imply any centralisation or hierarchy; they were just poor subsistence farmers. This situation gradually changed with the Iron Age. Immigrants may have formed some sort of aristocracy, however that is interpreted, and with the formation of the great broch and defended village complexes (and, possibly, the treb dykes) we have evidence of very powerful chieftains which is augmented by the Romans supposedly having actually concluded a treaty in 43 AD (though doubt has been thrown on this[54]). Roman goods are even found — an amphora from Gurness, for instance, would originally have held marine produce from Spain or Portugal. This type of society passed too, and while the Pictish period is one about which we know relatively little yet in archaeological terms, it is clear that the norm was undefended farmsteads scattered about on their land. In the last half of the period, at least, Orkney was close to the centre of Pictland, both physically and culturally, and had rulers of its own.[55] How such a society operated, in broad terms, can be seen for the succeeding period from the *Orkneyinga Saga*.

Acknowledgments

I would like to thank Teresa Hedges, my wife, for having looked over the grammar of this chapter and Anna Ritchie for having checked its archaeological content. The accompanying line drawings were specially drawn for the purpose by Angela Townsend and photographs kindly supplied by Mike Brooks and other photographers.

CHAPTER 3

Biological Characteristics
Evidence of Micro-evolution in the Orkney Islanders

Don Brothwell, Don Tills and Veronica Muir

There are clearly a variety of ways in which the people of Orkney can be considered, whether in the past or the present. The history of their material culture and society is being dealt with in various detail in other chapters, and of course rightly so, but it is equally important to investigate their biology as well. There is also certainly value in considering people in terms of their demography, physique, inherited characteristics, or patterns of disease, and these not only have academic interest, but are generally essential to a balanced evaluation of the Orkney population as a whole.

Our qualifications, as 'foreigners', for writing about the Orkney islanders are two-fold. Some years ago, in Deerness, one of us — Don Brothwell — excavated the best-preserved old Orkney cemetery so far found, and in fact it is the best Norse period sample we yet have from anywhere in Britain. In collaboration with a number of colleagues two of us — Don Brothwell and Veronica Muir — also undertook a sort of rounding-up operation, house-to-house visiting and trying to persuade very many Orcadians to give samples of blood and provide other information for eventual detailed laboratory study 'doon sooth'. The serological unit at the British Museum (Natural History) — BMNH — undertook the detailed study of these blood samples (Don Tills and colleagues). All the Orkney data is not archived and the range of information is indicated in the appendix. Some analyses have still to be completed, but this chapter provides an opportunity to review the range of information currently available.

The early Orcadians

Interest in the ancient human remains from Orkney extends back over a century. By 1862 the famous Victorian skeletal biologist John Thurnam was investigating material from the 'Knowe of Saveraugh' near Birsay, and in 1867 other bones from the 'Brough of Quoy Ness' on Sanday.[1] Garson (1883) had similarly discussed prehistoric Orkney material, and Sir William Turner (1915) reviewed the various evidence for variation in early Orkney peoples, in comparison also with other early Scottish material.[2] Since then, and over the years, further descriptions of old Orcadians have been made, although, until recently, no relatively large samples have been studied. For instance, Orkney short cist burials have been described by the anatomist Alex Low (1928-9) and the controversial burials from Skara Brae were considered by A. Robinson (1930-31).[3] Low also described the remains of ancient Orkneymen from the long stalled chambered cairn near Midhowe, Rousay.[4] Much more recently, there have been detailed studies made on large Neolithic bone assemblages from Quanterness[5] and Isbister.[6] In the case of more recent times, the Norse period is now well represented by the numerous burials from the early Christian cemetery at Newark Bay, Deerness.[7]

Although we only have this modest amount of skeletal material representing ancient Orcadians, we can say a little about them.

The Neolithic material from sites such as Isbister and Quanterness is reminiscent of material from other parts of Britain, and would suggest that those who crossed to the islands were typically of moderate stature, and long-headed. Although there is far less material from the Beaker period and into the Bronze Age, what scraps there are again suggest that the more well built, taller brachycephalics (roundheads), so well represented in Scottish short cists, often with beakers or food vessels, had also got to the islands eventually. What the population density was then is highly debatable, although later Bronze Age sites suggest a reasonable spread of people — either indigenous or of intrusive Bronze Age origin.

Until Norse times, there are then no skeletal samples complete enough to enable biological comment. Viking and Norse skeletons have been found and described for many years, although no large samples were available. Even the bones of St Magnus and St Rognvald have received close scrutiny and, to the relief of all good Orcadians, were shown by R. W. Reid in 1926 to be biologically acceptable Norsemen![8]

Some years ago, (1967-71), it was possible for one of us (Don Brothwell) to excavate the Norse period chapel and cemetery at Newark Bay, Deerness. This site was gradually eroding into the sea, and turned out to be more complex than anticipated, with two earth houses[9] and the chapel, over which was superimposed a late medieval manor house. About 250 individuals were excavated and some of the results of their study are briefly outlined here.

The Newark community was one of varying health. Infant mortality was high, far greater than in Orkney prehistory or recent times (Table 1).

Infant Mortality Rates (0-1 year) as deaths per 1000

ORKNEY	M.R.
Deerness Norse (pop. ?250)	260
Isbister Neolithic* (pop. ?341)	132
Orkney 1911-1915	73
Orkney 1966	17

EUROPE, GENERAL	
Scotland, General, 1911-1915	113
Shetland	66
Sweden	206
Berlin 1881-5	279
Moscow 1881-5	340

Average Adult Life Expectancy (at 20)		
Deerness Norse	Males (M)	40.4
	Females (F)	38.1
Isbister* (M) + (F)		29.2
Orkney 1966 (estimated)	Males	74
	Females	75

Table 1. Some demographic information on Orcadians, past and present.   *data from Hedges (1982)

As yet, the application of multivariate statistics to the evaluation of Orkney skeletal data has been limited, and in particular a consideration of the Neolithic people from

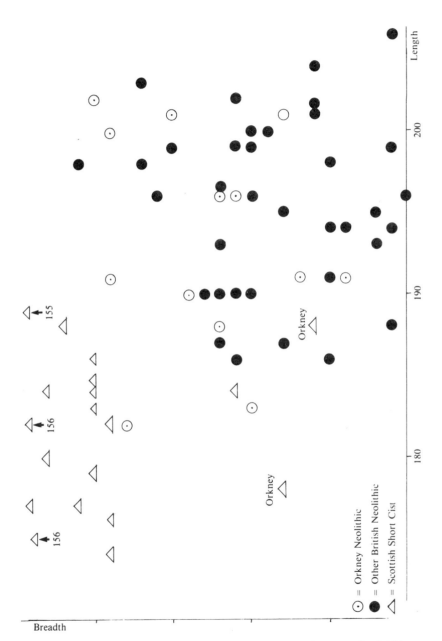

Fig. 20—Unidimensional variation in prehistoric Orkney and comparative British male crania.

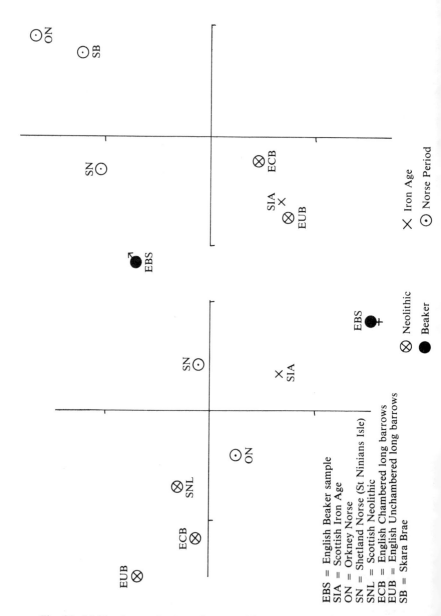

Fig. 21—Multivariate evaluation of ten cranial measurements for early Orkney samples and some comparative series. (Left = males; right = females). Canonical axes 1 and 2.

Quanterness and Isbister must remain for the future. It might be mentioned that there have been some comments about the physical distinctiveness of the Neolithic Orkney folk, but this does not seem to be demonstrable from simple comparisons of bone measurements although founder effect and local micro-evolution may have resulted in slight distinctiveness. Thus, for example, the plot of cranial length and breadth (Figure 20) for the Orkney Neolithic people, including Isbister, does not fully overlap the general British Neolithic distribution. Also, it will be seen that one Isbister individual falls surprisingly close to the somewhat separated Scottish short cist series, while two so-called Orkney short cist individuals were divergent in these bone measurements from the Scottish mainland people. In Figure 21, a number of early British series, including Orkney samples, are compared by the analysis of a whole series of ten cranial measurements. To the left, the males are given, and it will be seen that the Scottish Neolithic series (which includes Orkney material) is similar in position to the English samples. Also, of a somewhat different period, it will be seen that the two Norse samples — including the Newark Bay, Deerness sample — are separated from the other series and also show some possible regional differences as well. In the female comparisons on the right, the Skara Brae sample (just two individuals) is again compared with a variety of early populations, and it can be seen that the closest affinities for these two individuals are with the Orkney Norse (supporting earlier suspicions that these Skara Brae burials were more recent than the actual early settlement on the site).

The affinities or dissimilarities of earlier peoples can be assessed not only in metrical terms, but also as regards the occurrence of so-called non-metrical traits (extra sutures, variable foramina, extra 'wormian' bones etc.).[10] In the case of the Orkney Norse sample from Deerness, these were included in a comparative study of populations which may have been influenced by Scandinavian population movements.[11] The findings of this study were not altogether expected, in that although the statistical analyses of the non-metrical frequencies showed expected affinities between Norse Orkney people and some Scandinavian groups (especially Iceland), the Shetland sample appeared somewhat different. This Northern Isles difference, however, might be partly the result of sample size, and in a recent re-analysis of the Orkney group, using a large sample, the closeness of the Orkney and Shetland series is more apparent. Many earlier British series were included in the analysis, but mainly Scottish groups are given in Figure 22.

E

We have mentioned founder effect as one possible reason for the slight differences which seem to be showing up in some early Orkney series in comparison with other groups. To illustrate the significance of this effect, one can take for instance the apparent differential settling of Orcadians in parts of Canada. With the help of Canadian friends, we sampled 844 Orkney names listed in Canadian telephone directories, and covering 33 of the commoner Orkney surnames. Comparing the frequency of these with the changing rank order of surnames in Orkney over the past three hundred years as given by Gregor Lamb,[12] some interesting facts emerged. The Fletts appear to be relatively common both in Orkney and Canada. In contrast to the situation in Orkney, however, the Canadian Rendalls are over 50% less frequent than the Canadian Fletts. Moreover, although the Cloustons are not even in the changing rank order of 23 names most common in Orkney over the past three hundred years, they formed 10.3% of the Canadian names noted.

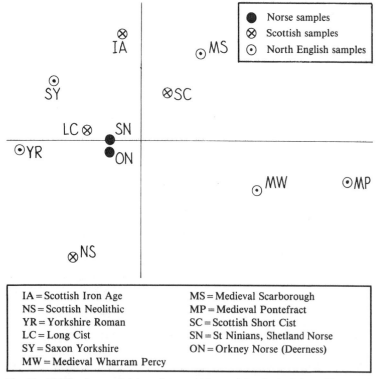

Fig. 22—Multivariate evaluation of non-metric cranial traits in Orkney Norse and some comparative samples.

Similarly, the surnames Peace (9.0%) and Isbister (6.4%) showed an increased representation in Canada. We do not wish to discuss this interesting question further here, but give it as an example of how some families can be more caught up in population movements (and of course some may 'survive' better reproductively in new settlements). This is evolution in action, but viewed at the level of surnames, not biologically!

In terms of stature (Table 2), the Deerness Norse demonstrated that — contrary to the image of tallness provided by St Magnus — Norse folk in general were relatively short, and indeed the Shetland Norse were even shorter. In comparison, modern Deerness people are on average taller, and this is so for other parts of the islands. The small-scale stature differences involved may reflect nutritional factors as much as genetic ones.

ARCHAEOLOGICAL	
Deerness Norse Ⓜ	171.1 cm (5ft 7¼in)
Shetland Norse	
(St Ninian's Isle) Ⓜ	169.1 cm (5ft 6¼in)
St Magnus	176.5 cm (5ft 9½in)
RECENT	
Deerness Males (adult)	174.7 cm (5ft 8½in)
Westray males (adult)	173.1 cm (5ft 8¼in)
Scotland, Northern Ⓜ	170.5 cm (5ft 7 in)
Scotland, Southern Ⓜ	171.0 cm (5ft 7¼in)
Scotland, Aberdeen Ⓜ	175.9 cm (5ft 9¼in)
Norwegians Ⓜ†	171.9 cm (5ft 7½in)
Sweden, Southern Ⓜ†	171.9 cm (5ft 7½in)
Iceland	176.6 cm (5ft 9½in)

Table 2. Stature* in Norse and recent Orkney male samples, compared with some Scottish and Scandinavian groups.

*Scottish (N + S) data from Clements and Pickett (1952); Scandinavian means from Reid (1926), Mahalanobis (1930), and Pálsson and Schwidetzky (1973).

†These are pre-World War II estimates, and thus perhaps from less well-nourished groups compared to more recent studies (but more comparable with the early Norse means).

While on the subject of stature, mention should be made of Marshall's growth studies on modern Orkney children.[13] Seasonal variation in growth is well established in European children,[14] and in view of the long light Orkney summer days and dark winters, it seemed clearly worth investigating Orkney child growth in relation to seasonal changes in daylight hours and temperatures. The results of this study provided much for debate, as the majority of children did not display a truly seasonal growth pattern. Factors beyond light and warmth are clearly important in child growth, and one might question whether, as there is a genetic component determining growth, future investigations in Orkney might usefully consider possible variation in child growth in relation to the 'Norseness' of grandparental surnames.

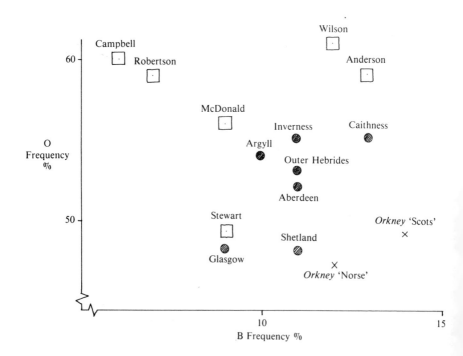

Fig. 23—Plot of O against B frequencies (of the ABO blood-group system) for a number of Scottish regions and surnames, together with 'old Orkney' and 'Scots' surnames.

Surnames and biological data in Orkney

Although in the course of the British Museum's Orkney project only a limited amount of time could be given to surnames in relation to questions of the biology of the Orcadian, they clearly have relevance in various respects. Gregor Lamb's *Survey of Orkney Surnames* was not then available, and we had only limited access to previous studies. Fortunately, the large compendium of Scottish surnames[15] gives good details on the majority of Orkney names. There is the possibility then of establishing 'old' Orkney names, as well as the more recent 'Scots' and other intrusive ones (linked mainly with agricultural settlement in the last few centuries). If we consider a few of these, as collected from regional lists, it is clear that considerable heterogeneity can be demonstrated on surname evidence — and this is clearly likely to be reflected in the genes. Ideally, of course, it would be more accurate to evaluate surname histories within a family over four or five generations, rather than to grandparents as recorded on our data sheets.

There is then the possibility that the separation of biological data on a surname basis, however crude such an endeavour may be, could assist in indicating a little more distinctly the more Norse components of the variation.

In fact, surnames are biologically interesting beyond Orkney. Thus, if for the ABO blood-group system (described more fully in the following chapter) we take the frequencies (in %) for the O and B patterns for certain Scottish surnames as well as for regions of Scotland (see Figure 23), the variation revealed in the one is very different from the variation shown in the other. Similarly, if we separate an 'intrusive Scots' component from an Orkney 'Norse' one, on surname associations, there is again some new variation revealed.

This type of separation can be attempted on all kinds of data. In the following table, the distribution of stature is given in association with 'old' Orkney names or more recent 'Scots' ones. Simply by dividing the sample at random one could expect some differences of course, but here the distribution for the 'Scots' series is sensibly different and displays an expected higher frequency of taller individuals (in line with the greater average stature in Scotland in general, compared with the Northern Isles).

	Stature range (in mms)							
	1600	1650	1700	1750	1800	1850	1900	Mean
'Scots' names			10.7	25.0	17.9	39.3	7.1	177.1 cm
'Old Orkney' names	11.4	17.1	31.4	28.6	8.6	2.9		172.8 cm

Table 3. Stature distribution by name in Deerness males
(% and average).

In fact both males and females show this difference, as the table below shows (even though there is a slight difference in mean age, which could have affected the results). In considering the differences between Orkney and Shetland, it is significant that the commonest surnames in Shetland (25% of the families and electors) are represented by nine names, most of which are not common in Orkney.[16] The ranking order of such names (in popularity) has changed a little from 1804 to 1954. Clearly biological frequency changes are linked with the well-being and relative success of families, fertility and reproductive success, nutrition and health, and the economic pressures which may differentially force some families to move from the islands.

A) Males 20+ years	Orkney	Scots	Difference
Number	35	28	
mean stature (mm)	1728.14	1771.36	43.21
standard deviation (SD)	60.007	54.94	
mean age	42.5	44.2	
SD	17.0	14.4	
B) Females 20+ years	Orkney	Scots	Difference
number	17	28	
mean stature (mm)	1582.76	1622.96	40.20
SD	51.02	56.45	
mean age	49.41	38.46	
SD	14.57	11.95	

Table 4. Overall stature in Deerness males and females, relative to Orkney/Scots names.

The mean is an average of the distribution; the Standard Deviation (SD) indicates the extent of variation around the mean.

Other differences in physique

Although as well as stature a variety of other measurements were taken on the Orkney islanders, a full analysis of these has not yet been completed. Nevertheless, some brief comments can be made. Table 5 gives some idea of the average dimensions representing the male physique of two Orkney groups from separate islands, Deerness (on the Mainland) and Westray (the latter data being kindly provided by Professor W. Marshall and the means calculated by Dr R. Harvey). It will be seen that, even allowing for modest sample sizes, the means are surprisingly similar, whether for total stature or weight, shoulder (biacromial) breadth, arm robustness or dimensions of the head. The one noticeable difference between them, in the range of variation in weight, is explainable by the difference in mean age. Thus, although in some biological aspects, the Orkney islanders show such marked inter-island differences, for physique there may be far more conformity.

Measurement	N	Deerness (AA = 43 yrs) Mean†	SD	N	Westray (AA = 28 yrs) Mean†	SD	U.K. (18 yrs) Mean†
Stature	63	174.7	6.13	49	173.1	5.85	174.7
Weight (kg)	44	78.0	13.21	47	75.5	8.50	63.0
Sitting height	61	91.9	3.06	49	92.5	3.00	92.0
Biacromial breadth	61	40.0	1.88	49	41.4	1.98	39.6
Upper arm circ.	61	29.5	2.98	49	30.8	2.10	26.3
Triceps skin fld.	57	0.94	0.37	49	1.15	0.52	0.89
Head length	62	19.6	0.70	48	19.9	0.64	19.6*
Head breadth	62	15.7	0.57	48	16.0	0.54	15.4*

Table 5. Variation in physique: Deerness, Westray and the U.K.

AA average age; N no. in sample; †in cms. except weight; *Scotland only.

UK means are mainly from Eveleth and Tanner, 1976.

Historical demography

During the time period covered by archaeological studies and the limited Norse writings, demographic information is severely limited. Skeletal samples allow some crude estimates of infant mortality, adult life expectancy, or sex ratios and so on, but the gaps in the information are vast. It would indeed be very interesting to know what happened to the Orkney population during plague times, and did Orcadians ever experience the famines and crop failures and livestock diseases chronicled by the Saxons in the South? We may never know, unless some special, chance, type of evidence is discovered (plague burial pits, for instance, or quantities of cereal with evidence of fungal disease).

But this situation changes in the middle of the 18th century, with the advent of records on population. The Orkney population rose from about 23,000 at the beginning of the nineteenth century to over 30,000 by the middle of the century, and it did not enter a trend of decline until the end of the century, since when it has dropped by over 10,000. To a varying degree, each island shows this same pattern. (More on population is given in Chapter 6.) With the increasingly precise information on regional population numbers, mortality and reasons for death, birth and parental details, and even details related to marriage, the pulse of Orcadian demography can at last be found. This has been a very fruitful, if highly specialised line of investigation.[17]

The special interest in Orkney demography is that the population is naturally broken up into a number of smaller island communities, varying in size and in degrees of isolation. This is an ideal situation in which to explore micro-evolutionary changes in a population which, following some intrusive movements of people into the area, then provides a stable and relatively unchanging state geographically 'isolated' from the rest of the country.

Demography can of course be divided into a number of separate dynamic processes, including mortality, migration and fertility. We have made some brief comments in another section of this chapter about life expectancy in relation to past and recent Orkney populations, and Evelyn Bowers discusses in Chapter 6 more detailed aspects of mortality. As regards British populations in general, studies of fertility — including variation in spatial fertility patterns — has progressed far less than other aspects of demography. Indeed, the analysis of fertility in Scottish populations by Jones (1975) was something of a pioneer work and nothing significant has been added to his findings.[18] For purposes of greater statistical reliability, Jones unfortunately combined information for Orkney and Shetland, and thus possible contrasts within the Northern Isles were not considered. In Figure 24 (a) it can be seen that the highest birth rates in northern Britain are mainly concentrated in the industrialised and urbanised counties of central Scotland, but that the island communities by no means show the lowest rates. Related to birth rate is of course the proportion of adults in the group of reproductive age, and it will be seen in Figure 24 (b) that, as a

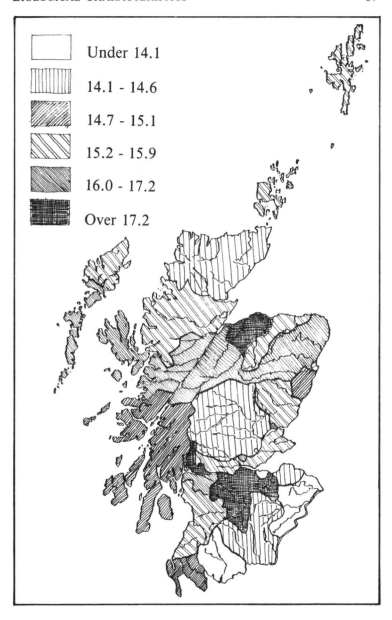

Fig. 24—(a). Average crude birth rate, 1971 and 1972. The rate gives the number of births per 1,000 population. Births data are corrected for usual residence of mother. *Source of data:* Registrar General (Scotland), Annual Reports 1971 and 1972. (After Jones, 1975).

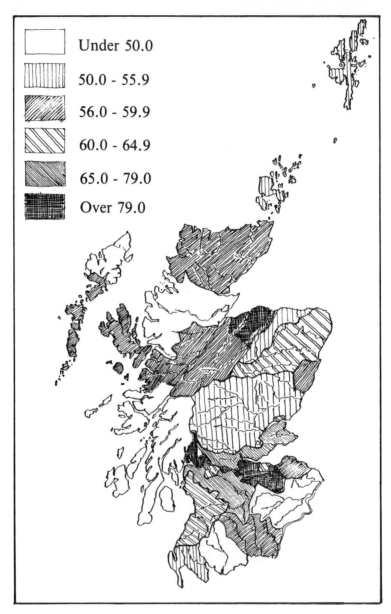

Under 50.0

50.0 - 55.9

56.0 - 59.9

60.0 - 64.9

65.0 - 79.0

Over 79.0

Fig. 24—(b). The 20-34 age group as a percentage of the over-50 age group, 1971. *Source of data:* 1971 Census of Scotland, County Reports.

whole, the Northern Isles are certainly not the most heavily
weighted as regards the proportion of elderly folk, although they
by no means show the most youthful age structure. Also, of
course, within Orkney some islands are heavily biased against a
youthful age structure, sadly reinforced by the education policy
which concentrates the young on the Mainland. This may have
been in theory educationally sensible, but it is demographically
disastrous.

Again, as in the case of fertility, there are few comparative
details of regional variation in terms of consanguinity, so the
recent study of inbreeding levels in Orkney by Roberts, Roberts
and Cowie (1979)[19] is not only a contribution to our
understanding of the Orcadians but of variation in Britain as a
whole. Although the pedigree analysis involved initially only 214
Orcadians, in order to establish the ancestries for the sample
some 50,000 searches were made into various records. Their

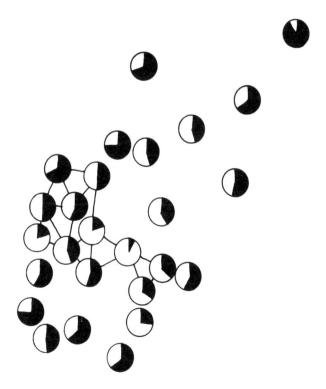

Fig. 25—Proportions (shaded areas of circles) in 1861 of marriages in which both
partners were born in the same Orkney parish. (After Boyce *et al.,* 1973).

conclusions from this work were that inbreeding levels are relatively high in Orkney, compared to the restricted information for other parts of Britain, with possibly some local variation. Although they found no evidence of a secular trend, Brennan's (1981) study of the Sanday population records that unions between close relatives decreased from 1800 onwards.[20]

This brings us to the question of marriage and aspects of mate selection, which is proving to be a very fruitful area of investigation.[21] The extent of marrying within one's own community in the islands has clearly been regionally variable, as the situation for 1861 (Figure 25) shows, and there is evidence that such a pattern of variation has changed through time. An example of the precise way in which marriage-associated movement within and into the islands can be analysed is provided by the distribution of distances between places of residence recorded at marriage on Sanday, totalled over the years 1855 to 1965.[22] Figure 26 shows clearly that the Sanday folk have usually selected their partners from within a ten mile radius, so that even the mainland of Orkney is excluded in this case. Few indeed lived beyond Orkney (i.e. over 40 miles away) before they married and took up residence in Sanday.

Not only are details of marriage revealing, but the members who do not marry are also relevant, especially in areas such as Orkney where this proportion of the population may be noticeable. Brennan records for instance that on Sanday, "high levels of celibacy and emigration have been observed: only 30 to 40% of all persons born in a given year married and at least potentially contributed offspring to subsequent generations; and the proportion of never-married individuals per birth cohort decreased from the late nineteenth century to the present".

Pigmentation

It is sobering to realise that hair and eye colour in Orkney have been the subject of investigation for the past hundred years. John Beddoe in 1885 recorded eye and hair pigmentation in no less than 568 Orcadians, noting that 71% had light eyes with associated 53% dark brown hair, and 15% of dark-eyed individuals were associated with 13% of dark hair. He also noted a 'red' hair frequency of 4.4%, confirmed recently on our samples (5.0% male, 5.6% female),[23] which is rather higher than most Scottish and Scandinavian samples. (Aspects of this are also noted in Chapter 5.)

John Gray in 1907 similarly included the Northern Isles in his detailed pigmentation survey of Scotland. Frequency patterns

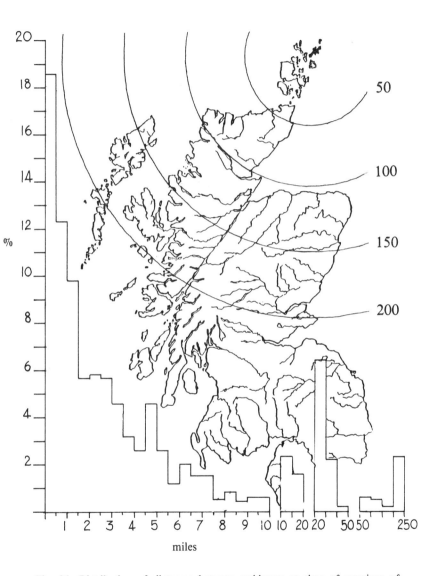

Fig. 26—Distribution of distances between residences at time of marriage of husbands and wives marrying on Sanday between 1855 and 1965. (50-mile circles marked from the south end of Sanday).

were complex, with the Caithness area and Northern Isles tending to contrast with more southern Scotland. However, his schemes often displayed some differences between Orkney and Shetland.

Study of recently-collected hair samples confirms that over 60% of the population have dark hair, with blondness relatively uncommon. In contrast to what one might expect, the hair colour is associated with very high frequencies of grey and blue eyes — especially in Sanday.

In Table 6, four broad categories of hair colour are listed for Orkney in comparison with Scottish and Irish samples,[24] in all cases using combined categories of the Fischer and Saller (1928)

	Orkney	Scotland	Ireland
Red (I-IV)	5.29	4.0	4.3
Blonde (A-L + N)	17.89	11.0	4.9
Brown (M, O, P-T)	41.06	39.0	35.1
Brown-black (U-Y)	35.77	46.0	55.7
Number studied	246	100	702

Table 6. Hair colour (%) for Orkney, Scotland and Iceland.

'hair colour table'. The frequencies vary but slightly, with the Orkney sample displaying the highest blonde percentage. Slight inter-island variation may occur (Table 7).

GRADES (combined)	1	2	3	4	5	6	
Deerness	1.3	1.3	10.1	26.6	38.0	22.8	%
Sanday	2.7	4.1	14.9	20.3	31.1	27.0	

Light blonde → Brown-black

Table 7. Variation in hair colour between islands

In the case of eye colour (iris pigmentation) we used one of the original sets of glass eyes devised by Rudolf Martin, and have been able to make some restricted comparisons with data from other parts of Britain collected by Grieve and Morant (1946),[25] in part by pooling some categories of data. Also, the data is compared with that from Shetland.[26] In comparison with England and Scotland, Orkney displays a much higher frequency of blue eyes, but there are remarkably similar overall frequencies for Orkney and Shetland (Tables 8 and 9, Figure 27).

Being controlled by multiple genes, pigmentary variation is not easy to evaluate precisely. We can at least say that eye colour conforms to the Scandinavian pattern. On the other hand, the frequent dark hair pigmentation might suggest that pigmentation was dominantly inherited, so that in a mixed Norse-Scots community, intrusive Scottish pigment-controlling genes would have maximum effect. Alternatively, regional Norse communities might have varied to the extent that those colonising Orkney contained more dark-haired individuals (only 30% of modern Norwegians are in fact blonde). A further question is clearly the extent to which Orkney pigmentation reflects genes surviving from pre-Norse times. It is difficult to see how this last question can be resolved, unless more variation can be detected in the actual chemistry of melanin pigment.

All facts considered, Orkney blondness and light eyes may well show Norse influence, but dark hair frequencies could even be a composite of a pre-Norse community, a darker Viking component, and more recent Scottish influences.

GRADES	A	B	C	D	E	F	G	
Orkney	2.9	7.2	20.3	6.5	10.1	10.9	42.0	%
N. Britain	6.8	11.0	19.2	5.5	19.9	26.7	10.3	

Brown → Blue

Table 8. Comparison of reduced (pooled) categories of eye colour for Orkney and northern Britain

Pooled categories	Martin numbers	Orkney		Shetland	
		No.	%	No.	%
I About pure brown	3 - 4	43	4.04	34	7.31
II More brown than grey or blue	5 - 8	158	14.86	92	19.78
III More grey or blue than brown	9 - 13	334	31.42	120	25.81
IV About grey or blue	12 - 16	527	48.58	219	47.10

Table 9. Eye-colour variation: Orkney and Shetland school children
(M + F)

Fig. 27—Proportions (shaded areas of circles) of grey, intermediate, dark- and light-blue eyes (Martin categories 12, 14-16) for Orkney and other areas of Britain. (After Boyce *et al.*, 1973)

Dermatoglyphics

The full analysis of large samples of finger and palm prints is a laborious business, and as yet only finger prints have been studied in detail and compared with other British and European samples.[27] Surprisingly — since large numbers of finger prints have been collected as a result of both forensic and anthropological interest — very little is still known of regional variation in Britain as a whole.

Population	No. in Sample	Whorls %	Ulnar loops %	Radial loops %	Arches %
Britain	5000	25.4	64.0	5.7	4.9
Orkney (total)	1886	26.1	61.8	5.2	7.0
Orkney Mainland	1154	25.4	62.3	5.3	7.0
Orkney Sanday	217	27.1	59.7	5.5	7.7
Orkney Deerness	127	25.6	61.5	5.0	7.9
Orkney Stromness	202	25.9	62.5	5.0	6.6
Orkney Kirkwall	238	27.3	62.9	4.4	5.4
Orkney North Isles	479	27.8	60.1	4.7	7.5
Orkney South Isles	252	26.2	62.6	5.4	5.9
Shetland	426	26.5	59.6	7.6	6.2
Scotland	537	29.2	60.4	4.6	5.8
Norway (males)	24518	25.7	61.1	5.8	7.4
Denmark (males)	8980	28.4	60.0	5.1	6.5
Iceland (males)	158	21.7	64.6	7.0	6.8
Faroe Isles (males)	446	18.9	66.4	7.3	7.4

Table 10. Frequency (%) for Orkney and some comparative samples. Both sexes are combined unless specified (European data from Harvey and Suter, 1983)

Considering first the within-Orkney variation, it is interesting to see the differences between the east, central and west Mainland samples, as well as the pooled North Isles and South Isles data (samples are admittedly small). In all but radial loop frequencies, the range of variation is over 2%. Very little difference was found in total ridge-counts (T.R.C.) for the Orkney samples.[28] The West Mainland shows a lower T.R.C. with an average of 110, as opposed to the Orkney average of 118 (ranging from 124 in Kirkwall to 112 in the South Isles). Both pattern-type and ridge-count frequencies were considered from the point of view of 'Old Orkney' and 'Scots' types of surname, but no significant differences were noted in this instance.

As far as the Norse-settled communities of Shetland, Iceland

F

and Faroes are concerned, there is similarity in whorl frequency between Shetland and the total Orkney figures, but Iceland and Faroe are distinct. Again, there are fairly high ulnar loop percentages in the Icelandic and Faroese samples, providing contrast with Norwegian and Danish figures as well as Orcadian and Shetland ones. (Chapter 5 goes into more detail on Faroese comparisons.)

Blood Studies

Since the classic note based on blood group results by Fisher and Taylor[29] concerned with Scandinavian genetic influence on parts of Scotland, there have been an increasing number of publications on the serology of Britain and beyond. In the last few years Orkney has produced a significant amount of serological data, and in our own project, fourteen different blood group systems or serological variants have been investigated. Details of the serological results are given in an appendix at the end of the book and in Tables 11, 12 and 13. The results lead one to diverse conclusions, and it would be wrong to suggest that frequencies simply confirm Scandinavian affinities. Indeed, it would seem important to remember that comparison of Orcadian with Scandinavian blood group frequencies could obscure true relationships if there have been any changes in Scandinavian groups since Norse times. Any comparisons must therefore be tempered with this awareness of possible change in both Orkney and comparative groups. Steffensen[30] and others have suggested that the proto-Scandinavians in Iceland were characterised by relatively low A frequencies, and this is the situation in both Orkney and Shetland. However, when Orkney surnames are used to divide the data into 'Norse' and 'non-Norse' components (Table 11), the A frequency is in fact 4% higher in the 'Norse' component,[31] and there is also a 4% difference in the Rhesus negative frequency, although the 'Norse' component is the lower one in this case. It should be noted that inter-island variation is quite noticeable for some genes, over 10% in the case of A_1 (of the ABO system), the contrast being most marked between the North Isles and South Isles samples. In the case of the MNS system, there is a 23% S frequency-difference between the East Mainland and South Isles, with some degree of difference generally between north, south, east and west. For all Orkney regions, and in totality, M frequencies are surprisingly low (16.4-25.8%) in comparison with results from other parts of Britain, Norway and Iceland. (The various blood-group systems are described in more detail by Derek Roberts in the following chapter).

In the case of the P, Lutheran, Kell and Duffy systems, there is further evidence of inter-island variation, with some frequencies noticeably divergent from comparable Scottish, English, Norwegian and Icelandic ones. For instance, in the Duffy group, Fy^a is generally higher in Orkney than in any of the comparative samples. Other serological traits also show variation. Gamma globulin (Gm) frequencies distinguish Orkney from both Scotland (Table 12) and Shetland.[32] Haptoglobin frequencies within Orkney vary by nearly 14% and in total diverge from both Scottish and Norwegian values by between 6% and 10%. In the case of the red cell enzyme adenylate kinase, the gene frequency for AK^2 is 44.8% for Britain as a whole, 31.7% in Ireland, 38.9% in Finland and 56.6% in Iceland.[33] The regions of Orkney are surprisingly variable for this allele, and it appears to be absent in the East Mainland, with up to 46% variation between other samples (all small). In the areas where it occurs, the average is 55.6%, a figure similar to that for Iceland.

	Old Orkney		Scots		Total	
	No.	%	No.	%	No.	%
O	83	46.62	186	49.34	269	48.47
A	64	35.96	120	31.83	184	33.15
B	22	12.36	54	14.32	76	13.69
AB	9	5.06	17	4.51	26	4.68
Rhesus Negative	32	17.98	84	22.28	116	20.90

Table 11. Some Orkney blood group frequencies in relation to surnames (using data of Allan and Lewes)

The enzyme 6-phosphogluconate dehydrogenase provides further evidence of inter-island variation (10% for the PGD^c gene). The average Orkney PGD^c frequency of 1.6% is lower than a pooled English series (21.5%) or a sample for Iceland (22.2%)[34] and seems to be the lowest found yet in Europe.

Beyond these group by group comparisons, it has been possible to use much of the serological data together in multivariate calculations of overall genetic distances. More is said in the following two chapters about these Orkney 'distances' in relation to some other European populations, and here it is sufficient to concentrate on the findings of the overall inter-island and British comparative results. Unexpectedly, there is a remarkable amount of variation *within* the islands, and although the West Mainland and South Isles are positioned relatively close together, the East Mainland and Sanday communities are clearly distinct from one another and the other groups (Figure 28). This must surely be linked to founder effect, the differential survival and expansion of some families, and to ongoing local micro-evolution. Two serological illustrations emphasise that point. During the BMNH Orkney Project an abnormal haemoglobin (previously identified and called HbE Saskatoon) occurred in a sample of 398 individuals.[35] It had been originally identified in Canada, and family studies appeared to show that it was inherited from a 'Scottish' father. But it does not seem to occur on the Scottish mainland, and the Canadian settler was likely to have been an Orkneyman. Given time, and family reproductive and economic success, the Orkney HbE (Saskatoon) gene could be expected to spread in areas where it was carried by Orkney settlers.

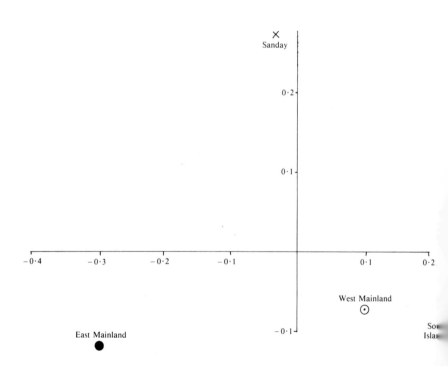

Fig. 28—Genetic distances of regional Orkney samples (using combined serological data).

Ref.	Blood donor sessions Town	No. Tested	Gm (1, 2)	Gm (1, −2)	Gm (−1, −2)
2	Brora	108	18.52	31.48	50.00
3	Golspie	100	27.00	24.00	49.00
4	Tain	230	21.74	33.91	44.35
5	Invergordon	138	29.71	25.36	44.93
6	Alness	167	20.36	32.33	47.31
7	Dingwall	185	21.08	37.30	41.62
8	Fortrose	136	18.38	36.76	44.85
9	Beauly	106	23.58	33.02	43.40
10	Inverness	633	23.06	31.28	45.66
11	Nairn	354	25.71	32.20	42.09
12	Forres	238	20.17	31.93	47.90
13	Grantown	201	19.90	37.81	42.29
14	Kingussie	142	19.01	35.92	45.07
15	Fort William	191	23.04	29.32	47.64
16	Kinlochleven	110	21.82	33.64	44.55
17	Montrose	210	24.29	30.00	45.71
18	Dundee	182	24.18	34.61	41.21
19	Perth	156	21.79	32.05	46.16
20	Auchtermuchty	146	23.97	29.45	46.58
21	Glasgow	1000	23.00	32.30	44.70
22	Stirling	100	29.00	27.00	44.00
23	Greenock	100	24.00	33.00	43.00
24	Rothesay	100	26.00	32.00	42.00
25	Kilmarnock	100	23.00	33.00	44.00
26	Ayr	100	24.00	39.00	37.00
27	Lockerbie	100	24.00	31.00	45.00
28	Dumfries	150	22.67	32.00	45.33
29	Castle Douglas	100	27.00	33.00	40.00
31	Wigtown	145	22.76	39.31	37.93
32	Stranraer	100	22.00	36.00	42.00
	Mainland totals	5828	23.01	32.57	44.42
33	**Stornoway**	**114**	**31.58**	**28.95**	**39.47**
34	**Orkney**	**154**	**20.13**	**40.26**	**39.61**
35	**Shetland**	**146**	**23.29**	**34.25**	**42.47**

Table 12. IgG (Gm) frequencies (in %) for regional Scottish and
Northern Isles samples (Izatt, 1973)

A different story is provided by variation in an erythrocyte
enzyme. Welch and Mears[36] carried out starch gel electrophoresis
on blood from 406 Westray islanders and found no less than
twelve inherited variants. Previously studies on samples from
various other parts of the world had at that time produced only

one variant! A further search in Orkney material[37] has so far not
produced any more. This indophenol oxidase variant is a mutant
allele which has survived particularly well in Westray, its
occurrence being linked with the degree of common ancestry and
inbreeding.

	Number examined	Number of electrophoretic variants	Frequency of the most common allele
Westray	406	12	0.985
North Ronaldsay	56	0	1.000
London	2500	0	1.000
Europeans (general)	6500	5	0.9996

Table 13. The incidence of indophenol oxidase variants in some
European samples

Colour Vision Deficiency

Although a number of different defects can occur in colour
vision, for the purpose of this analysis all red-green defects have
been placed together. In view of their sex-linked inheritance,
with females uncommonly involved, we present here only the
male data. Both Orkney adults and children were tested, using
the Ishihara pseudo-isochromatic charts. Minor judgment errors
in reading the charts were not scored as evidence of deficiency.
The overall Orkney 'colour blindness' frequency is 6.2%, which
is lower than most other northern British frequencies, although
there is an especially low (and puzzling) rate of 3.5% in
Edinburgh.[38] The Orkney frequency is nearly half the Norwegian
figure of 10.1%,[39] and is much lower than the Shetland
frequency (Table 14).

Post[40] argues for a general east-west and north-south gradation
in British frequencies, although his case is not altogether
supported by some regional frequencies. Moreover, he considers
that these 'clines' may be explained by the population history
(especially movement of people in the past and settlement
history) and the phenomenon of relaxed selection. While we
would agree that earlier population movement and settlement
must have contributed significantly to the broad overall pattern
of variation in Britain, it seems important to consider that
intrusive groups may have been small and founder effect
therefore significant in determining differences.

Wick and Inverness area	6.7
Aberdeen	6.1
Dundee	5.6
Kirkcaldy	7.0
Edinburgh	3.5
Stirling	5.9
Galashiels	7.8
Newcastle	7.3
Dumfries	10.9
Paisley	8.7
Glasgow	7.0
Motherwell	7.9
Shetland	9.0
ORKNEY	6.2

Table 14. Some 'colour blindness' frequencies — Northern Britain
(in %)

There are clearly differences in frequency between islands[41] (Table 15). This is not the result of sample size, and in fact the two largest samples (East and West Mainland) show a difference of 8%. Sibs were excluded as much as possible.

Regional variation	Total tested	Colour blind	% of males affected
West Mainland	495	27	10.8 (N = 251)
East Mainland	493	4	2.8 (N = 251)
North Isles	208	6	5.5 (N = 109)
South Isles	154	6	7.0 (N = 86)
Total Orkney	1350	43	6.0 (N = 697)

Table 15. Regional variation in 'colour blindness' for Orkney.
(N = number in sample)

Taste Blindness

The ability or otherwise to taste the bitter quinine-like substance phenylthiocarbamide (PTC) has been investigated since 1931, but only in the early 1960s were Orkney people tested for a taste-ability for this substance.[42] In the most recent survey, wide variation in response was found, and it was not easy to divide the subjects into precise taster and non-taster categories. Nevertheless a separation was made, and the results are presented in Table 16. Even allowing for the fact that the inclusion of relatives may modify estimated frequencies somewhat, it still seems likely that Orcadians have higher frequencies of non-tasting than generally seen in the British Isles, including Shetland.[43] The high Orcadian frequencies can not be explained by Scandinavian affinities, as the non-taster frequencies for Norway, Sweden and Denmark range from 18.7% to 31.8%.

Population	No. tested	% non-tasters
Orkney	567	42.85
Kirkwall	243	36.21
Sanday	75	38.67
Shetland	489	28.22
Scotland	206	32.00
County Durham	735	31.8
SE England	441	31.5
SW Wales	1005	27.6

Table 16. Non-taster frequencies for Orkney and some other British samples (%)

Medical Biology

There is a growing literature on the regional geography of disease in Britain, and in particular the detailed data and maps of Melvyn Howe[44] call attention to some quite noticeable contrasts between the Northern Isles and mainland Scotland. This shows well in the rates for ischaemic heart disease and cerebrovascular disease (stroke), where Orkney has a poor health record (Figure 29). Such differences may be due to subtle environmental factors, but it would be interesting to investigate this variation more closely in relation to population and surname history.

Less common disease has also received attention. Berry [45] and more recently Roberts et al,[46] have noted the high rate of multiple sclerosis in the Orkney islands and in Scandinavian Countries. Muir[47] investigated tylosis, a well defined familial skin condition. Fortunately, unlike its occurrence elsewhere, it seems to have no association in Orkney with cancer of the oesophagus.

There seems little doubt that malignant tumours ('cancer') are considerably influenced in their occurrence by a variety of environmental factors (interesting in themselves), but to what extent is there a genetic background to tumour liability? Orkney, with its genetic affinities both with Britain and Scandinavia, could be revealing in this respect. Only limited data can be considered here, and we have selected only certain parts of the

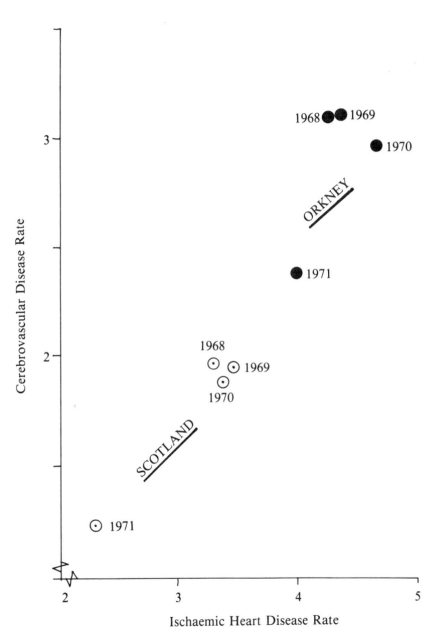

Fig. 29—Variation in the Orkney and Scottish frequencies for cardiovascular and ischaemic heart disease.

body where malignancy causes varying mortality. In the case of stomach and breast cancer (Figure 30), the Orkney rates are close to those for other regions of Britain, but contrast very markedly with Swedish, Danish, Finnish and Icelandic figures. The Orkney rates for cancer of the oesophagus and prostate are higher than more southern British figures, and prostate frequencies are lower also in Denmark, Sweden and Finland. But oesophageal cancer is noticeably higher in Denmark and especially in Sweden. Orkney cancer frequencies thus seem to be generally divergent from Scandinavian ones, to the extent that one might tentatively conclude that environment is dominant to hereditary factors in initiating cancer in the populations discussed. But what are the environmental factors in some forms of malignancy? Why for instance is breast cancer low in Orkney, higher in Denmark and extremely high in Sweden? Indeed, as seen in Table 17, we can also ask why breast cancer deaths have been lower in Deerness and the South Isles over the past century than in Orkney as a whole (the sample sizes being admittedly small). Better diagnosis and surgery does not explain this, although it could explain the reduction in mortality in the case of ovarian tumours. Again, why does Orkney show relatively high oesophageal and prostate figures in comparison with southern Britain? One is certainly left asking whether genetic factors can at times be as important as environmental ones.

Organ involved	Deerness and South Isles		All Orkney	
	Number	%	Number	%
Stomach	10	15.9	19	10.9
Breast	2	3.2	20	11.4
Uterus	4	6.3	7	4.0
Pancreas	1	1.6	9	5.1
Prostate	3	4.8	11	6.3
Leukaemia	1	1.6	2	1.1
Ovary	4	6.3	1	0.6
Colon & Rectum	8	12.7	14	8.0
All other sites	30	47.6	92	52.6
Total	63		175	

Table 17. Deaths from malignant tumours in all Orkney (1967- 1971) and in Deerness and the South Isles (1865-1965)

What then is the pattern of malignancies in Orkney families? This could be a fruitful area for research, but we can present

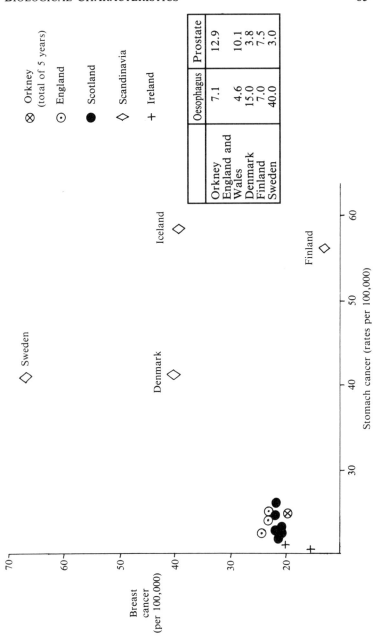

Fig. 30—Variation in British and other European breast, stomach, oesophagus and prostate cancer rates.

only limited findings here. Again, by reference to records of the past century for Deerness and the South Isles we have charted the frequencies of deaths from the major killers (tumours and vascular diseases) in a series of families. Not only are there differences between families as to whether mortality is precipitated by cardiovascular or neurovascular disease, but some families seem to be generally 'low cancer risk' families, while others show 'high risk' frequencies. Considering a larger range of families in this way, we tentatively divided the mortality information into two groups, depending on whether the surname was an old Orkney one or Scots and more recently intrusive (Table 18). Compared in this way, the actual family differences are submerged, and in fact there are no significant differences in these two components.

Surname group		Cardiovascular disease	Neurovascular disease	Malignant tumours
Old Orkney names	No.	68	47	37
	%	44.7	30.9	24.3
Scots and others	No.	42	31	15
	%	47.7	35.2	17.0

Table 18. Relative frequencies of mortality from malignant tumours and vascular diseases in relation to old Orkney and other surnames

Perhaps a final comment on Orkney medical biology should include a little more on the past. Infectious diseases such as tuberculosis have been important killers during the 18th and 19th centuries and may have caused differential selection, and gene pool change in the Orkney population. There is no certain Norse evidence for it, in Orkney, but it was present in early Icelandic populations. Frequencies are low in Orkney today, but as Table 19 shows, prior to 1915, it commonly occurs in mortality records as the cause of death. Moreover, about 60% of the deaths are in individuals of reproductive age, with some families being hit harder than others. Back in Norse times it is far from easy to pinpoint health problems. The Deerness Norse had relatively good oral health, but joint (rheumatic) disease was clearly a problem and was advanced in various larger joints in some individuals. Familial aspects of rheumatic diseases are now being investigated in far more detail in some areas, and it is to be hoped that eventually the population of Orkney might be seen to be worthy of special study, not only because of its genetic diversity but also in relation to environmental factors.

Of special note in the Deerness Norse is the fact that leprosy had probably arrived in the islands via Scandinavia by the 10th century (on the evidence of one skull). Large parasites, in the form of tapeworm, were probably affecting 2.0% of the early Newark people, a figure based on the occurrence of calcified echinococcus cysts in two individuals.

Age group (yrs)	Deaths	% of all TB
0 - 4	0	0
5 - 9	1	1.1
10 - 14	0	0
15 - 19	11	12.4
20 - 24	20	22.5
25 - 29	25	16.8
30 - 34	10	11.2
35 +	32	36.0
Total	89	100

Table 19. Age composition of deaths from tuberculosis* in Orkney prior to 1915 (restricted sample).   *mainly pulmonary.

Conclusions

The Orkney population of today can be seen in a way as the sum of its past. How simple or complex is the history of the communities? Were there successive layers of migrants moving in, mixing, differentially surviving ? Have evolutionary factors caused trait or family survival to a different degree in different island groups or even socio-economic divisions?

Biological data are relevant to the proper solution of a variety of questions concerned with Orcadians of the past and present. But there are no quick answers, and the data presented here show the complexity of the situation as much as pointing towards answers. The biological information, from bones or blood, suggests some affinities between Orcadian and Scandinavian, but interesting differences. We are left questioning whether the Viking and later Norse settlers were really like modern Norwegians. There is still the uncertainty that some of the variation, such as in pigmentation and some blood group frequencies, might show the perpetuation of pre-Norse genes in the community (rather than more recent Scottish intrusive ones).

More than one line of biological enquiry could eventually be very fruitful, including the association of scientific work with detailed surname investigations.

Acknowledgments

We wish to thank most warmly, the very many Orcadians who have helped in these investigations. Our special thanks go to Mr A. Bain, Dr I. Haddow, Mr A. Warlow and the heads of various Orkney schools, who have helped in various ways with the project. Thanks also to all those who assisted in the initial collection of data, and to Robin Harvey for useful comments and information when the manuscript was in preparation.

Our one apology is to the (now not so) young Magnus Grimond who, as a result of a resounding blunder on our part, was the one person involved in our study *before* we received back a letter of permission from his parents!

During the conference in Kirkwall on the Orcadians, Mr John Hedges and the Curator of Tankerness House Museum, Mr Bryce Wilson, kindly permitted one of us (Don Brothwell) to examine unpublished Isbister material (assisted by Mrs D. Lorimer).

CHAPTER 4

Genetic Affinities

Derek F. Roberts

History and archaeology tell of a succession of peoples in Orkney. There were the Neolithic folk who left us Skara Brae, later perhaps the Picts and the Celts, and then the Norse and the Scots. Despite their cultural effects on the islands, there is very little evidence as to who most of these people were, and the attempt to answer that question is the theme of the present book.

Only for the later comers to Orkney is there evidence about the extent of the biological impact of the new arrivals upon the people who were already in occupation. For the earlier changes, we do not know whether the newcomers eliminated their predecessors, whether they intermarried with them on a massive scale (either peacefully or after their conquest and partial destruction), or whether in fact the newcomers were few in number and their biological effect — despite their cultural or political significance — relatively slight. Various approaches are suggested by authors in this book; one possible way is through the evidence of genetics.

The bodies of animals and plants are made up of *cells,* which contain various substances and structures, including a *nucleus.* It is within this nucleus that we find the material that determines the characteristics of the organism as a whole. This material is carried on thread-like *chromosomes.* In every cell of a normal human being, there is a nucleus with 46 chromosomes. The original cell from which each individual develops is formed from the amalgamation of an egg cell from the mother with a sperm (male cell) from the father. Each of these parent cells has 23 chromosomes; fused together, they give the 46 chromosomes that delineate the various characteristics of a new human being.

The chromosomes themselves are made of a backbone of protein, around which is arranged a double helix of desoxyribose nucleic acid (DNA). DNA is a long chain formed out of only four basic building blocks — substances known as nucleotides, repeated in various sequences. There are literally countless ways of forming DNA, depending on the order of these nucleotides. Each particular sequence of DNA is connected with a particular characteristic of the living organism. This was the discovery which led to the breaking of the 'genetic code' — the recognition that a sequence of nucleotides on the DNA in the chromosomes corresponds to an observable characteristic of the living organism.

The DNA of the chromosomes controls the way that the cell makes proteins, which are the basic ingredients of a living organism. A crude analogy might be with the way that a punched card inserted in a knitting machine controls the manufacture of a jersey. Groups of nucleotides on the chromosomes are called genes, with each gene corresponding to the production of a particular protein in the organism.

Each of us receives half of our genes from our father, set out along the 23 chromosomes from his sperm cell that originally fertilised our mother's egg cell. From that egg cell, we receive a further 23 chromosomes with the other half of our genes. Thus for each particular protein that has to be synthesised in our bodies, we have two genes, which by controlling the production or lack of production of a particular protein in us, control a characteristic we display. For example, the presence or absence of a particular pigment in the iris of our eyes determines our eye colour.

These two genes, one from each parent, may be identical with each other, or they may (since our parents will not be identical in every aspect) differ slightly in the effects they have the potential to produce. If a person gets two slightly different versions of a gene, both genes may manifest, or it may be that only one does so, in which case the gene whose effects do come through into a characteristic of the organism is said to be *dominant*. One of the many examples of dominant genes can be found in the system of blood groups.

The concept of human blood groups came about as the result of a problem that occurred with blood transfusions; sometimes the attempts were successful, but at other times blood from one person did not mix well with blood from another. The *serum* or liquid from the one person's blood caused the red cells from the other to clump together or agglutinate. The conclusion was that there were several different types of blood, characterised by differences in the red cells and the serum. A substance on the red cell called an *antigen* reacted with *antibodies* in blood serum to cause clumping.

In the ABO blood group system, there are four types. People

of group A have the A antigen on their red cells, and the anti-B antibody in their serum. Group B is characterised by the B antigen on the red cells and the anti-A antibody in the serum. A transfusion of plasma (i.e. red cells and everything else apart from the serum) from a group B person to someone of group A would have the serious — indeed possibly fatal — effect of putting red cells with B antigens into serum containing anti-B antibodies which would clump them.

It is possible to have neither an A nor a B antigen on the red cells, and blood like this is described as group O. It has both anti-A and anti-B antibodies. Blood with neither of these antibodies but with both A and B antigens is called group AB.

Which blood group you have depends on your genes. An A gene enables your body to make A antigens, while a B gene controls the B antigen. Someone with an A gene from one parent and a B from another will have blood of group of AB. However, a person with an A gene from one parent and an O from the other will manifest only the A gene in his or her cells. A is said to be *dominant* over O; and conversely O is recessive to A. The only time a person is blood group O is when he or she receives the O gene from both parents.

The *phenotype* of someone of blood group A is said to be A; genetically they may be either AA or AO, and so we must distinguish between their appearance or phenotype and their genetic composition or *genotype*.

Today there are many blood group systems known, detected by a variety of methods but principally by the agglutination procedures — the MNS system, the P system, the Rhesus system and others. There are also other blood characters that are controlled in a simple genetic way. For instance in the red cells there are certain enzymes whose particular form is controlled by a single gene (an *enzyme* is a type of protein that assists the progress of certain chemical reactions). Also, in the serum of the blood, the liquid which carries the various red cells and other corpuscles, there are a number of proteins, several of which are controlled by a single gene. Again the presence of these proteins gives information on gene frequencies. Quite apart from the red cells of the blood, which carry oxygen through the body, the serum also carries the white cells which provide protection against intrusions from bacteria, viruses and foreign proteins. A particularly informative system is that of the Human Leucocyte Antigens (HLA).On the white cells (leucocytes) there are antigens which stimulate the production of antibodies, and these antigens are controlled by genes. These genes are those principally concerned with immunological reactions.

Although our parents die, their genes live on, with every cell in our body holding in its chromosomes half our mother's genes and half our father's genes. In the same way, our own genes continue in our children's bodies, and so on. When we look at the inhabitants of an island group such as Orkney, we can therefore alter our focus from the particular individuals and move down to the genes that are held in each body. Taken together, the genes form a pool, which is, as it were, shared out and held in trust by the individuals making up the population at any one time. This gene-pool is, like the population, a continuous and dynamic entity. It is permanent relative to the individuals who are born into it and then die out of it — it is there before the individual is born and after he dies. The gene-pool forms the genetic constitution of the population.

What we see, of course, in the individuals forming the population, are physical characteristics, produced by the internal genes held within the cells. For certain characteristics, it is possible to determine their distribution and frequency in the population. This is possible, for example, with characters such as the blood groups and particular proteins. Thus tests for blood groups can lead directly to the identification of particular genes in a population. By taking a sample of the population, and counting the number of individuals with particular blood group characters, we can calculate the *frequency* of each of the genes involved. This can be done for each gene or system separately. But sometimes the genes for two or more systems are situated close together on the same chromosome, in which case the frequency of the different combinations in which they occur can be calculated. These combinations are termed *haplotypes.*

Although people are born and die, the genes continue, and there is a tendency for the gene frequencies to be stable from one generation to the next. But populations evolve. Evolution of a population is in genetic terms merely change in its gene frequencies with time. One of these processes of genetic change is obviously immigration and emigration. Each time somebody comes into the population and marries an indigenous spouse, half of the genes of each of their children will have come from outside.

There are other processes which change gene frequency. First of all, there is *mutation.* Since the gene is formed of a series of chemical substances — nucleotides — on a chromosome, physical or chemical change can produce an altered gene. Secondly, a new gene produced in this way can spread, if possession of it is advantageous; equally well, if possession of it is a disadvantage, the gene frequency will go down, and the gene may be eliminated in the course of time. This is the process of *natural selection.*

A third process of gene frequency change particularly important in small populations is random change, or *genetic drift,* due to the chance nature of the process by which an individual transmits one or other of each pair of genes to each offspring. The possible importance of this process of random change is stressed by the authors of the next chapter.

The question for Orkney is to try to describe the gene-pool of the population, and from that to see which other populations the Orcadians most closely resemble genetically. In order to carry this out, blood specimens were collected from 413 apparently normal, outwardly healthy individuals from various parts of Orkney. These blood specimens were examined for the presence of different blood groups and other substances.

Phenotype and gene frequencies

The phenotype frequencies in the main sample of 413 Orcadians are set out in Table 20, together with the gene frequencies derived from them. The HLA antigen frequencies from a subsample of 100 individuals, along with corresponding gene frequencies, are given in Table 21. Some comparative gene frequencies are listed in Table 22 in which results from Shetland and from an earlier survey in Sanday and Westray in Orkney are also included.[1]

The Orkney gene frequencies (Table 20) show immediately a number of interesting features.

In the ABO blood-group system, the high B gene frequency in Orkney supports the previously reported figures of 11.3% by Brown in 1965 and 11.7% by Boyce *et al.* in 1973; indeed, it is slightly higher than either of these.[2] The only sample which is slightly different is that of Allan and Lewis in 1969, who had a rather lower, though still high, B frequency.[3] Undoubtedly the A gene frequency in Orkney is surprisingly low and the B frequency remarkably high for a population thought to contain a considerable Norse element, for present-day Scandinavian (Norwegian and Danish) populations tend to have much higher A and lower B frequencies. Only the east coast folk of Caithness show ABO blood-group frequencies similar to Orkney. Elsewhere in Northern Europe, only populations of the eastern Baltic (Finland and Poland) have B frequencies generally higher than Orkney. It seems likely that the earlier Scandinavian peoples who contributed to the Orkney settlers were sharply distinguished from the modern Scandinavians, whose gene frequencies have

System	Phenotype	Number Observed	Frequency %	Allele/ Haplotype	Frequency %
		BLOOD GROUPS			
ABO	O	170	41·2	p_1	16·7
	A_1	101	24.5	p_2	6.6
	A_2	39	9·4	q	13·3
	B	72	17·4	r	63·4
	A_1B	26	6·3		
	A_2B	5	1·2		
		413			
Rhesus	CcDEE	1	0·2	C	48·2
	ccDEE	9	2·2	c	51·8
	CCDEe	1	0·2	E	16·7
	CcDEe	69	16·7	e	83·3
	ccDEe	46	11·1	D	64·8
	ccddEe	2	0·5	d	35·2
	CCDee	86	20·8		
	CcDee	152	36·8	CDe	47·2
	Ccddee	2	0·5	cde	33·9
	ccDee	4	1·0	cDE	15·6
	ccddee	41	9·9	cDe	1·6
		413		Cde	0·6
				cdE	0·7
				CDE	0·4
MNS	MMSS	22	5·3	m	55·2
	MMSs	62	15·0	n	44·8
	MMss	42	10·2	S	26·6
	MNSS	8	1·9	s	73·4
	MNSs	85	20·6		
	MNss	111	26·9	MS	22·9
	NNSS	3	0·7	NS	3·7
	NNSs	7	1·7	Ms	32·3
	NNss	73	17·7	Ns	41·1
		413			
P	P +	340	82·3	P_1	58·0
	P −	73	17·7	p	42·0
		413			
Duffy	Fy^{a+b+}	170	41·6	Fy^a	45·7
	Fy^{a+b-}	102	24·9	Fy^b	54·3
	Fy^{a-b+}	137	33·5		
		409			

System	Phenotype	Number Observed	Frequency %	Allele/ Haplotype	Frequency %
Kidd	Jk^{a+b+}	179	44·2	Jk^a	49·0
	Jk^{a+b-}	109	26·9	Jk^b	51·0
	Jk^{a-b+}	117	28·9		
		405			
Kell	Kk	27	6·5	K	3·5
	KK	1	0·2	k	96·5
	kk	385	93·2		
		413			
Lutheran	Lu^{a+b+}	24	5·9	Lu^a	3·2
	Lu^{a+b-}	1	0·3	Lu^b	96·8
	Lu^{a-b+}	380	93·8		
		405			
Lewis	Le^{a+}	26	12·7		
	Le^{a-}	179	87·3		
		205			

RED CELL ISOENZYMES

System	Phenotype	Number Observed	Frequency %	Allele/ Haplotype	Frequency %
Adenosine deaminase	ADA 1-1	359	88·6	ADA^1	94·2
	ADA 1-2	45	11·3	ADA^2	5·7
	ADA 5-2	1	0·2	ADA^5	0·1
		405			
6-phospho-gluconate dehydrog-enase	AA	396	98·0	PGD^A	99·0
	CA	8	2·0	PGD^C	1·0
		404			
Lactate de-hydrogenase	LDH N	404	100	LDH N	100
Malate de-hydrogenase	MDH N	404	100	MDH N	100
Adenylate kinase	AK 1-1	363	89·9	AK^1	94·8
	AK 1-2	40	9·9	AK^2	5·2
	AK 2-2	1	0·3		
		404			

System	Phenotype	Number Observed	Frequency %	Allele/ Haplotype	Frequency %
Acid phos-	AA	52	12·9	P^a	36·5
phatase	BA	177	43·8	P^b	59·2
	BB	140	34·7	P^c	4·3
	CB	21			
	CA	14	3·5		
		404			
Phospho-	PGM 1-1	235	58·9	PGM^1_1	71·5
glucomutase	PGM 1-2	128	32·1	PGM^2_1	24·9
locus 1	PGM 2-2	35	8·8	PGM^7_1	0·1
	PGM 7-1	1	0·2		
		399			
Phospho-	PGM_2 1-1	404	100	PGM^1_2	100
glucomutase					
locus 2					

SERUM PROTEINS

System	Phenotype	Number Observed	Frequency %	Allele/ Haplotype	Frequency %
Haptoglobin	1-1	78	19·1	Hp^1	42·4
	1-2	184	45·1	Hp^2	57·6
	2-2	140	34·3		
	Neg.	5	1·2		
	2-1M	1	0·2		
		408			
Transferrin	CC	402	98·5	C	99·3
	CB	6	1·5	B	0·7
		408			

Table 20. Phenotype numbers and frequencies, and gene and haplotype frequencies, in the Orkney sample.

been considerably modified by later migrants from elsewhere in Europe.[4]

In the MNS blood-group system, the frequency in the Orkney sample of gene M appears close to Norway and Denmark. The Orkney MS haplotype frequency is rather high and thereby also close to Norway and Denmark, but the low NS frequency appears to set the Orcadians apart. Indeed, Orkney seems to have an NS haplotype frequency at the extreme lower end of the European range which is only approached in one or two local valley populations in Norway, and in parts of the English Lake District. In the Lewis system Orkney, with its 13% of individuals of Le^{a+} phenotype, is clearly distinct from Denmark and Norway, and again falls at the lower extreme of the European range. In these few systems alone, then, Orkney appears quite distinct.

Of the other systems, the P^1 gene frequency is a little high for northern Europe, though it is approached in one or two localities in Sweden and north-west Germany. In the Rhesus system, the cde haplotype frequency is rather low, though not as low as on the Faroe Islands, and resembles the Norwegian valley population of Setesdal. The Fy^a gene frequency in Orkney is a little higher than in Scotland. The AK^2 gene is a little elevated in frequency. But generally in all the other blood-group and enzyme systems the Orkney frequencies fall in the range usual in north-west Europe, though there is a suspicion that they may tend to be more towards the extremes of these ranges than in the middle.

The HLA types in Table 21 provide further evidence to help interpretation. These indicate elevated frequencies of A1, A11 and B7, and indeed the Orcadians appear to be ultra-European in the direction of the differences. For the Orkney A2 gene frequency (37%), the nearest populations are in Iceland and the Hebrides (both 31%), and the Orkney figure is only exceeded by two samples (38%) among the several from Sweden. For A11, the nearest to Orkney (11%) are Northern Ireland (9%) and Iceland (8%). The B7 gene frequency of Orkney (22%) is only exceeded by the 23% of Iceland and of one (Västerbotten) out of several samples from Sweden, though several Lapp samples are consistently as high or higher (21-29%).

Genetic distance and relationship

Comparison of single individual characters is interesting, but it may tend to mislead. Subjectively, one's attention is immediately drawn to the characters of unusual frequency. Objectively, there is the possibility that each particular character may have been

HLA Antigen	Phenotypes %	Gene frequencies %
A1	34	18·8
2	60	36·8
3	25	13·4
9 (incl. 23,24)	9	4·6
10 (incl. 25,26)	13	6·7
11	20	10·6
W19 (incl. 29,W30,31,32)	17	8·9
28	1	0·5
B 5	13	6·7
B 7	39	21·9
B 8	24	12·8
B 12	31	16·9
B 13	6	3·1
B 14	10	5·1
W 15	14	7·3
W 16	1	0·5
W 17	9	4·6
W 18	3	1·5
W 21	2	1·0
W 22	2	1·0
W 35	2	1·0
27	12	6·2
W 40	11	5·7

Table 21. HLA Antigen and gene frequencies

subject to drift or selection, and may have thereby altered from the level in the gene-pool established by the founding population and subsequent migration. However, although these processes may affect particular characters, they are much less likely to have operated in the same direction on the frequencies of a number of characters. It is therefore preferable to examine a number of characters simultaneously.

For example, we have noted that for the A and B genes, the Orkney and present-day Scandinavian figures (Norwegian and Danish) are some distance apart. On the other hand, for the M gene Orkney and Norway are quite close. What we want to do is make an overall calculation of distance of Orkney from

		Cumbria	Ireland		Orkney†		ORKNEY§	Shetland	Iceland	Norway	Denmark
			Southern	Northern	Sanday	Westray					
Approx. number of people tested*		800	1700	300	110	350	413	300	1600	200	430
					BLOOD GROUPS						
ABO	A_1	18	13	12	9	13	16.7	13.1	13	21	20
	A_2	8	4	5	6	6	6.6	6.1	6	10	8
	B	7	7	6	17	9	3.3	8.9	6	6	8
	O	67	76	77	68	72	63.4	71.9	75	63	64
MNS	MS	25	27	28	22	23	22.9	31.2	16	20	22
	Ms	29	29	26	40	34	32.3	27.7	42	31	30
	NS	6	6	5	2	6	3.7	2.4	6	9	7
	Ns	40	38	41	36	37	41.1	38.7	36	40	41
Rhesus	R_z	0.2	0	0	1.0	0.3	0.4	0.2	0	0	0
	R_1	42.0	40.0	40.0	46.3	44.5	47.2	45.2	44.1	43.5	39.8
	r'	0.4	0.4		0	0	0.6	0.4	0.4	1.0	1.0
	R_2	10.8	15.7	14.4	13.6	13.5	15.6	13.6	16.6	16.4	16.6
	R_o	1.9	1.4	1.4	0	0	1.6	2.5	1.2	0.6	1.5
	r"	1.9	3.6	0.5	1.5	0	0.7	0	0.8	0	0.8
	r	42.7	42.1	43.7	37.6	41.3	33.9	38.2	36.8	38.5	40.2
Duffy	Fy^a	38	42	41	50	44	45.7	46.9	43	42	41
Kell	K	5	4	5	4	3	3.5	5.0	5	4	4
Lutheran	Lu^a	4	2	2	2	—	3.2	4.2	2	4	4
P	P^1	29	48	45	39	38	58.0	43.5	40	—	—
					PROTEINS AND ENZYMES						
Haptoglobin	Hp^1	35	38	41	42	38	42.4	42.2	43	38	40
Adenylate kinase	AK^1	95	97	96	95	97	94.8	95.8	93	96	96
Acid phosphatase	P^a	32	34	33	32	—	36.5	31.4	37	38	34
	P^b	65	62	63	62	—	59.2	63.6	55	55	60
Phosphoglucomutase	PGM^1	72.9	74.3	78.6	68.3	82.0	75.1	79.7	83.7	77.7	80.1
6-phosphogluconate dehydrogenase	PGD^A	97.2	98.5	98.1	97.9	98.5	99.0	98.7	97.9	—	—
Transferrin	Trf C	99.5	99.0	98.7	100.0	—	99.3	99.5	99.9	—	—

*Varies for different genes

†Earlier survey (see Chapter 3)

§Individuals from many parts of the islands

Table 22. Gene and haplotype frequencies (%) of blood groups and serum proteins for Orkney, Shetland and other areas. (These frequencies which are based on data in the corresponding table in R. J. Berry and J. L. Johnston, *The Natural History of Shetland,* are for illustration only and apart from the column of overall Orkney figures are not the data used in the distance analyses described in the text).

Scandinavia, taking a number of different features into account, and then compare the Orkney-Scandinavia genetic distance with that for Orkney-Scotland, Orkney-Iceland, and so on.

The mathematical techniques of multivariate analysis provide the means for making such a calculation. Several methods of measuring genetic distance have been devised, based on different assumptions, and it is desirable to employ more than one for a satisfactory interpretation of the results. In the analysis provided here, genetic distance was calculated by the methods of Edwards,[5] Nei[6] and Sanghvi.[7]

The first stage of the work was to compare a selection of the Orkney gene frequencies with those for other populations, collected from the literature. This comparison was made by calculating the genetic distance of Orkney from the other populations by two of the different methods, that of Edwards and that of Nei.

One of the difficulties in making such comparisons between different populations is that complete data are rarely available on all the various loci that it would be desirable to include. Thus when comparing populations in pairs, the number of features that can be used may vary. In the first stage of the work described here, not less than seven, and not more than nine, systems were used in any one comparison.[8] Thirteen comparisons were made, to give Orkney's genetic distance from thirteen other populations.

The results of this calculation are shown in Table 23. Both methods used show that the greatest distance is from Iceland,

| | Method of: | |
	Nei	Edwards
West Germany	20	358
Norway	23	445
The Netherlands	49	489
Belgium	52	573
England	59	671
Denmark	61	633
Sweden	85	739
Shetland	89	737
Scotland	113	1145
Wales	124	832
Eire	162	1022
Northern Ireland	215	1150
Iceland	328	1389

Table 23. Genetic distances from Orkney (7-9 loci) $\times$ 10^4

followed by Northern Ireland. The closest is West Germany, followed by Norway. Indeed, the results by the two methods are quite similar, for there are only three shifts of rank, two of a single place and one of two places. Both sets of results show that Orkney is closer to Scandinavia and countries bordering the North Sea than to Iceland, Northern Ireland, Eire and Wales. Distance from Scotland seems to fall with this latter group, and distance from Shetland is in an intermediate position.

These distances should not necessarily be regarded as definitive. First — as previously noted — the number of systems used is not constant in all comparisons. Secondly, the populations included were not necessarily homogeneous. Some gene frequencies relate to one locality within the population, other gene frequencies to another, and some (for example, those for the English) relate to highly heterogeneous samples. The next step, therefore, is to concentrate on homogeneous samples, namely those where the same individuals were included in the testing for each system, and could be identified with a particular locality or area.

Four closely-defined populations, all examined in the same laboratory, were taken — Orkney, Shetland, Cumbria (where historically Scandinavian influence was also strong), and Whickham (a suburb of Newcastle-upon-Tyne). Fifteen systems were used, containing in all a total of 42 genes or haplotypes.[9]

The results of this comparison of Orkney with Shetland, Cumbria and Whickham show the distance of Orkney from each of the other three populations to be very much the same. By Edwards' method, Orkney appears slightly closer to Cumbria (.0426 distant), with Shetland next (.0446 away from Orkney), and then Whickham (.0532). By Nei's method, Orkney is closest to Whickham (.0016), followed by Shetland (.0018) and then Cumbria (.0021).

These results were then augmented by others from a wider geographical area, taking in some from the same laboratory but incorporating also others from the literature that had been extensively tested. Some slight changes were made in the list of genetic loci used; otherwise, however, the Orkney, Shetland, Cumbria and Whickham material remained the same, and was incorporated into a list with the Isle of Man, Northern Ireland, Eire and, to give perspective, Belgium and Poland.

The results are shown in Table 24, and it will be seen that, between the outcomes of the different methods, there is less agreement than before. By Edwards' method, Orkney remains close to Cumbria and Shetland, with Whickham a little further away, but Eire is as close as Whickham. Belgium and Poland are the most remote from Orkney, but Northern Ireland and the Isle of Man are nearly as distant. With Nei's measure, Northern Ireland comes out to be the farthest from Orkney, followed by Poland; Eire appears as next in order of remoteness. At the other end of the scale, Whickham, Shetland and Cumbria retain their order of proximity to Orkney, but Belgium comes in the list with the same figure as Shetland, and thus is ahead of Cumbria. If these calculations of genetic distance are carried out using a third method, that of Sanghvi, the sequence is the same as with Nei's.

	Nei	Method of: Sanghvi	Edwards	Harpending
Whickham	17	23	558	73
Shetland	21	27	456	76
Belgium	21	27	721	121
Cumbria	24	31	442	83
Isle of Man	27	35	628	154
Eire	35	47	549	102
Poland	49	64	819	225
Northern Ireland	55	74	638	147

Table 24. Genetic distance from Orkney (13 loci) $\times$ 10^4

Comparing the results of the different methods, the rank order of distances is seen to vary to some extent according to the method used. It seems that at relatively short genetic distances, even when they are based on a large number of systems, random effects may alter the rank order of distances. Nevertheless, it is possible from these analyses to make some generalisations. All three methods used agree in demonstrating the genetic proximity of Orkney to Cumbria, Shetland and Whickham. All also agree in demonstrating relative remoteness from Poland and Northern Ireland, and an intermediate position for the Isle of Man. Eire is shown as quite remote by two of the methods, Belgium by one. These are the two principal changes of rank, in fact, and the varying positions of Eire and Belgium reflect the different assumptions of the different methods. Overall, however, these findings are compatible with the conclusion of the previous analysis shown in Table 23, namely that the closest Orcadian affinities are with North Sea populations rather than Atlantic.

These tables show distances from Orkney; thus two other places, each equally distant from Orkney, may not necessarily be close to each other. For example, in Table 24, Nei's method puts Shetland and Belgium at the same distance from Orkney. This

PRINCIPAL COMPONENTS ANALYSIS FOR GENE FREQUENCIES IN 9 POPULATIONS

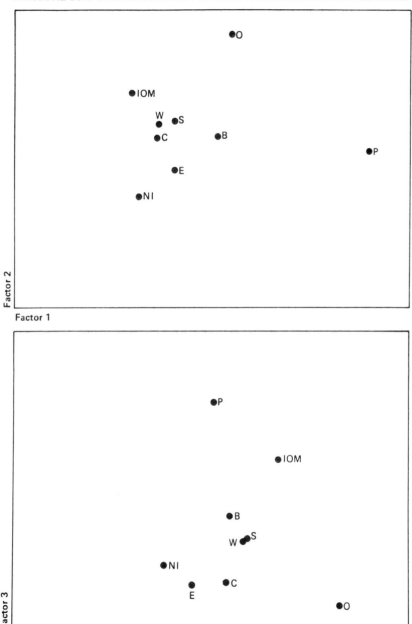

Figure 31. Genetic distance analysis shows that the Orkney population stands rather apart from the eight others.

implies that the sum total of all the genetic differences of
Shetland compared with Orkney on this basis is the same as the
sum total of all the differences between Belgium and Orkney. It
does not, however, mean that the differences in each case are the
same. On a map of Europe, the distance from London to
Shetland will be seen to be roughly the same as that from
London to Milan; but Shetland and Milan are far apart since the
distances from London are measured in different directions!

On a map of Europe or the world, we can specify places by
two co-ordinates, such as latitude and longitude, or else by so
many miles north and east of a reference point. If we were using
just two genetic characters to compare populations, we could
display our results on a two-dimensional chart very much like a
grid map. For the present investigation into 13 separate
characters, we would need a space with 13 dimensions to
represent the results. Although we cannot visualise something
like this, it is, from a mathematical point of view, only a little
more difficult to handle.

There is available a mathematical process which reduces the
full set of 13 figures to only a few underlying factors. The
process will not be gone into here, but the results of applying it
are shown in Figure 31. The idea is that although the various
populations differ from each other in relation to 13 different
features, the main differences can be summed up by two or three
key factors. The important thing about Figure 31. is not the
mathematical complexity by which it was reached, but the way in
which it shows genetic distances between different populations.
Before, in the single lists, all we could see was how populations
differed from one particular population taken as a reference.
Now, in Figure 31, we can see for any two populations how
much or how little they resemble each other genetically.

In the first diagram of Figure 31, the populations are set out
according to the values of the first two of the main factors that
are derived from the original 13 characters in order to sum up
the overall differences. Again, the closest to Orkney are
Shetland, Whickham and Cumbria, and all three of these turn
out to be close to each other. Just as close to Orkney, but in
slightly different directions, are the Isle of Man and Belgium.
Northern Ireland and Eire are farther away, and so is Poland in
a quite different direction.

The second diagram of Figure 31 plots Factor 2 against Factor
3. Again, Shetland, Whickham and Cumbria are very close
together and closest to Orkney. Farther away are Northern
Ireland and Eire, and the Isle of Man and Belgium in quite
different directions, while Poland is altogether remote. In this

diagram, as in the first, Orkney's position is conspicuously separate from even the closest of the other populations.

There is another method of comparing populations, developed by Harpending and Jenkins.[10] It is not a genetic distance in terms of differences in gene frequencies, but is a measure of relationship — that is to say, it measures the probability that a gene found in two populations derives from an ancestor common to both. It therefore leads to a slightly different final diagram of genetic affinity (Figure 32). As with Figure 31, the important thing is not the complex mathematical processes that are required to reach it, but simply the relationship it displays between the various populations on the diagram. Again, Orkney is closely related to Shetland, Cumbria, Whickham and Belgium, less so to Eire, Northern Ireland and the Isle of Man.

The analyses shown in Figures 31 and 32 add a further dimension to the interpretation. Not only do they support the suggestion that the closest Orcadian affinities are with the North Sea populations; they also indicate that despite these affinities Orkney remains quite distinct and individual.

PRINCIPAL COMPONENTS ANALYSIS FOR HARPENDING'S R MATRIX

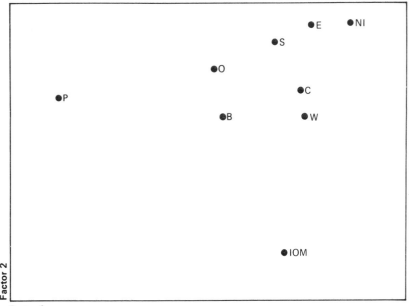

Figure 32. Genetic relationship of Orkney to the eight populations.

Conclusion

Taking all these analyses together, the distance analyses and the diagrams appear to distinguish the Orcadians from the people of the Gaelic fringe of western Europe, often regarded as representing a relict population into which more recent arrivals have brought genes from outside. Scrutiny of the separate blood systems shows that the Orcadians are characterised by extreme gene frequencies in some — B, NS, Lewis, and HLA-A2, A11 and B7 — and by their distinction in the diagrams from those populations to which they seem to be genetically closest. Perhaps, then, the Orcadians retain a strong element of an extreme, ultra-European population, contributions from which are found in varying degrees in other populations, and particularly in those bordering the northern North Sea. Though their gene-pool has also been modified to some extent by immigrant genes, they would thus represent the remains of a relict population, in the same way as, but different from, those of the Gaelic fringe.

It may be, of course, that genetic drift has acted to produce these extreme gene frequencies, though it seems intrinsically unlikely that drift would alter all of them in the direction of the extreme of the European range. Or again, the gene frequencies may have been subject to natural selection, representing more extreme effects of the same selection pressures as have operated in the same direction in other north-western European populations; there is as yet no evidence of what such selection may be. The suggestion that the Orcadians remain an outpost of an ancient population, diluted but not totally replaced by immigration from related populations from north-west Europe and particularly Scandinavia, appears a simpler interpretation.

Acknowledgments

Acknowledgment is gratefully made to the Trustees of the Marie Stopes Foundation for their support and interest in this analysis.

CHAPTER 5

Relationships of the Orcadians:
the View from Faroe

Robin G. Harvey, Diana Suter and Don Tills

In this chapter the relationships of the Orcadians are approached from a northwesterly direction, from the Faroe Islands, where since 1977 the Sub-Department of Anthropology of the British Museum (Natural History) has been carrying out an extensive study of the physical and genetic characteristics of the Faroese people.[1] During the course of this work the Orkney Islands have figured prominently in comparisons between the Faroese and neighbouring populations in the North Atlantic region. As a result, we have been able to obtain an insight into the biological affinities of the Orcadians from the position of the Faroe Islands, which occupy geographically a central place in relation to the neighbouring areas of Iceland, Ireland, Northern Scotland, the Northern Isles and Norway.

Historical

Unlike the Northern Isles of Scotland, there is at present no evidence for any Neolithic or Bronze Age settlement in the Faroes. Celtic hermits, mentioned in the writings of the Irish monk Dicuil (825 AD), are believed to have been the earliest inhabitants. According to radiocarbon dates, they may have reached the islands during the 6th century.[2] They were probably driven off by the Vikings who arrived early in the 9th century and established their settlement — somewhat later than those in Orkney but in advance of those in Iceland.

Unfortunately there is no Faroese equivalent of the Icelandic *Landnámabók* to give an indication of where the Vikings came from; however, it is probable that in addition to voyaging from Norway, some ventured to the Faroes from established settlements in the Orkney and Shetland Islands, and from the Scottish mainland, Ireland and the Hebrides. The *Færeyinga Saga* records the presence of Einar the Hebridean, who became a close companion of Sigmund Brestisson, the Norseman who brought Christianity to the Faroes.

H

Administratively and economically, the Faroes have been principally tied to Denmark, but the proximity of the Orkney and Shetland Islands has always presented the Faroese seafarers with attractive prospects for fishing and trading.

Methods of analysis

In the previous chapter, Derek Roberts has described how we can compare two populations genetically, by the method of 'distance analysis'.[3] The data used by Professor Roberts were the frequencies of blood groups and blood (serum) proteins. For our own survey we used a number of the same genetic markers, but also fingerprints; they are not under such simple genetic control as the blood factors, but they do still have a large genetic component.

We looked at the four main types of pattern formed by the ridges of skin on the fingers — *arches, radial loops, ulnar loops* and *whorls.* We investigated to what extent each of these patterns was present in the Faroese, and then brought together all four sets of results to give a total overall degree of

Left Hand

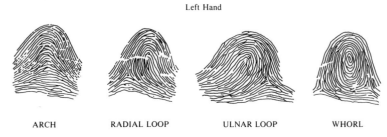

ARCH   RADIAL LOOP   ULNAR LOOP   WHORL

Figure 33. The four main types of fingerprint pattern.

'fingerprint distance' (or *dermatoglyphic distance*) between Faroe and other populations. This distance tells us to what extent the Faroese differ from — or are similar to — neighbouring populations in their fingerprint patterns. Table 25 lists the various aspects of the characteristics that we studied of the Faroese Islanders.

Genetic distance

The results of these surveys show that, genetically speaking, the distance today of the Orkney Islands from the Faroes is considerable. For example, Table 26 shows the results of a calculation using investigations on six blood groups and four serum protein and enzyme systems.[4] For these particular ten

Type of Study	Approx. Sample Size
Register of names	1550
Family birthplace data	1530
Blood samples	690
Finger prints	920
Palm prints	600
Anthropometry (adult Males)	230
Hair samples (including matching to colour scale)	880
Eye colour (matches to colour standards)	600
Skin colour (measurements and/or observations)	600
Colour vision deficiency tests	790
Photographs (standardized facial)	90

Table 25. Details of the physical anthropological study of Faroe Islanders conducted by the British Museum (Natural History) in association with Odense University, Denmark 1977-79.

factors taken together, Orkney emerges with England as its nearest neighbours, followed by Denmark and Eire, and then Ulster, SW Scotland, and the Isle of Man and Iceland together: the Faroes are much further away, almost at the foot of Table 26. Figure 34 shows this more clearly, and also illustrates the degree of similarity or difference between all the various populations in the table. In Figure 34, the Faroes along with Lewis in the Western Isles stand out quite separate from the main cluster of populations. We believe the reasons for this to be random genetic drift, which operates particularly strongly on

Population	Distance (× 1000)
England	30.9
Denmark	40.9
Eire	42.1
Ulster	57.0
S.W. Scotland	59.3
I.O. Man	61.6
Iceland	61.6
Norway	66.3
Cumbria	69.7
Wales	70.7
Faroes	104.2
Lewis	119.4

Table 26. Genetic distances—ranked from Orkney

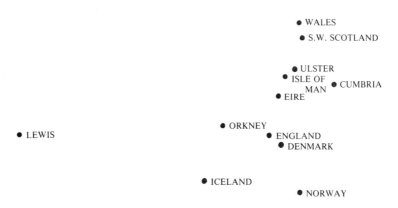

Figure 34. Genetic distance plot based on gene frequencies for six blood group
and four serum protein and enzyme systems.

small, isolated populations. In a big enough population, the number of genes present stay stable from one generation to the next, but in smaller communities, where for instance the number of people carrying a particular gene may be in the tens or twenties, the life or death of a few individuals can make a significant difference to the total gene pool of the next generation, and the effect of random events can build up to an overall change in the genetic character of the population.

In the case of the Faroes, the population was for a long time small (probably no greater than 5,000 from 900 to 1800 AD) and the rate of immigration was very low.[5] The result is a distinctive array of genetically determined characteristics which, in a large number of genetic systems, place the Faroese towards the extreme limit of the range of frequencies for northwestern Europe.

In other words, the relative isolation of the Faroes has meant that in the Faroese population over the centuries certain genetic traits have changed in frequency, simply because of the small population numbers. Similar effects may have operated also on the gene pool of the Lewis Islanders, studied by Prof. E. J. Clegg.

There are several other points that should be made about the data in Table 26 and Figure 34. Firstly — and rather surprisingly — for this particular combination of genetic systems the sample closest to the Orcadians was the English one, mainly from London and the South-East. However, it is interesting that the next closest are Denmark and Eire.

Next, it is important to note that the populations used for this comparison were selected on the basis of the availability of genetic data. This means that we have had to leave out, for instance, the people of North-East Scotland, who share with the contemporary Orkney population a high frequency of the blood group gene B.[6] Also, of course, there is a considerable amount of variation *within* each of the populations used. For example, when looking at blood genetic markers, the range of variation between regional populations within Iceland is almost as extensive as that for national population samples throughout the whole of North-West Europe. Clearly, we have to be very careful when speaking about an overall Icelandic pattern of genetic factors, or about an overall pattern for any other population. Until we know more about the full extent of variation within these populations, the genetic distance comparisons must be regarded as rather imprecise. Nevertheless, they are still worth making, so long as the assumptions on which they are based, and the problems of interpreting them, are clearly understood.

Fingerprints

For the survey of fingerprints, Figures 35 and 36 show the overall distance between the Faroese and other populations. Figure 35 is for males, Figure 36 for females. The actual distances themselves, against Orkney as a baseline, are listed in Table 27, but Figures 35 and 36 allow comparisons between any or all of the populations plotted. The Orkney data are from the extensive study of Dr V. Muir.[7]

All these figures have some distortion of scale, so cannot be used for direct quantitative measurements from the diagram itself, but they do illustrate the overall pattern. Figure 35, for males, shows that the nearest to Orkney are Norway and Iceland, followed by Denmark and the Scottish mainland. Next come South-East England and Cumbria, each at about the same

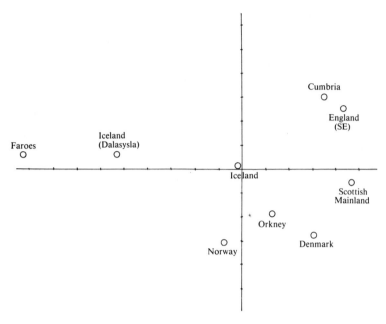

Figure 35. Dermatoglyphic distance (males) based on the frequencies of four
fingerprint patterns (Fig.1). [Data source: Harvey & Suter (1983)].

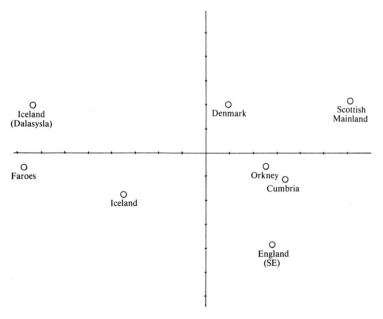

Figure 36. Dermatoglyphic distance (females).

distance from Orkney. The most remote populations in this selection are those of the Dalasysla region of Western Iceland, and the Faroes. With the variation in fingerprint pattern frequencies having a high genetic component, the distant position of the Faroes can be accounted for by the effects of random genetic drift.

The relationships of the females (Figure 36) appear as broadly similar to the males, although the total Icelandic sample is far less close to Orkney than for the males, and the Scottish mainland sample is more distant from Orkney than are the Cumbrians and the English.

Hair colour

We can also compare populations on the basis of hair colour, and measure categories such as blondness, redness and dark brownness. This has been done for several populations, using the same international standard for each — the Fischer-Saller Hair Colour Scale — on samples that as far as possible were matched for age. The Orkney sample, of 246 people, was scored by Suter

Males	
Population	**Distances (× 10,000)**
Iceland	5
Norway	5
Denmark	13
Scottish Mainland	14
S.E. England	23
Cumbria	24
Dalasysla (Iceland)	42
Faroes	110
Females	
Population	**Distances (× 10,000)**
Denmark	1
Cumbria	2
S.E. England	18
Scottish Mainland	33
Iceland	61
Dalasysla (Iceland)	167
Faroes	209

Table 27. Dermatoglyphic Distances—ranked from Orkney

in 1979.[8] The results for the various populations are shown in Figure 37.

For blonde hair, the Faroese, Norwegians, Danes and Icelanders form a cluster, with blondness for about 30% of the population and dark brown hair for around 20%. However, within this cluster there are differences, and the cluster becomes less homogeneous when redness is considered. The Norwegians — and, to a greater extent, the Swedes — are outstanding in having very low frequencies of red hair.

The Orcadians occupy an intermediate position between Scots and Icelanders on the fair-to-dark scale, but the proportion of redheads in Orkney, at 5.3%, is higher than that reported for Ireland (4.3%), Scotland (4.0%), or Iceland (4.3%).

Eye Colour

The eye colour of 1,063 Orcadians of both sexes, aged between 5 and 18 years, was recorded by Muir,[9] using thirteen categories of the Martin eye standard. There are problems in comparing

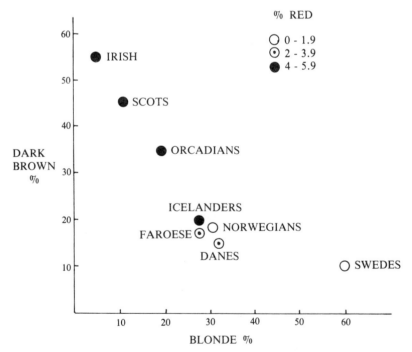

Figure 37. Hair colour variation. [Data source: Suter (1979), Harvey & Suter (unpubl.), Pálsson & Schwidetzky (1975)].

different populations, as over the years different investigators
have used different methods of colour assessment; to avoid these
problems, only two major classes of eye colour shade have been
used for Figure 38. 'Light' includes all blue and grey eyes; 'dark'
spans the range of brown eye colour from light to dark. In
general, in the populations shown, there is a fairly consistent
relationship between the proportions of dark and light eyes in the
populations: those with the highest proportion of light eyes have
the lowest proportion of dark, and vice versa. The exception is
the Irish sample, which has a high frequency of intermediate or
'mixed' shades. On the two scales of measurement the Scots are
closest to the Orcadians, but have darker eye colour. The
Faroese are next, with a higher proportion of light eyes, followed
by the Icelanders.

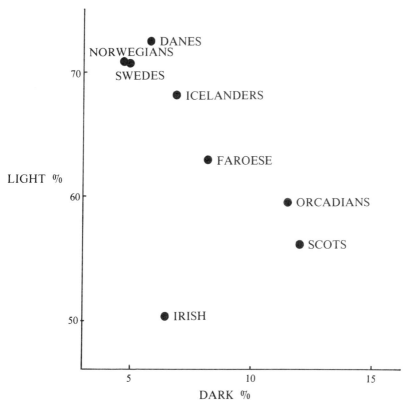

Figure 38. Eye colour variation. [Data source: Harvey & Suter (unpubl.), Muir
(1977), Pálsson & Schwidetzky (1975)].

Conclusions

Before drawing any conclusions from these results it would be wise to express again a few words of caution about their interpretation.

Firstly, there is variation within all populations, and in a number of our populations we do not know enough about this internal variation to be able to say with confidence that we have obtained a representative sample.

Secondly, there are insufficient data on the population size of the Orcadian communities during their early settlement history, and on the extent of migration, for us to be able to tell whether or not random genetic drift has been operating, although in the preceding chapter, Derek Roberts concludes that it probably has been unimportant in Orkney. Notwithstanding, drift and inbreeding are factors which may act over the years to differentiate communities, and if they have operated in Orkney at some stage in the past, they would have influenced the genetic composition of the Orcadian population today.

Thirdly, we do not know to what extent natural selection may have operated on such characteristics as the blood types. For example, it is possible that individuals of certain blood groups may have had greater resistance to major epidemic diseases such as the Black Death.

Finally, the gene frequencies for contemporary Scandinavians, Scots, British and Irish may be substantially different today from what they were at the time of settlement and population expansion in Orkney and elsewhere.

The inescapable conclusion is that the biological affinities of the Orcadians are not particularly clear-cut. In terms of 'distance', they seem to be poised between on the one hand the Scots and the Irish, and on the other the Scandinavians and partially Scandinavian-derived populations. It is possible that the English from the South-East of Britain should be included in the latter category, although the unexpected closeness of the English sample in the genetic distance analysis should not be taken as conclusive evidence of any remote or recent admixture from the South-East of the UK into the Orcadian population. Rather, it indicates that for this particular combination of genetic markers the two populations have similarities in their gene frequencies which defy any straightforward anthropological explanation at the present time.

In general, the results do not support a hypothesis of comparative isolation for the whole Orkney archipelago. This finding is certainly in accordance with the historical evidence.

Biologically the results are what might be expected from a mixture of Celtic, Scottish-Gaelic and Scandinavian ingredients during the forty or so generations that have elapsed since the Vikings first established their Orkney communities. As to the proportions of these ingredients, genetic studies may help, but this is something which must await future anthropological investigations.

Acknowledgments

We are grateful to Dr Veronica Muir for permitting us to use unpublished data from her PhD. thesis in our inter-population comparisons. We should also like to thank Prof. D. F. Roberts for the use of dermatoglyphic data for Cumbria in our distance analysis.

CHAPTER 6

Length of Life
and Age at Death in Orkney

Evelyn J. Bowers

The possibility of unusual longevity in the Northern Isles has historical precedents; older writers frequently commented, for instance, on the apparent long lives of some Shetlanders. In 1862 J. R. Cowie, who wrote his MD thesis on the people of Shetland, calculated that the male death rate in the islands between 20 and 70 years was 51.2%, compared to 90% in Scotland as a whole; in Shetland one fifth of the adult population survived to over 80, compared to only one thirteenth in Scotland.[1] The 1971 Census showed 6.6% of the Shetland population to be over 75, and 1.4% over 85; the relative proportions in Scotland as a whole at the time were 4.2% over 75, and only 0.7% over 85.[2]

Also in Shetland, a difference was noted between the length of life of men and of women. Writing in 1809, A. Edmonston commented that women usually lived longer than men and preserved their faculties better; his theory was that women may have been "less exposed to excessive and desultory labour".[3] Whatever the reason, the pattern was still there in 1851: the Census of that year showed that the proportion of females aged 70 years or more was ten per cent higher in Shetland than in Scotland generally, while in 1951 the excess was even more marked. In 1971, women outnumbered men by two to one amongst the over-75s in Shetland.

The difference in longevity between men and women in Shetland could reflect to some extent emigration, voluntary or forced, and the risks of life in fishing communities. It has, for instance, been estimated that by the time of Trafalgar there were approximately three thousand Shetlanders in the British Navy: this figure, the result of the pressures of island poverty and the virtually unrestricted operation of the press gang, represents no less than half the adult male population of the islands.[4] In more

peaceful times, there were opportunities in the Hudson's Bay
Company in Canada and at the Greenland whaling, for which in
1862, for example, more than five hundred young men joined
ship in Lerwick. In the same year, a further 142 Shetlanders
enlisted in the Royal Naval Reserve.[5] Many of the Shetland men
who left home for these various forms of employment never
returned; neither did the 105 fishermen lost in the dreadful storm
of 1832.[6]

Even allowing for the strong influence of emigration amongst
the male Shetlanders, there is still the observation by Cowie in
1862 that children were frequently born to women up to 50 years
of age. In general, there are a number of Shetland incidences of
long life, in both sexes. In the parish registrar's record for the
island of Unst for 1850 to 1945, during which time the
population of the island averaged 2,000, A. T. Cluness noted the
deaths of four centenarians, with four more reaching 99, nine 98,
four 97, and sixteen 95 or 96. One man from Uyeasound served
as a cooper in the same place and for the same firm or its
successors for no less than eighty-four years.[7]

> He began as a boy of twelve and continued until he was
> ninety-six, when he retired, finding that "the work was
> getting beyond him." He enjoyed his pipe and a quiet
> evening's fishing at the pier in front of his house. Work,
> and a pipe, and cleanness of mind and body were his
> recipes for a long life.

Of one lady in Unst who lived to 103, Cluness quotes a
description he was given:

> "She was able to move about the house when she was over
> the hundred years. She was carefully tended by three
> daughters and she looked younger than any of them, with
> rosy cheeks and bright eyes. She loved fun, and enjoyed a
> gossip, and was full of old songs and old tales."[8]

Longevity in Orkney

Does Orkney show comparable examples? Present-day
Orcadians can quote the example of Mrs Margaret Ann Clouston,
who celebrated her 106th birthday in 1986 and indeed was
looking after her own house until recently. Ex-Provost George
Robertson of Stromness, initiator of many community projects,
used in his 90s to enjoy going round the local golf course in a
score lower than his age. At the age of 90 he produced a book of
memoirs in which he remarked that

my longevity may be accounted for by heredity and golf, moderate smoking (cigarettes and pipe) and food. I never was a drinker.[9]

The *Orkneyinga Saga* says that the first Bishop of Orkney, William the Old, had at the time of his death in 1158 been a bishop for sixty-six years. That would, if so, make him at least 86 years old at death, and at least 70 when he joined Earl Rognvald on a journey to the Holy Land.[10]

Rev. James Wallace (d. 1688), who was minister first in Sanday and then in Kirkwall, observed:

> By reason of the temperance of their Dyet and wholesomenes of the Air, the People usually live to a great Age. A Man in the Parish of Ham dyed not many years since, who liv'd upwards of Fourscore Years with one Wife, in a marry'd estate. There is also a Gentleman, yet living in Stronsa, who was Begotten of his Father when he was an hundred Years old, and who did live till he saw this same Man's Children.[11]

Even allowing for possible exaggeration in information provided to Wallace, these reported ages appear not to exceed figures that have definitely been authenticated on occasion elsewhere.[12] They do certainly suggest a contrast with some other areas such as London. A contemporary of Wallace was John Graunt, the pioneer of demography, the analysis of population structure and change. Graunt studied the Bills of Mortality, the weekly records of deaths and baptisms which went back to the end of the 16th century, to analyse birth and death rates in London. In his compilation of mortality data, published in 1662, he reported that less than one Londoner out of a hundred lived past the age of 80 years.[13]

There is evidence of a general lengthening of life since then; for example, after studying records for European royalty, Peller reported in 1967 an increase of ten years in maximum life span between 1650 and 1850.[14] Such a rise does not mean that the pattern of life spans over the centuries has been a simple one of slow and steady increase: an earlier study of Roman funerary inscriptions showed life spans reaching 100 years.[15] Thus the more recent European increase in life span should be seen as something of a return to a previous condition, after a period of decline. Orkney, however, judging by the kind of figures quoted by Wallace, appears not to have undergone such a decline but rather to have retained an earlier pattern of longevity.

Little over a hundred years after Graunt's figure of less than one Londoner in a hundred living past 80, the Rev. George Barry noted in the *Old Statistical Account* that in Kirkwall and the parish of St Ola many of the inhabitants reached the age of 80 and 85, and "some to 90".[16] The *Old Statistical Account*, compiled by Sir John Sinclair of Ulbster in Caithness and published by him in 21 volumes between 1791 and 1799, was based on answers to a 166-item questionnaire circulated to all the parish ministers of Scotland, and is a mine of information for the study of the society of the time. The apparent pattern of long life reported by Barry amongst the people of Kirkwall and St Ola does not appear to have been uniform over all of Orkney. The Orphir entry, for example, speaks of "very few" of the people of the parish (pop. 826 in 1795) as attaining the age of 80.[17] The effects of extreme poverty, and also the resulting emigration, mean that the population structure of the time is clearly complex, with a number of different factors operating.

James Fea (1775), in a book of proposals for economic development, speaks of

> the bulk of our inhabitants being reduced to extreme misery, without a possibility of relieving themselves, by any means they can use. An instance of this is, that such as are employed in the Iceland fishery, are obliged to work for four months in the year, for thirty shillings; which certainly shews the greatest distress at home, or it cannot be supposed, that they would leave the Country, to work for such wages.[18]

The emigration itself, which intensified throughout the 18th century, would have taken many young and healthy Orcadians away from the islands for a time, but many also did come home again when their time of service was over, so their temporary absence would not necessarily affect longevity figures substantially. However, they might settle in a different parish from the one from which they originally came, or take a house in Kirkwall. Heavy emigration from a parish could also indicate living conditions of a particularly depressed nature, to the extent that longer lives were less common.

Supporting the overall impression of reasonably long life spans at the time, there is the report from another book by James Fea, in 1787, that

> These islanders are generally longer livers than in the more southern parts of the kingdom, a man being hardly

reckoned old at fourscore, and several living to above an
hundred; it has even been known that these centenaries
have been able to earn their bread by hard labour: all of
which is ascribed to their temperance and frugal way of
living, being strangers until of late to the luxuries of
wealthier nations.[19]

Despite the heavy emigration from Orkney in the 18th century,
a counterweight to it developed with the rise of the kelp
industry, which in the boom years from 1780 to 1830 employed
at its peak 3,000 people;[20] emigration was too well-developed a
tradition to be ended, but the kelp boom helped to stem the
overall population decline.[21] The *New Statistical Account* of 1842
was published at a time when in Orkney population figures had
been rising since the Census of 1811, with the natural increase in
births outweighing the loss by emigration. On general health and
length of life, the North Ronaldsay entry reports that

> The people are uncommonly healthy and robust. Excepting
> a very few who die in infancy, these seldom exceed one in
> a twelvemonth, deaths among the young are exceedingly
> rare. By far the greatest number of deaths take place on
> those who have reached sixty-five or upwards, and yet
> comparatively few outlive eighty. Occasional instances of
> very great longevity will be found no test of the general
> healthfulness of the population, or of the average term of
> life; and it is precisely among a population like that of this
> island, that these attain their maximum, where are
> accustomed to laborious occupations and exposure to every
> kind of weather, which tend, in the first instance, to render
> the bodily frame hardy and robust, and, at the same,
> prevent it from reaching an extreme old age.[22]

Some interesting examples of long life are given in *Descriptive
Notes* by George MacGregor Jnr. (1893):

> *The late Mr Wm. Laughton, Caldale, St Ola.*
> Mr Laughton died a few years ago at the ripe age of 98
> years. Although in early life his occupation was varied, he
> followed a number of years the 'big' herring fishing . . .
> From the meridian of his life until a few years before his
> decease, Mr Laughton farmed with much success the farm
> of Caldale . . . Although Mr Laughton was never what
> they call 'TT', he was at all times moderate in the use of
> alcohol as a beverage, and likewise used tobacco and snuff

Stromness lifeboat crew, c. 1930

The Housegarth Band

with comparative moderation. It may be mentioned that, some years before his death, there were five members of the Laughton family — brothers and sisters — alive at the time whose ages averaged 85 years.

The late Mr Yorston, Shoemaker, Kirkwall.
This worthy citizen died in Kirkwall, on the 8th July, 1888, at the great age of 101 years . . . Mr Yorston during his long business career (which was close application to the shoemaking, less five seasons at the Davis Straits) was highly and deservedly respected as a quiet, industrious, Christian man. Snuff and tobacco he used none, and as to the use of spiritous liquor was always very moderate.

Mr Benjamin Halcro, Farmer, Petertown, Orphir.
Mr Halcro, now (1890) approaching 100 years, hale and hearty, and of happy disposition, is of medium height, stoutly built, and of a dark complexion, and in early days, I am told, was very wiry and muscular. He sits from eleven to six o'clock in one of those old fashioned straw-backed chairs, looking out at a window which takes in a magnificent view of Hoy Sound, the Island of Graemsay and the Hoy hills, and is carefully nursed by his daughters, Mrs Sinclair and Miss Halcro.

Benjamin was born, and spent his years up to boyhood, at South-heather, by Hobbister, Orphir . . .

Benjamin was married in the year 1828, his wife by whom he had four daughters, having been spared him for over fifty-six years . . .

When a boy about thirteen or fourteen, Benjamin's parents sent him to Stromness to learn the shoemaking trade, but he did not serve out his apprenticeship, because the quality and quantity of the food he received from his landlady (the wife of his master) was inadequate for his necessary support . . .

In early life, although he had wrought at different employments (one of these being a trip to the Davis Straits) from the prime of his life up to twenty-six years ago, he farmed successfully Orrakirk, Petertown, Orphir . . .[23]

Amongst the others mentioned by MacGregor as having been to the Davis Straits was a Rackwick man who was said to be at the time of this account "about 100 years of age".

J

Orkney population patterns

The increase in world population over the last century and a
half is thought to be due predominantly to the decrease in infant
mortality.[24] Nevertheless, the increase in life span, as seen in the
increased proportion of elders in society, makes an important
contribution to population growth in some parts of Western
society at present.[25]

Orkney displays the increase in the proportion of older people
that is seen in other parts of Western society, but the situation is
complicated by emigration. A peak in population of 32,225 was
reached at the time of the Census of 1861, and thereafter came a
decline as emigration again exceeded the natural increase. A
century later, for every 100 people there had been in Orkney in
1861, there were only 58.[26] This was part of another more
general pattern in much of Western society, the movement of
population from rural areas to the cities, and over the same
hundred years Shetland only retained 55 people per 100,
Sutherland 52, and Berwick 61. 'The drift from the isles' was a
major subject of discussion in Orkney in the 1950s and 60s, with
the rate of depopulation building up to a peak between 1951 and
1961.[27] Amongst the causes was the decline in employment on
the farms, with the continuing mechanisation of Orkney's main
industry, agriculture, and the amalgamation of smaller units. In
more recent years, however, the population has started to
increase once more, due to several factors, including the trend
from the cities to 'get away from it all' to rural areas, increased
employment opportunities in Orkney from the arrival of the oil
industry in the 1970s, and the decline in emigration from the
islands due to decreasing prospects in the Merchant Navy and
overseas.[28]

Within the overall Orkney population trends, there are
variations. Kirkwall, for instance, as the county town, has
continued to grow in population, and a pattern of movement in
to Kirkwall from the outer isles shows no sign of slackening. The
exception to the picture of falling population in the isles is
Westray, the most populous, where the fishing industry has
grown steadily, due to determined community effort and local
investment.[29]

Another sort of pattern occurred in the parish of Walls in the
island of Hoy: the Royal Navy's Scapa Flow base at Lyness
employed an estimated 200 local men on general duties through
the Second World War, and the existence of the base meant that
the total population of Walls and the neighbouring island of
Flotta hardly altered at all between 1931 and 1951, a period in

which Eday's population fell by 35%, Stronsay's by 33%, Rousay 26%, and North Ronaldsay 25. The closure of the Lyness base in 1957 meant a sudden and massive depopulation of the working age group, and within a year the proportion of over-65s in Walls was almost twice the general Scottish percentage.[30]

The basis for life in Orkney over the past 5,000 years or so has been farming and fishing, and from the potential food production from the land and the sea the population even in remote times may have been within the range of the figures of the last two centuries. This emerges from considerations by Gordon Childe[31] and by Colin Renfrew[32] of the evidence from the Neolithic period, while Ronald Miller (1976) suggests a population of between ten and twenty thousand in the broch period:

> The sheer labour of collecting and building such a mass of stone makes it seem unlikely that a broch would be built for less than 100 people, say twenty to twenty-five families. Their position, with good arable ground, hill grazings behind and sea fisheries (except for the interior of the West Mainland) in front make such a population feasible. In all the Orkney brochs would thus suggest a minimum population total of some 10,000 but if there was a slave population living in subjection to the broch folk, this total might well be doubled.[33]

If the seventeenth-century population of Orkney could provide a thousand men to die for the Royalist cause at Carbisdale, under Montrose in 1650,[34] then the overall figure at this time was probably in this range also.

Orkney mortality patterns

With different individuals living to different ages, these ages at death form a pattern, a *mortality pattern*. In a stable environment, this distribution would remain stable, and would be characteristic of a population. If, however, the environment changes, a new distribution gradually takes shape as the pattern of ages at death alters. The distribution of ages at death determines the overall structure of a population, i.e. the numbers of individuals in each group. For example, over the past century and a half Orkney has in common with many other places seen major changes in medical care and hygiene practices, and so infant and childhood mortality have greatly declined. As the years have gone by, the increased number of survivors from childhood have grown to adult life and their deaths have gradually spread through the mortality pattern. At any one time, a study of the age structure of the living gives a profile of the population that is shaped by the mortality pattern.

Although modern medical developments have increased the number that survive from birth to enter the population system, the causes of eventual death in any population are largely outwith the control of its members. The typical length of life of individuals in the population is shaped by their heredity and their environment — on what they are and on what influences and events they are exposed to.

A study of Orkney mortality was carried out using data recorded in the civil *Registers of Mortality* for certain parishes for the years 1860 to 1964.[35] The parishes taken were Birsay, Burray, Deerness, Hoy, Sanday and North Ronaldsay, along with a twenty per cent sample of the Kirkwall population, and

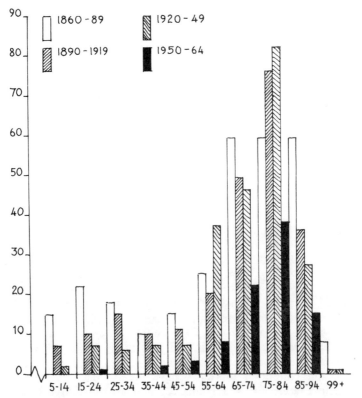

Fig. 39. Distribution of ages at death in Birsay, in ten-year intervals (males)

the ages at death of nearly 8,900 people were tabulated in five-year age groups, male and female.

In the tabulation, deaths over the age of 99 years were assimilated into the age class 95-99. In the entire set of data for Orkney in the period examined, there were five people with recorded ages over 99. They were all women, and scattered over the various regions of Orkney. The distribution of centenarians appears consistent with that for England and Wales.[36]

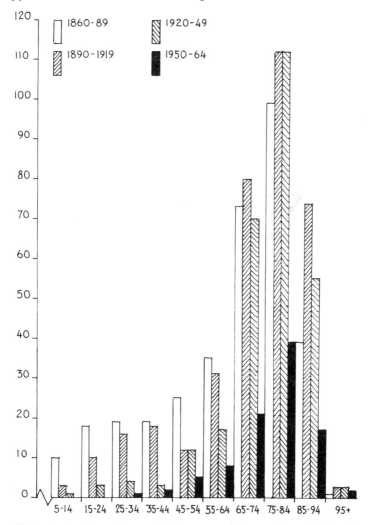

Fig. 40. Distribution of ages at death in Birsay, in ten-year intervals (females)

In these analyses, the age group from birth to 4 was considered separately as the focus was on longevity and factors affecting infant and childhood mortality are likely to be different from those having their impact later in the life cycle.[37] The time period involved, 1860 to 1964, has been divided into four sections: 1860-1889, prior to the spread of germ theory; 1890-1919, from the development of germ theory to the close of the First World War; 1920-1949, from the end of the War to the introduction of antibiotics; and 1950-1964, a half-size period in the era of antibiotics.

Figures 39 and 40 show how the data is tabulated. The figures show the distribution of ages at death in Birsay, for males and for females, taken for these diagrams in ten-year intervals. The most common age of death can readily be seen from each figure: for men and for women, on this ten-year-interval scale, it is in the 75 to 84 group, and the peak has remained in this group through the four periods under study. Out of the various classes that the ages at death fall into, this 75-84 class is called the *modal class* (the word *mode* having the same meaning as in the French phrase *á la mode* or 'fashionable' to describe this peak class).

The average person in Birsay does not, however, die at this modal age, as the totals in all the other age-groups or classes exceed it. One measure of the average can be obtained by looking for the individual who is exactly half-way along the scale as far as age at death is concerned, that is, half of the population live longer than him, while the other half live shorter lives. To find this point, we simply count along the classes until we have covered half the population; this point is called the *median,* and the median age in a distribution like this is a measure of the length of life that can be expected for a newly-born infant.

Another type of average can be found by the standard process of adding up all the ages of the population in the sample and dividing by the total; this is called the *mean*. It is the age at death which would be observed if everyone died at the same age.

Table 28 shows the result of the analysis of ages at death in the seven parish areas chosen, with the ages taken in classes of five-year intervals. Following the median age through the four periods, for each parish, it will be seen that it steadily increases over time; in other words, life expectancy is increasing. The mean age rises too, as time goes on. We might to some extent expect these increases as part of a general pattern of longer life spans in Western society. An interesting aspect that is less expected is the constancy of the mode, the location of the peak

Time	1860 to 1889			1890 to 1919			1920 to 1949			1950 to 1964		
	Modal Class	Mean	Median	Modal Class	Mean	Median	Modal Class	Mean	Median	Modal Class	Mean	Median
Males of:												
Birsay	70-74	61	71	80-84	67	74	75-79	69	74	80-84	74	76
Burray	70-74	52	60	75-79	60	68	80-84	63	69	70-74	72	74
Deerness	75-79	60	67	75-79	65	74	80-84	69	73	75-79	75	77
Hoy	75-79	60	68	75-79	58	67	80-84	66	70	*		
Kirkwall	75-79	52	58	70-79	61	69	65-69	69	70	70-74	67	70
Sanday	70-74	57	65	75-79	67	73	75-79	70	73	80-84	76	77
S. Ronaldsay	80-84	58	67	75-79	60	68	75-79	68	73	75-79	69	73
Females of:												
Birsay	80-84	63	70	80-84	70	76	75-79	75	78	80-84	75	78
Burray	80-84	54	64	75-79	62	71	75-79	65	75	60-64	74	75
Deerness	80-84	66	73	75-79	66	72	80-84	71	75	75-79	77	79
Hoy	75-79	60	70	75-79	61	70	75-79	67	71	*		
Kirkwall	80-84	56	65	70-74	60	69	80-84	72	74	80-84	72	76
Sanday	80-84	62	70	80-84	65	72	80-84	70	74	80-84	75	80
S. Ronaldsay	80-84	59	67	75-79	62	70	80-84	69	74	80-84	76	79

* There are too few deaths in Hoy in the most recent period for analysis.

Table 28. Measures of central tendency of ages at death: Modal Class, Mean and Median, deaths above age four years.

of the distribution. As time goes on, this peak seems to be staying at more or less the same age group, while the distribution readjusts around it.

Table 28 gives the pattern by parishes, with men and women taken together, in the 28 cases given by looking at the seven parish areas for four time periods each. When the data for men and women was examined separately, a modal age at death of between 80 and 84 was found for women in 18 out of the 28 cases. In several of the other cases, the modal age class was 75-79, and a change of one or two individuals would have moved it to the next older class. In the Kirkwall sample between 1890 and 1919 the peak was at a lower age group, with 29 deaths between ages 70 and 74, 27 between 75 and 79, and 25 between ages 80 and 84; a factor operating here could well be the great influenza pandemic.

For Orkney men, the modal class of ages at death appears to be 75 to 79 years of age, but there is more variability among males than among females in this characteristic, as in many others. The 75-79 group comes out as the modal class in 16 out of 28 instances. In four cases the mode falls in the previous age bracket; and in five, in the subsequent one.

The birth to 4 age group, treated separately in the analysis, is capable of producing a mode, particularly in older times of higher infant mortality. This in fact happens for girls in the period up to 1890 in all the areas studied, apart from Birsay, but after that the mode already identified in the older age-groups — the senescent, or aging, mode — is higher. For boys, the mode is in the infant age group for all the areas in the first period, and also for the South Ronaldsay and Kirkwall cases in the second; after this, decreasing numbers of deaths in the first five years of life leave the senescent mode as the overall peak.

The constancy of the senescent modal age, over various parishes of Orkney and through various periods, leads to the question as to whether or not this modal age is a characteristic of the people of Orkney — in other words, a biological feature. Observations of the high senescent modal age at death in various areas have been known for many years, but their biological significance appears largely to have gone unappreciated. A study of males in England and Wales for 1871-1880, made by Karl Pearson, showed a senescent mode in the early 70s, but exceeded by an infant mode in the first year of life.[38] French data examined by Pearson also showed a senescent mode in the early 70s.[39] More recently a distribution of ages at death of Hungarian males, 1959-1961, gave a senescent mode of 75, exceeded by an infant mode in the first year of life.[40]

It is interesting to note that we can still get a peak like this in an infant age group in the overall distribution of death rates of a national population: the presistence of an infant mode in such data contrasts with its disappearance from Orkney. One reason may be that size of population may influence infant mortality. Certainly infectious diseases that would die out in small populations can remain endemic in large ones, and may contribute to the difference noticed here.

The Dane, P. L. Panum, in his classic work on the 1846 measles epidemic in the Faroe Islands, reported a high modal age at death there also. The Faroes, like Orkney and Shetland, were colonised by the Norse in the Migration Period (about the 9th century), but later with the rest of the Norwegian territories came under the crown of Denmark with Norway. Panum states that

> When we . . . compare the rate of mortality on the Faroe Islands with that of Denmark, we shall see that while the greatest mortality among us is found between the sixtieth and the seventieth years of live, on the Faroes it is between the eightieth and ninetieth years.[41]

Panum based his statement on an examination of the Church Registers of Mortality, and did not distinguish between the two sexes. He attributed the greater longevity of the Faroese to the absence in the small populations of Faroe of infectious diseases which occurred commonly in the large populations of Denmark.

In Shetland, however, already noted as being characterised by longevity, infectious diseases have been described in a phrase of Berry and Muir (1975) as being "particularly rampant" in the history of the islands.[42] This suggests that the idea of an absence of infectious diseases is not an adequate explanation of the observed longevity. The occurrence of a high modal age at death in Faroe and Shetland as well as in Orkney argues for a genetic basis for this characteristic since the populations of these three island groups have varied from one to the other by an order of magnitude, and epidemic diseases have not spared Orkney and Shetland.

This analysis supports the hypothesis that the modal age at death is a biological feature which is under genetic control and is probably maintained by balancing selection. This support comes from the consistency of this feature of the mortality distribution in seven Orkney parishes in four time periods in spite of changes in medical care and health and hygiene practices which have produced a marked increase in life expectancy. In the absence of genetic control, the mode would be expected to vary at random and not exhibit a consistent pattern.[43] The consistency also suggests that the factors influencing this selective maintenance have not changed over the period under study in Orkney. These results are consistent with the idea that life span at the individual level is directly controlled by the process of natural selection.[44] The results do not support a recent suggestion, based on extrapolation of the general increase of life expectancy, that a senescent mode around 85 is to be expected in Western society.[45] For that to become the case an advance in the mode would be required and there is no sign of any such movement in the Orkney data from 1860 to 1964.

This analysis also shows no change in the maximum length of life in the people of Orkney since 1860. The occurrence of long lives in traditional societies is supported by data from Orthodox Church registers for the Aleutian Islands[46] in the early period of contact with settlers, as well as from the previously-mentioned work of Panum for Faroe and Cowie for Shetland. The life span in Orkney is only slightly shorter than that reported for Abkhazia[47] in the USSR and is similar to that for Vilcabamba[48] in Ecuador when data from these regions are subject to rigorous verification. Orkney can be seen to be another area characterised by long life for appreciable numbers of the inhabitants, a feature which has been part of the ecological adaption of the population of Orkney for a long time.

Some Reminiscences of a Centenarian

Mrs Margaret Ann Clouston

(Mrs Clouston celebrated her 106th birthday on May 17th 1986. Her cousin, the late Mrs Jessie Alexina Craigie, was also one of Orkney's centenarians. These reminiscences are taken from two interviews made on Mrs Clouston's 104th birthday by Kathryn Gourlay of BBC Radio Orkney and retained in the station's Orkney Sound Archive.)

I was born in Rousay—Claybank, that was the name of the house. I was born in 1880. My father was a farming man—he was a ploughman working service. Seven pound and a half a year—that wasn't much! A shilling would have bought a lot of errands then. He'd have gotten sugar and maybe an ounce of tobacco for that too. It was better in those days: there was little money but it was cheaper—it's very dear now.

My grandfather's farm was Fjalquoy in Rousay, but he was born in Quandale—that's a district that's not occupied now. My grandfather built a new house at Fjalquoy, a grand house with upstairs in it and bay windows, about the time that I was born. The old house had a hole in the roof, for the smoke to go through, and a backstone. My mother didn't like it. She was a young wife, married one of the sons. She didn't like it—smoke in the house. You would come in at the door and the backstone was there with the links at either side of it and the pots and the kettles all on that, and a hole in the roof of the house for the smoke to go out of.

And they ate 'soor fish' in those days and a woman came there to be a servant and said, "I can't take that rotten fish." She wasn't used to it, she was a Caithness woman. 'Soor fish' was when it was just beginning to rot—I can't take that rotten fish either!

They built the new two-storey house out of stone—no bricks then. The stones were quarried out of the ground. You could quarry them and lift some of them square. I've worked in a quarry myself—never thought anything at it!—quarried flags and lifted them out and helped. I was hungry then—not a penny to rub together. I'd eat anything I could get my hand on. We never thought about what it was—maybe a raw turnip. We just peeled it with our teeth and ate a piece out of it when we were hungry. There wasn't so much to live on then as now; you wouldn't have got a sweet biscuit or anything.

When we were all done with being born there were thirteen of us, but they didn't all live—two died in infancy. But it was wonderful: eleven was a lot—it was a grand football team!

My mother could go to the peat hill and carry home a sack of peats on her back and make a grand fire for us. She had plenty of stuff, fish heads and fish livers, tatties and cabbage and she'd make right good meat. And we'd spoon it in us just like that—grand! And they didn't need cod liver oil like what they do need now: we got our livers, the real thing and that was why we were so hardy. That's what makes you live to a hundred and four! The fish livers were all cooked up to us, and right good it was with our meat. That's the thing that makes a hardy folk. We ate the fish off the heads and the heads is the best—the most nourishing of all and folk throw it away!

I remember a terrible influenza. Everybody was in, and the few that were on their feet went about and helped—a terribly bad influenza, a lot of folk died. And there was plenty of snow on the ground then—there's no snow like it now, no hail, no frost hanging from the roofs of the houses—what a difference! We used to down with the icicles and suck them and make our lips all cracked; it's fine and fresh—health for folk!

At the time of this influenza I would have been six or eight. I was lying by the fire with my head on a creepie. I could go to the shop and buy my errands and bring them home too. Everybody was ill and there was just me and my brother up and the rest were all ill. And the folk that could go on their feet were feeding the other folks' kye. That was a long time ago!

We all had different jobs to do—bearing water and going to the shop with errands and going for the milk and getting a pail and going for kirned milk to bake with. I was not very much at the school, let me tell you that! I had to work and notice the bairns for my mother—I was the oldest lass. We had to carry baskets of turnips for the kye. That was what they got in the winter, and they were right mad for it. They got their turnips and the straw after it. And their byres were properly cleaned and the kye were bedded with straw. The byres were kept clean—you could walk inside without dirtying your feet. We had brooms and we swept the byres clean.

When I was twelve I went to Flaws in Evie to herd kye. We didn't have to herd kye the whole year, we just herded in the bonny summer months. There were no dykes and fences then. You had to herd the kye to keep them out of the crop, back and fore like that. On rainy days we took a shawl with us and held it over our heads and a great big plaid held about us. When it was wet we just held it down and got wet, and dried again—a bit of water never hurt you! We were running with bare feet among the thistles—we just had our bare feet many a time. We liked to run then with no boots on us!

I was nineteen when I married and he was twelve years older than me—old men's the best! Never marry a fisherman—it's a hard life when they're at the sea and coarse weather comes and peedie boats: very, very worrying. Waiting for them all the time and hearing they're coming in on a very coarse day and hauling their boat to a better piece and you hear them coming and you're glad to see them.

He was not a very strong man, he didn't last a long while—consumption was rife in those days but they can master it now. It was enormous, the number of folk that had consumption, and I was at the houses with it and I said I'm surely immune from it for I never took it, working so much among it, you see.

He went out every day; every morning he rose with the tide. When the tide was in they had to get up and go to sea, and they were small boats. We sold some of the fish and dried them on the dykes and pressed them, and we sold them in Kirkwall. Salted fish—the merchant bought them and sold them out of

Kirkwall. Lobsters were very cheap in my young days. Lobsters were only a shilling, and they got eleven pence sometimes. That was the way we were kept down, you see. We could dress ourselves and go to the kirk too, all the same.

We had a set of clothes we kept aside and only put on on a Sunday for going to the kirk. What a grand day we had—everybody was walking then. There were no cars or anything; everybody was walking. What a grand time we had on the road, all speaking together! Fourteen miles was the size Rousay right round it, and I've been round it on a Sunday, every bit of it and at my auntie's home at night for tea and milking the kye then. We'd go home at eight o'clock, running pieces of the road to get home on time when we were delayed. We had grand fun—that was great times then as well as now. Far better—dances at night, and all. And it was spoken about for a while. Now they never speak about a dance, it's just that common.

My father was the only fiddler on Rousay for a great while, and he taught the other ones to play. He was a grand fiddler; he just fairly fitted into the dances and the time. Polkas and schottisches and the Four Couple Reel and the Flowers of Edinburgh. There were dances that came in and they learnt them from Kirkwall: Rory O' More and Strip the Willow and the Queen Victoria.

We had a grand walk at our wedding, everybody went out with their partners and my father was there with the fiddle playing and played the whole road home and we were going with him—I suppose we did maybe fully two miles. We married in the house, decorated up for it. Plenty of whisky and plenty of ale and plenty of cakes and plum pudding and sweeties. We had our dance and we had our walk—the Quadrilles and the Lancers—that's dancing!—and they take the sweep and everybody takes hands and they sweep in and that's good dancing!

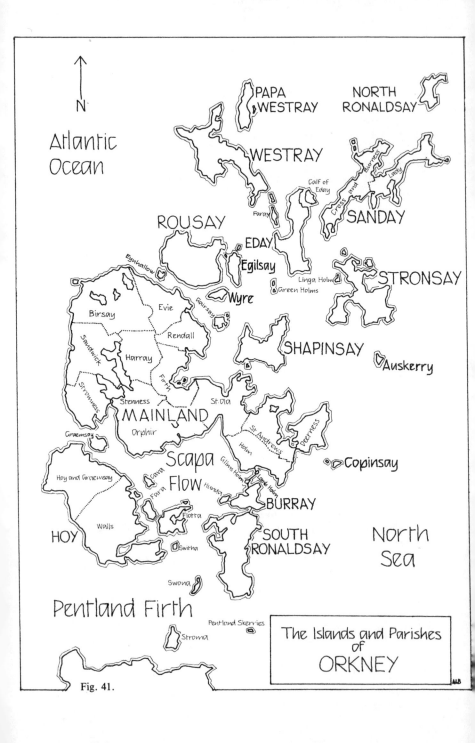

The Islands and Parishes of ORKNEY

Fig. 41.

CHAPTER 7

Traditions and Customs

Howie Firth

In 1773 the Rev. George Low visited North Ronaldsay and in his description a year later of the island remarked: "Sometimes the calf has a better apartment than the heir of a family that can boast of twenty-four generations of uninterrupted lineal succession!"[1] The priority given to the farm animals would not be unusual even into comparatively recent times in a community like Orkney which depends so heavily upon agriculture; but the comment about the ability to trace back twenty-four generations is, as J. Storer Clouston observed in a paper in 1926, extremely significant.[2] It means that Low clearly has an actual case in mind, and Clouston pointed out one good reason for the care taken with such oral records.

> The peculiarities of the odal system of inheritance, with its lack of documents and its feature of all the descendants of the original owner having rights in the land (unless they had been formally extinguished), obviously made it necessary to keep an oral pedigree very strictly and correctly, and for a long distance back, just as in the Highlands oral pedigrees were necessary for purposes of establishing the chieftaincy.[3]

One Shetlander of the last century is said to have been able to trace a family back through 27 generations.[4] North Ronaldsay itself is the island where the minister read to some of the older people Thomas Gray's poem *The Fatal Sisters* soon after its publication in 1768. The poem, based on an old Norse text, tells of a vision which occurred in Caithness at the time of Earl Sigurd of Orkney's defeat and death at Clontarf, but after the North Ronaldsay minister had read a verse or two of Gray's translation to his listeners, "they interrupted the reader, telling him they knew the song well in the Norse language and had often sung it to him when he asked them for an old song."[5]

To us today, word of mouth might at first seem a particularly
unreliable way of passing on information, and so it can be if
there is only one speaker and one listener. But W. B. Yeats
described how in the *Parochial Survey of Ireland*

> it is recorded how the story-tellers used to gather together
> of an evening, and if any had a different version from the
> others, they would all recite theirs and vote, and the man
> who had varied would have to abide by their verdict. In
> this way stories have been handed down with such
> accuracy, that the long tale of Deirdre was, in the earlier
> decades of this century, told almost word for word, as in
> the very ancient MSS. in the Royal Dublin Society. In one
> case only it varied, and then the MS. was obviously wrong
> — a passage had been forgotten by the copyist.[6]

This system of collective public checking is a key point in the
oral process. The written word remains, as long as no one
actually destroys it (or discreetly tampers with it!), so it can be
preserved passively, by simply leaving it alone. Oral information,
however, does not have a separate existence apart from the
speakers, and it can only be kept alive by a process of continual
activity. It is in some ways analogous to the information in the
memory banks of an older type of electronic computer, which
would be lost if ever the electric power to the system were to be
switched off. A society depending on oral tradition alone for its
data and references, its laws, history and traditions, must set
absolute standards for accuracy. Examples come from many
areas; the poet-singer of Arabia, for instance, was described as

> a recognised authority who dare not for his life deviate by
> a word from the known facts. Should he err, he is forever
> disgraced. No one reads or writes, therefore their memories
> are acute to a degree practically unknown in Europe.[7]

Plato made this very point in his dialogue *Phaedrus* (c. 370
BC) when he told the tale of the Egyptian god Thoth who
invented writing and described how it would improve the wisdom
and memory of the Egyptians. On the contrary, replied the king
of Egypt, "those who acquire it will cease to exercise their
memory and become forgetful; they will rely on writing to bring
things to their remembrance by external signs instead of on their
own internal resources."[8]

In his paper of 1926, J. Storer Clouston examined some stories
handed down into recent years within Orkney families about

Three people with a great knowledge of traditional Orkney life and events: (above) Willie Thomson of Neven, North Ronaldsay, (below left) Mrs Margaret Ann Clouston, (below right) Peter Leith Snr. of Appiehouse, Stenness

their origins, and though this is an area obviously open to bias and distortion, he still managed to find some surprisingly accurate details. There was, for instance, the story of how the ancestors of the Leiths had bought the little township of Onston in Stenness. The story said that a cow had been thrown in to make up the price.

> Actually, as the charter of 29th August, 1546, is still there to show, the animal was 'ane horss the price XXX schillingis'; but except for turning this charger into a cow, the tale is literally true. Think of a trifling matter of this sort being remembered for nearly four centuries, while the whole agricultural and administrative system of a hundred and fifty years ago has been clean forgotten.[9]

Amongst other traditions that Clouston noted with interest was the story of the first Vikings who landed on Rousay being met by warriors with glittering spears, and the tradition of two men who fought a duel on the Holm of Papay in which they both lost their lives. These, Clouston argued, could well be genuine oral records of events that had actually happened — Vikings being confronted by armed forces of Picts in one case (although we should note Professor Almqvist's qualification on this interpretation in a chapter 9) and the early Norse practice of duel on holms, in the other. "They seem to me," he said, "like small loopholes in a thick wall, giving glimpses of a distant country and a far horizon. And the prospect they show, is in the one case of an Orkney at least twelve hundred years older than the Orkney we live in, and in the other case probably getting well on for a thousand."[10]

The Norse settlement

Storer Clouston's excitement at an item of folklore that might throw some light, however fragmentarily, on the coming of the Norse to Orkney is not hard to understand; for almost no other event in the history of the islands has had such a long-term impact, and yet we know virtually nothing about it. There are no accounts of the arrival of the early settlers, and even in the *Orkneyinga Saga* the islands only come into view in the time of the Norwegian king Haraldr *hárfagri,* Harald Fine-Hair or Fairhair.

> One summer Harald Fine-Hair sailed west over the North sea in order to teach a lesson to certain vikings whose

K

plunderings he could no longer tolerate. These vikings used to raid in Norway over summer and had Shetland and Orkney as their winter base. Harald conquered Shetland, Orkney and the Hebrides, then sailed all the way to the Isle of Man where he laid its settlements in ruins.[11]

There are references to this expedition in several other sagas, but little additional detail, and even the date of Harald's arrival is far from agreed, varying from c. 850 at the one extreme to c. 900 at the other.[12] With a lack of documented evidence, indirect arguments such as those from place-names studies have been essential, but the lack of documented evidence has not prevented very definite views being expressed.

For some time now, a standard model for the analysis of most aspects of island culture, in Shetland as well as Orkney, has been what might be called the Primitive Viking Model — the idea that the arrival of Norse colonists in the period of the 8th/9th centuries was "cataclysmic, a wave sweeping before it every vestige of the former inhabitants and their culture",[13] and that all aspects of island culture are to be explained as essentially based on Norse transplants, originating from this time. This is putting the idea in its starkest possible form, and it should be stressed that over the years there have been a number of eminent voices raised against it, but nonetheless this general way of looking at the Norse influence has seeped into so many areas of study, and coloured indirectly so many interpretations of data examined therein, that it is essential to formulate it explicitly here.

The picture this model of the Norse arrival gives us is of a kind of fault line cutting across Orkney tradition and culture somewhere around 800-900AD, with the Norse on one side of it, and an unknown culture — possibly Pictish — on the other. To cover against eventualities, some authors do allow for the survival of handfuls of suitably menial servants or slaves, male and female. One of the most authoritative assessments of the period of transition accepts that Christianity may have survived the Norse arrival but that

> In other fields the Picts gave little or nothing to the Scandinavians, and the future of the Northern Isles belonged essentially to the Scandinavian world . . . As frequently emphasized in this chapter, the Picts were overwhelmed politically, linguistically, culturally and socially. That is why, after so many centuries, the Northern Isles are still so Scandinavian in outlook and character.[14]

Fig. 42. Orkney in relation to north-west Europe

If the people of Orkney are essentially the descendants of Norse colonists, possibly augmented by a few overwhelmed indigenous slaves and servants, we should expect Orkney folklore to show strong similarities to that of Norway: we would indeed be looking for an underlying base of transplanted Norse folklore. When we examine Orkney folklore in practice, however, this is not what we find. There are elements that show a Norse flavour; but often what stands out are motifs in which Norway is noticeably deficient.

To take one example: the mermaid is one theme that we would at first sight expect to be a common thread running through the folklore of the seagoing communities of the Northern Isles and the West Norwegian coast. Certainly Orkney is rich in such stories, Walter Traill Dennison indeed remarking: "I have heard a hundred times more about mermaids from the lips of Orkney peasants than I ever saw in books."[15] Dennison quotes a number of very detailed descriptions of a subject that seems to have been very familiar in his native island of Sanday:

> Her face was most lovely, and her form perfect in shape and proportion, while her golden hair, descending below her waist, was her matchless crown of beauty, adorning her head, and falling over her snow-white skin in wreaths of golden tissues. With regard to her posterior all my informants agreed that, when in the water, she had a tail; the men holding that her tail was an integral part of her body, while the old women declared this tail to be a skirt, fastened at the mermaid's waist, and forming, when its wearer was on land, a beautiful petticoat embroidered with silver and gold; when the mermaid was in the sea her petticoat was gathered together and shut up at its lower end, at once concealing the mermaid's feet and forming what foolish men called a tail. I have often heard stiff arguments among the old folk, as to whether the tail was a part of her dress, or was a part of the mermaid's body.[16]

But by contrast to this strength of mermaid stories in Orkney, legends about mermaids in Norway "have never been especially common".[17] Such Norwegian accounts as there are tend to make the mermaid or *sjókona* less attractive than in the stories of Orkney and other areas like it.

> It is dangerous to come too close to the mermaid, and when she appears it is usually a sign of bad weather. But it is also said that she sings when there is a favorable wind.

If someone acts contrary to her wishes, she can avenge
herself in the most horrible fashion.[18]

And remarkably in Shetland, where one would tend to expect,
if anything, an even richer haul of mermaid stories than in
Orkney, such accounts are, as Ernest Marwick pointed out,
"somewhat rare".[19] He was, indeed, able to gather out of the
whole of Shetland just two stories involving mermaids, and in
both of these the mermaid has a rather subordinate role.
Dennison quotes a Shetlander who said: "Such an idea as a
Mermaid I never heard of till I saw it in some English work of
fiction." His own experience in Orkney, remarked Dennison,
was "exactly the reverse".[20]

Stories of mermaids still survived in Sanday into recent years,
with the late Willie Meil in 1969 telling Ernest Marwick of the
old belief.

> They said that if a mermaid cam to you, she would ask you
> what tide it was, do you see, if you were on the sea; she
> would grip the gunwales of the boat: well would you —
> what would you say to her? Ah well, if you answered her
> right, you were taen doon wi her [to the bottom of the sea].[21]

The significance of the mermaid theme is that it is a very old
one, which reaches back along the coast of Britain and Ireland
and down past France and Spain to the Mediterranean. The
beautiful woman with yellow hair, coming out of the sea,
appears in classical Greek mythology as Aphrodite arising from
the foam, and the mermaid legends do seem to coincide to a
degree with the old west Atlantic route from the Mediterranean
Sea. The Primitive Viking Model of Orcadian tradition would
suggest a fault-line between Orkney and mainland Scotland,
cutting off the mermaid stories at the Pentland Firth or at least
allowing one or two to diffuse across to the South Isles of
Orkney. The fault-line in this case, however, is between Orkney
and Shetland, leaving Orkney connected to a continuum going
back down the west Atlantic coast of Britain, with Shetland
nearer to Norway.

The fallback position is to postulate that the mass of mermaid
lore in Sanday came in to the island subsequent to the Norse
period with an influx of immigrants from mainland Scotland, for
instance in the Stewart period. But if this were to be taken as a
serious hypothesis, we should have to put forward some evidence
to substantiate it — and we should also have to explain why the
same body of lore was not brought into Shetland, where it has

been estimated that approaching a third of the seventeenth-century population may have been of Scots origin.[22]

Leaving open the possibility that there was some as yet unidentified influx of people into Sanday on such a scale as to overwhelm the Norse descendants in matters of folklore though nothing else, we do have the option of a simple interpretation of the existence of the mermaid stories. It could be that they were in Orkney before the coming of the Norse and that they survived afterwards. It is fair to say that in most other areas this possibility would be the one taken seriously. In Cornwall, for instance, politically part of England for centuries, no one would suggest that the mermaid stories there were obliterated by the English annexation but later re-introduced by immigration.

The significance of the apparent fault-line between Orkney on the one hand and Shetland and Norway on the other has to be qualified in various ways. There is a hiatus in all Nordic folk tradition caused by the scale of the effects of the Black Death; there is the gap opened up between Orkney and Shetland after the Battle of Florvåg in 1194, following which Shetland was directly governed from Norway whereas the Orkney earldom had much less close links; and there is also Dr T. M. Y. Manson's perceptive observation that the relative simplicity of sailing due west from Norway to Shetland's long land-mass makes possible the consideration of much earlier contact and settlement from Norway to Shetland.[23] But these factors only serve to highlight in the present context the fact that in general 'Scottish' folklore did not come in to Shetland with Scottish annexation and partial settlement, strengthening the argument against the Orkney mermaid stories originating from the 'Scottish' period.

It is necessary to take a little time over this point because the Primitive Viking Model has become so deeply entwined into so much study of Orkney's past that it is sometimes very difficult to separate out the data from the interpretation. The Model has seduced as many scholars as the mermaid ever did, and no example shows this more clearly than the case of the trows.

Of trows and trolls

There are many stories in Orkney and in Shetland of these little people, who live in hills and mounds, often Neolithic or Bronze Age sites, into which they might lure a human fiddler to provide music for the dancing which they loved so much. They might also take brides or children into the hill, leaving behind a 'trowie' replacement — 'trowie' meaning 'poor' or 'sickly'. Cold iron or a steel knife was one protection.[24]

Now from this description it is clear that the Orkney and Shetland trows are essentially the same as the Scottish fairies. This has been clear to a number of observers, including Sir Walter Scott on his voyage north in 1814:

> The *trows* do not differ much from the fairies of the Lowland, or *Sighean* [*sidhichean*] of the Highlanders. They steal children, dwell within the interior of green hills and often carry mortals into their recesses.[25]

The little trow is very different from the Norwegian *troll* — the ugly giant creature who lives up in the mountains, captures and eats humans, gnawing on their bones, and hurls rocks in quarrels with his fellows. The troll fears only the light of day, which turns him instantly to stone. Yet the two words are clearly closely connected, and there is a good case for arguing that the name *trow* was applied by the Norse in Orkney. If we believe that Orkney folklore is essentially a Norse transplant, there is little alternative to following the suggestion made by Ernest Marwick, in an outstanding and definitive paper of 1972, that "in Orkney the Norwegian trolls became diminished in size owing to the greatly reduced scale of the landscape".[26]

But if we take our attention for a moment away from the word and look simply at the phenomenon itself, it is clear that there is a very great difference between the little trow with his music and dancing and the big slow bone-crunching troll. The same terminology seems to be in use for two quite separate concepts.

The modern Norwegian word *troll* has in fact two meanings. One is 'troll, monster, ogre'; but there is another and less specific one — 'any kind of supernatural creature'.[27] This aspect of the word is not new: the Old Norse *troll* translates into modern Norwegian as *troll* or *uvette* ('evil spirit').[28] Words derived from *troll* display a similar range of meaning. ON *trolldómr* means 'sorcery, magic, witchcraft'. ON *trollkerling* indicates on the one hand a troll-woman, especially an old one; but it can also be used for a witch.[29]

In other words, when the Norse arrived in Orkney in the 8th or 9th centuries, they had a word which could be applied to various kinds of supernatural creatures. If the Orcadians told them about creatures of hill and mound who stole people away from their homes, then the Old Norse word for 'spirits' or 'sorcerers' — namely, *troll* — would be an appropriate one to apply. Thus we would have the application of a Norwegian word to an Orcadian phenomenon, rather than having to postulate the creation of the Orcadian phenomenon by gross distortion of a Norwegian one (and conveniently into a Scottish shape!).

To show that such a process is possible is not, of course, to prove it, but it does provide an explanation of the facts with the minimum of hypotheses. And there is a further supporting argument.

If the Norse did not distort their concept of trolls to create the Orkney trows, then they must have continued to keep the idea of a troll as a separate entity, whether they regarded the creature as having been left behind in Norway or as having relatives in Orkney. In various parts of Norway there is a word *jette* which is used for a troll: it is related to the ON *jötun*, Mod. Nor. *jotun*, which we translate as 'giant'. (The 'j' in all these words is pronounced as 'y'). If the Norse in Orkney were finding suitable creatures to apply this word to, it would suggest that the original concept of the giant 'troll' was not distorted into something else but continued in existence.

And that is exactly what we do find, in Ernest Marwick's same paper of 1972: he very lucidly identifies the Orkney link with the *jötnar* (Mod. Nor. *jotner*). There are very specific legends in both Orkney and Shetland of giants in which this word is used, and — most significantly for the 'troll' connection — a number of the stories refer to giants being turned into stone by the rays of the morning sun. Amongst the sites Marwick points to is the standing stone in Rousay that is known as the Yetna-steen, a clear derivation from *jötun:*

> One can easily discover the legend of the giant turned into stone in the Yetna-steen, which goes down immediately after midnight on New Year morning to the Loch of Scockness for a drink. In the parish of Birsay there is a similar legend about the Stone of Quoyboon, which finds its way each New Year morning to the Loch of Boardhouse, but is always back in its place *before dawn.*[30]

If we take the word *jötun,* found in the 'Yetna' of Yetna-steen, and follow it back to Norway, we can look at one example in a story gathered by Richard Bergh in Porsangerfjord, right up in the north of Finnmark, beyond Karasjok and Kautokeino. There the *fjellsamer,* the mountain Lapps, told him of the tale of *Jettanas* who dared not be outdoors when the sun shone. He had a servant-man to work for him, but planned to eat him. When the man found out what was in store for him, he escaped, with a comb, a whetstone, and a bottle of water. As Jettanas came in hot pursuit, the man threw down first the comb — which turned into a forest, chopped down by Jettanas; and then the whetstone — which became a mountain which Jettanas had to smash.

The final hope of protection was the water-bottle, which produced a great expanse of water, as big as a sea, to block the path of the giant.

> *Jettanas la seg ned for å drikke opp vannet. Men mens han drakk, kom solen frem. Og Jettanas sprakk og ble til stein.*

> Jettanas lay down to drink up the water. But while he was drinking, the sun came up. And Jettanas burst and was turned to stone.[31]

The culture of the Sami people, of course, is quite distinct from that of the Norwegians, but there are enough similarities between this story and the Rousay one to suggest that it would be interesting to make a detailed survey of the northern distribution of this widespread legend, of the form generally known as "The Magic Flight".[32] Any conection, however, may be complex, since stories about people and giants being turned into stone, often into Neolithic standing stones, are widespread through Scotland, England, Ireland and Wales, as are stories of stones that move.[33] We could be looking at a theme with a pre-Norse origin, reinforced and added to by the settlers from Norway.

Already we can see that the idea of Orkney folklore as a Norse transplant can lead us into difficulties or indeed contradicitions; a better way forward — and indeed a more logical one — is to think in terms of a pre-Norse base overlain by a Norse layer.

Now that we have extricated the trows from the clutches of the Norwegian trolls, we can examine them for what they are, a species of 'little people'.[34] In that connection, as Dr Alan Bruford describes in a note to this chapter, they have more in common with the fairies of Gaelic tradition than with the Norwegian *huldrefolk*. Scott's original impression of the trows, later shared by others such as Duncan J. Robertson,[35] was correct, and the Orkney fairies are in that lower underlying body of tradition that was in the islands before the Norse and survived their arrival and settlement.

Saints and settlements

As well as direct transmission by word of mouth, there are other ways by which the beliefs of one generation are preserved for analysis by a future one. In order to get acceptance, the early

Christian church did not totally oppose every aspect of the older religions it encountered, but instead incorporated a number of what it felt to be tolerable features. The advice of Pope Gregory to the mission of Augustine to the English was to destroy the idols in the temples, but not the temples themselves, which should be converted into churches.

> In this way, we hope that the people, seeing that its temples are not destroyed, may abandon idolatry and resort to these places as before, and may come to know and adore the true God. And since they have a custom of sacrificing many oxen to devils, let some other solemnity be substituted in its place, such as a day of Dedication or the Festivals of the holy martyrs whose relics are enshrined there.[36]

As a result of this strategy, the sites of Christian churches can often give clues about older pre-Christian religious centres, and even the figures they were dedicated to. Several rather unlikely figures have been absorbed into the canon of Christian saints.

Among the Scottish saints who emerged out of the transition to Christianity is St Bride, an amalgam of the possibly historical St Bridget of Kildare in Ireland together with the much older Brigit, the Celtic goddess of fire who was also patron of poetry, healing and smith-craft, and the guardian of marriage, the hearth and women in birth.[37] As well as being a significant figure in Irish mythology, she also gave her name to the powerful British tribe of the *Brigantes*,[38] and the Christianised cult-centres come through into place-names like the Kirkbrides in Galloway and Kilbrides up the west coast and islands, Brydekirk in Dumfries, and of course East Kilbride.

The distinction between gods and goddesses is an important one. For the people who emerged into the Neolithic Age in Europe, the so-called 'Old Europeans', the new ideas of cultivation of crops were symbolised in the concept of the earth as a woman giving birth to new life but also receiving the dead as part of an eternal cycle.[39] In this way of looking at the process of life and death, the earth was primary, with the rain from the sky a valuable adjunct that was seen as the fertilisation of the female earth. The moon, with its relationship to the female bodily cycle and to the tides of the earth, was regarded as a controlling influence, and to the three phases of the moon, waxing, full and waning, there corresponded three forms of the one goddess; she could appear as maiden, mother or old woman.

The Indo-European cattle-herders of the plains of Central and Eastern Europe placed a different emphasis on the relative importance of earth and sky. To them, the potency of the male sky-god, in the form of rain, was what dominated their pattern of life. The fruits of the female earth were something to be taken and enjoyed before moving on to the next one.

The advance of the patriarchal Indo-Europeans into Old Europe can be seen by the extent to which the older female goddesses gradually became absorbed into the male pantheon, becoming daughters, sisters or wives of the sky-god.[40] In the Mediterranean areas and among the Germanic peoples to the north there was much less fusion, and females in Norwegian tradition, for instance, tend to have little power and such as they have is often for malevolent purposes. (The mighty Germanic goddess Nerthus, described by Tacitus, becomes by the Viking Age the less significant god Njörðr).

Thus in Norway the underlying religion before Christianity is dominated by male figures, and few dedications of the St Bride type would be expected. Specific female saints are hard to find in Shetland too, apart from the isolated instance of St Sunniva in Unst who is suspected of being, along with her countless virgins who sailed to Bergen, an invention of the Norwegian Church.[41] But in Orkney female saints can certainly be found, and a number of chapels and place-names refer to Bride. There is a Bridesness in North Ronaldsay,[42] a Breedakirk in Eday,[43] a Bride's Noust with a chapel site in Graemsay,[44] a chapel on the point of Breetaness in Wasbister in Rousay,[45] and a St Bride's chapel site near the Noust of Bigging in Yesnaby, Sandwick, with a tradition of a holy well with curative powers nearby.[46] There is also a St Bride's chapel site on the island of Papa Stronsay.[47]

Papa Stronsay is of course notable for its connection with the early Christian fathers or *papae*. The significance of such a community is that it may well have suffered less disturbance with the Norse influx than elsewhere in Orkney, and so may afford us a clearer window into the past.

In the other island of the *papae*, Papa Westray, there is also a female saint, Tredwell or Triduana, who is reputed to have plucked out her eyes to avoid the attentions of the Pictish king, Nechtan son of Derili. But as W. J. Watson points out, similar stories are told of other female saints, including Brigit,[48] and the eye motif is a strong one in the picture of the earth goddess — the eye is linked with the womb and with the moon.[49] Watson noted that there is an old Irish word *tredan* which comes from an institution in the Celtic Church, the *triduanum ieiunium*, 'three days' fast', which suggests that the word *triduana* may be more of a title than an ordinary name, and the connection with three adds support to the idea of a link with the older three-fold goddess.[50]

Generally, much remains to be done in investigating the dating and distribution of chapel dedications, but the pattern in Papay certainly looks pre-Norse, with St Tredwell's chapel on a broch site and another ancient site being occupied by the kirk of St Boniface. The presence of Tredwell and Boniface dedications in the same island is significant in view of a story that Triduana was one of the two abbesses who accompanied Boniface on his mission from Northumbria to Pictland c. 715. The Tredwell tradition in the island is a strong one, added to which Hugh Marwick noted the absence in Papay of farm names of the *-garth, -ston, -by* and *-bister* type, usually associated with the early Norse settlement. The inference is that the Norse left the island for the most undisturbed.[51]

While in Papa Westray, there is also evidence that another female cult-figure, whether connected with Triduana or not, survived into Norse times. On a day early in February, boys in the island used to go out with torches and look for the *gyros,* bigger boys dressed as older women and wearing masks. The gyro would wear a skirt and hit out at the younger boys with a rope or a tangle. The word *gyro* looks like a derivation from the Old Norse *gýgr,* 'ogress', and the occasion was close to the time of the festival of St Bride, Candlemas, a time when the old custom of the fire-goddess Bride had become Christianised into a festival of light.[52] The *gyro* in Papey could therefore be a survival of a ritual involving the goddess Brigit.

There are other fragments that look more like survivals of pre-Norse belief than Norse implants. There is from Sanday what Walter Traill Dennison calls

> a popular notion, perhaps more stongly held than any other superstitious idea regarding marriage. This was a religious horror of pork at a wedding feast. This rule was once violated by a sacrilegious sceptic. And, horrible to relate, on the morning after the night of the 'pork wedding', wedding house and wedding party were found burned to ashes. Nothing was left by the avenging fire except a single chair, saved from the flames by having the priest's gloves hung on its back. Tradition gives no account of the priest's safety, so that his gloves must have possessed greater sanctity than their owner.[53]

More detail of this story is given in what seems to be a quite separate account, recorded by Dr William Wood, who practised in Sanday in the 1820s, and preserved in a notebook of George Petrie, Sheriff Clerk in Kirkwall in the middle of the last century. William Wood was the contributor of a description of the antiquities of Sanday in the *New Statistical Account* of 1842 and the accuracy of his observations has been commented on. His version of the Sanday legend fixes the site of it on the Knowe of Skartan, on the south-east side of Otterswick Bay. Despite sea erosion, Dr Raymond Lamb, who located Dr Wood's account of the story, has identified the remnants of stone structures and midden refuse, which show the knowe was the site of a settlement. The story says that the priest at the wedding came from the nearby Peterkirk, a little way along the shore.

> What is probably the church enclosure can still be made out, and this appears to have been built on top of some prehistoric structure; a deep well-chamber of the type common in brochs lies right on the edge of the banks, where the sea must very soon break through into it. It is of great interest that this church, although not a parish church, was always referred to as a kirk and not as a chapel, and the story, by assigning its own priest to it, further suggests that it had some higher than average status.[54]

In the agriculturally-oriented religion of the Neolithic, the pig has great significance, with sculptures of pigs known from all parts of Old Europe and dating from every period, and associated with the goddess who represented the earth's fertility.

> The fast-growing body of a pig will have impressed early agriculturists; its fattening must have been compared to corn growing and ripening, so that its soft fats apparently came to symbolize the earth itself, causing the pig to become a sacred animal probably no later than 6000 BC.[55]

A thorough survey of the North European distribution of the pork taboo would be worthwhile, but there is certainly a general contrast between, on the one hand, the Scottish Highlands and Wales, where until not so long ago there was a great reluctance to eat pork,[56] and on the other, Norway, where there seems to be none and where indeed there are no traces of the pig having any religious significance in the Neolithic period.[57] This leads to the possibility that here again we may be looking at some tradition that may have carried over in parts of Orkney from before the

Norse arrival.[58] It should also be added that the analysis of the
sea-eagles' bones at Isbister by John Hedges has opened up the
whole field of the use of totems in prehistoric Orkney,[59] and in
connection with the pig we have not only Neolithic possibilities
but also the Iron Age in which there are Irish examples of
particular heroes being forbidden to eat the flesh of a specific
animal.[60]

The oath by the stone

As well as various legends applying to specific places in
Orkney, there is one custom (now discontinued) of particular
interest. This involves the so-called Stone of Odin.

The Stone of Odin stood in the vicinity of the two rings of
standing stones in Stenness until 1814, when it was removed by
an unpopular landowner and subsequently broken up. It had a
hole through it, into which limbs were passed for prevention or
cure of particular diseases, but it was also notable for its use by
lovers making vows.

> There was a custom among the lower class of people in this
> country which has entirely subsided within these 20 or 30
> years. Upon the first day of every new year the common
> people, from all parts of the country, met at the Kirk of
> Stainhouse, each person having provision for four or five
> days; they continued there for that time dancing and
> feasting in the kirk. This meeting gave the young people an
> opportunity of seeing each other, which seldom failed in
> making four or five marriages every year.

That account was given by R. Henry, minister of Greyfriars
Church, Edinburgh, who presented a drawing of the Stones of
Stenness to the Society of Antiquaries of Scotland in 1784. It is
quoted in Joseph Anderson's introduction to Low's *Tour,*
published in 1879. Henry goes on to describe a procedure which
ended with the lovers joining their right hands through the hole
in the Stone of Odin, and swearing an oath of fidelity. "This
ceremony was held so very sacred in those times," he says, "that
the person who dared to break the engagements made here was
counted infamous, and excluded all society."[61]

The purpose of the ceremony was, in Mr Henry's understanding, "to secure each other's love, till an opportunity of
celebrating their nuptials", but Ker, who visited the stones in
1780 with Dr Groat from Kirkwall, says that the doctor told him
that the lovers in fact "proceeded to Consummation without

further Ceremony.'' Taken with the binding nature of the promise — Dr Groat said that "no Instance was ever known of their refusing to keep their agreement afterwards'' — what was taking place seems to be more in the nature of a marriage, than an engagement.[62]

Mr Henry also described another custom:

> It was likewise usual, when husband and wife could not agree, that they both came to the Kirk of Stainhouse, and after entering into the kirk the one went out at the south and the other at the north door, by which they were holden legally divorced, and free to make another choice.[63]

A form of wedding ceremony surviving so long through centuries of the Established Church seems unusual enough, but a divorce system, carried out within the church building itself, seems remarkable. There are very strong parallels here with accounts of a custom that was reputed to have taken place in Ireland on the occasion of the great annual assembly at Tailtiu (in English, Teltown) in County Meath. Writing in 1836, John O'Donovan spoke of a particular hollow on the site called Lag an Aonaigh or Laganeeny (the Hollow of the Fair).

> Here according to tradition marriages were celebrated in pagan times. A well springs in the centre of this hollow, a short distance . . . to the south of which a wall . . . [now a ditch] was erected, and in this wall there was a gateway closed by a wooden gate in which there was a hole large enough to admit a human hand. This is the spot at which marriages were celebrated according to the old manner following. A number of young men went into the hollow to the north side of the wall, and an equal number of marriageable young women to the south side of the wall which was so high as to prevent them from seeing the men; one of the women put her hand thro' the hole in the gate, and a man took hold of it from the other side, being guided in his choice only by the appearance of the hand. The two who thus joined hands by blind chance were obliged to live together for a year and a day, at the expiration of which time they appeared at the Rath of Telton and if they were not satisfied with each other they obtained a deed of separation, and were entitled to go to Laganeeny again to try their good fortune for the ensuing year. This tradition has given rise to a phrase in the country 'they got a Tailteann marriage' by which it meant

that they took each other's word for nine months. The
natives of Telton think that there was a great deal of fair
play in this marriage . . .[64]

As to the way of ending the marriage, one subsequent writer
says that the couple would stand back to back on a nearby
earthen fort called Rath Dubh (the Black Fort).[65] Another says
that the man and woman walked up two adjacent mounds and
turned their backs on each other.[66]

In the *Old Statistical Account* of 1793, the minister of the
parish of Eskdalemuir in the county of Dumfries describes a
similar tradition, in connection with an old annual fair, which
had been by that time discontinued.

At that fair, it was the custom for the unmarried persons of
both sexes to choose a companion, according to their
liking, with whom they were to live till that time next year.
This was called *hand-fasting,* or hand in fist. If they were
pleased with each other at that time then they continued
together for life; if not, they separated, and were free to
make another choice as at the first.[67]

There are other accounts of various types of temporary
marriages in Scotland and Wales, and one, in Argyll, is
connected with St Ciaran, who is also associated with the
Teltown Fair in Ireland.[68] The handfast marriages at the Stone of
Odin — for this is clearly what they were — seem to have been
continuing after those elsewhere had stopped.

The idea of the oath by the stone is an old and powerful one
whose roots could well go back through the Iron Age to the
Bronze Age, and various examples are known which sometimes
survive in isolated places. According to the *Kanu,* the customary
law of the mountains of Albania, "the oath by [upon] the stone
. . . is among the most important and most frightening oaths
which the Albanian of the mountain knows."[69] It is a
frightening oath because it has a cosmic significance. The
swearer of the oath connects himself in to the universe and opens
himself completely to the absolute processes of law and justice
that flow through it. It is somewhat analogous to a man who
designs a new man-powered aircraft and jumps off a cliff to take
the first test flight in it himself. If he is right in his construction
plans, all will be well. If he is wrong, then the laws of
aerodynamics will inevitably carry him to his downfall.

The oath by the stone is connected, too, with the procedure of
holding a piece of earth when swearing, as in a Gaelic tale, or

indeed putting earth into the mouth after making an oath, as in an Iranian story.[70] In several Iranian languages, the phrase "to eat an oath" is used for "to swear an oath".[71] Commenting on this, Heinrich Wagner notes that expressions such as "I shall eat (or drink) such and such a thing if this and that happens" are current in a number of modern European languages.[72]

The political significance of this type of oath in Bronze Age and Iron Age society is illustrated by this story. How *do* you form political units of tens of thousands of individuals out of the scattered and independent peoples of the time? The answer lies in the power of the oath, and also in an assembly fixed in space and time, which *has* to be attended. People gather there at specific times of the year, or in time of crisis, and the various political decisions of war and peace are announced, while such new oaths as are required are made. Hence, for instance, the political significance of the great annual assembly in Ireland at the festival of Lugnasad, which in later times became the Lammas Fair. It was the occasion for "public business", legal proceedings and the issue of special ordinances; and also, as we have noted, a time for handfast marriages.[73]

Before proceeding further, we should emphasise one important point. The origin of the Lugnasad customs, and indeed the idea of one-year marriage, could go further back in time than the Iron Age or indeed the Bronze Age. The joining of hands through a stone may well have connections with ideas of fertility, and the one-year life of the marriage represent the cycle of the seasons, but the aspect of the proceedings that enabled the custom to survive for so long was the *legal* and *political* one: the nature of the oath. Just as today the hand on the Bible has significance for adults in a court of law, or "cross my heart and hope to die" for children, so did the oath on the stone or the oath by the elements in Bronze Age and Iron Age times. In fact, without it, the political structures of the period would have been much weaker. If you beat the neighbouring tribe in battle, how do you stop them coming back next year? The oath by the elements gives you an alternative to total slaughter. It binds them securely, and so an overlord can rule simply, from a distance.

The oath by the stone is also connected with the use of coronation stones — like the stone on Tara in ancient Ireland, which shrieked when the rightful king stood on it.[74] Particular Scottish clans had their own special stones for inauguration of the Chief — the 'Bear Stone' of the Forbeses and the 'Falcon Stone' of the Hays, for example[75]— while until the middle of the last century there stood near St Columba's tomb in Iona the 'Black Stones of Iona'. They were so called "not from their

L

colour, but from the black doom that fell on any who dared to violate an oath sworn upon them. As recently as the reign of James VI, two clans who had spent centuries in bloody feud met here and solemnly pledged themselves to friendship."[76]

But back to Orkney, and the Stone of Odin. There is the obvious and immediate attempted explanation for it, as a Norse custom, brought across by the early Norwegian settlers. There are, indeed, descriptions in Orkney folklore of 'Odin's aith', which apparently brought short-term success to the swearer but then eventual bitter consequences.[77] According to the Edda-poem *Hávamál* Odin swore an oath on a golden ring, but there seems to be no Norwegian pattern of oath-stones associated with him and a number of saga references to oath-rings appear to involve Thor instead.[78]

If we choose to assume that the custom of linking hands through holed stones was brought across from Norway, we have to explain why it is that a similar custom is found in other areas where the Vikings certainly did not bring it. Also, if the custom were a Norse one, it is rather strange that we do not seem to have any records of it in Norway.

The alternative possibility is that the Orcadians were indeed using the stone for handfast marriages when the Norse arrived, and that the incomers adapted to the custom, and associated it with one of their gods which seemed to be the most appropriate. There are several strands to Odin's character, war-god, death-god and magician, but it has been argued that he was originally an oath-god, a form of all-seeing sky-god equivalent to the oath-god in whose name assemblies such as the Irish Lugnasad were convened.[79]

There are other hints as to the survival in Orkney of oath-stones and associated customs. There is, for instance, a particularly interesting sentence in Walter Traill Dennison's tale of Johnie Croy and the mermaid, where he says that "Johnie went down on his knees and swore by the meur-steen (generally a standing stone or boulder where district Things were held) that he would court the beautiful creature though the wooing would cost him his life".[80]

The connection of the oath-stone and the Thing is interesting, because it suggests that the Norse settlers in Orkney may have chosen for their law assembly a site that was already used for just such a purpose by the native people.

Evidence that standing stones retained legal significance well into historic times comes from records collected by George Petrie, and given to the writer of an article in a Scandinavian review, published in Copenhagen in 1852.[81] One of the documents concerned a judgment made in Kirkwall in June 1514 by 'Nicoll, Haw Lawman of Zetland and Orkney for the tyme'. The question under consideration was whether a certain Nicoll Fraser or Frysell had sold lands legally, since his brother Alexander claimed that he had not been given opportunity to buy them first, as was his statutory right. However, it was shown that Nicoll Fraser had indeed made such an offer, and indeed repeated it at "divers and sundry times in *courtis and heid stanes*". This having been proved, the lawman declared the transaction valid. But note the significance of "heid stanes" in the same context as "courtis".

We can also note another document quoted by Petrie, which recorded a claim made by Edward Etkin and his wife that Bernard of Kamsto and his heirs had taken by force a patch of land that had previously belonged to Edward Etkin's mother-in-law. Pressing their case, the Etkins published their claim "at Tyng and Stein".[82]

We do have to take into account the existence of the Old Norse *stefna*, 'law-court', and indeed when Storer Clouston transcribed the above documents he made this interpretation of 'stane' or 'stein'.[83] Two of Orkney's courts were apparently different from the Lawting, the Wapen*stein (vapnastefna)* which met in February, and the Hirdman*stein (Hirðmannastefna)* which met in January. However the earliest reference to the Hirdmanstein, in 1438-9, does suggest that a stone was involved for the swearing of some oath,[84] and in the reference to "Tyng and Stein" two different sites are mentioned, one at Kirkwall at the Tyng or Head Court, and the other "in to landward quhair it effeirit", i.e. in the parish in which the lands were situated. The site in the case of the claim against Bernard of Kamsto was interpreted by Petrie as the standing stone in St Andrews parish, where Kamsto (today Campston) is situated.

Thus as the various fragments come together we see an underlying pattern coming into view of stones in public places, oaths and the law. The strength of the system can be seen from the extent to which aspects of it survived, in particular the pattern of handfast marriages at the Stone of Odin and the associated divorces in the Stenness Kirk. These were the continuation of a system that was in operation in Celtic society long before the coming of the Norse to Orkney. The system was so strongly based in society that remnants of it continued in areas like Stenness until well into the 18th century.

If such a system survived the Norse arrival, together with various other civil, legal or political uses of the stones, can we really continue to support the idea of some kind of over-

whelming genocidal wave in which the indigenous Orcadians
were wiped out and cleared from the islands?

The place-name arguments

The argument for the vanishing of the native population goes
back time and again to the place-name record and to
Wainwright's classic chapters on 'Picts and Scots' and 'The
Scandinavian Settlement' in *The Northern Isles* in 1962. It is
worth looking in some detail at what it was that Wainwright
actually said: first of all it should be noted that far from ruling
out Celtic place-names, he accepted that there were "a
substantial residue of elements that are Celtic in origin and
form".[85] That residue came from a list of approximately sixty
Celtic elements in Orkney and Shetland place-names which
emerged from the studies of Hugh Marwick and Jakob
Jakobsen. If anyone should have been able to draw out a hidden
Scandinavian root in a place-name, it should have been the great
Faroese philologist, and indeed Jakobsen to begin with did
believe that no pre-Scandinavian place-names had survived.
However, as his studies developed, he found a hard core of
place-name elements in Shetland that appeared to him Celtic
rather than Norse. Marwick, who himself produced a list of
nearly thirty apparently Celtic elements in Orkney place-names,
asked Jakobsen on one of his last visits to Orkney if he thought
that as many as one per cent of Orkney place-names might be of
pre-Norse origin. "Oh, much more than that," was the reply:
"anything probably from five to ten per cent."[86] That might
well, as Marwick himself subsequently remarked, be going to the
other extreme, but as Marwick also added, coming from
someone of Jakobsen's experience, it could not be lightly
ignored.

Wainwright went through the combined lists of Marwick and
Jakobsen, and removed any about which there could be the
slightest doubt. First out were a number which seemed to lack
adequate early documentation; then a group that he felt could
still be more likely interpreted as Scandinavian; and then a
further group that although Celtic in origin were known to have
been adopted by the Scandinavians as loan words at an early
date. Still, at the end of all that, there was that "substantial
residue". They were there, and Wainwright accepted them; but
they were, in the archaeological context of the day, the wrong
sort of Celtic.

Although the Celts were spread across Europe from the
Iberian peninsula on the one side to the Black Sea on the other,

almost nothing of the Continental Celtic languages survives, apart from the names of a number of people, places and tribes, and some fifty inscriptions in Gaulish. As David Greene points out, very little would be known about Celtic if it were not for the British Isles, where two groups of so-called Insular Celtic languages have taken shape.

> The early state was simple enough; British was spoken in Britain and Irish in Ireland, though scholars prefer to call them Brythonic and Goidelic respectively . . . The simple situation of Brythonic in Britain and Goidelic in Ireland did not last long; during the fifth century AD the Irish began to penetrate into British-speaking Scotland, and the English (if I may call them that for short) into the southern part of Britain, and soon British was everywhere on the retreat except in Wales and Cornwall; outside these territories the last stronghold was Strathclyde, where Cumbrian may have held out until the eleventh century. But if British lost heavily at home it made one new colony, for large numbers of British emigrated across the sea to what had been the Celtic region of Armorica, displacing the Roman tongue by British and establishing what still bears the name of Brittany.[87]

The two Insular Celtic groups, Brythonic and Goidelic, are sometimes categorised by their different treatment of a particular sound inherited from Indo-European. This sound, which gives *qu* (kw) in a number of languages, is retained by the Goidelic group, becoming simply *c* in later Irish — hence Irish *ceathair* for 'four'. But in the Brythonic languages it became *p* instead — thus Welsh *pedwar,* 'four'. The fragments of the Gaulish languages seem to show the same pattern, and for that and other reasons the concepts of P-Celtic and Q-Celtic developed as two hypothetical branches of a hypothetical Common Celtic ancestor. Against that, it has been pointed out that the q/p change is found in other language groups apart from Celtic, and that what we should be remarking on instead is the extent to which Irish and Welsh differ not only from the hypothetical Celtic ancestor, but also from each other. To explain a number of strange features of Irish and Welsh, some of which are not even Indo-European, it is now argued that the languages developed in the British Isles in contact with languages already existing and that

> the invaders represented . . . a fairly thinly-spread ruling class, so that we should not regard Irish and Welsh as

languages which were imported into their respective countries, but as languages which are really indigenous in the sense that they have grown up as the result of all the linguistic and social influences which have touched Ireland and Wales over more than two thousand years.[88]

Thus we have two streams of Celtic in the British Isles, each representing a synthesis of an original Celtic tongue with earlier and unknown languages. Here we shall not attempt to speculate as to how the q/p change may or may not have come about, and whether it might have been due to an overall pattern in the Celtic languages or whether it might have been influenced by other languages in the British Isles. The Q and P notation is in the present context merely a convenient label to denote two language-groups. Bearing in mind the complexity of each, we can use for the moment the Q and P terminology to bring out the contrast between the two, and look at what Wainwright made of the "substantial residue" of Celtic names that he had left in Marwick and Jakobsen's place-name root list for Orkney and Shetland. The bulk of the elements in the list turned out to be Goidelic; in fact, Wainwright maintained, not a single element could unequivocally be said to be P-Celtic.[89]

The interpretation that could be put on that would seem today to be that the people who were in Orkney before the Norse had a strain of Q-Celtic stock. But Wainwright was not looking for Q-Celts; only P-Celts could be fitted into the archaeological structure of the time for Orkney. A model had gradually emerged in which two main Iron Age regions of Scotland were identified by their fortifications, with the brochs in the north and north-west (the Western Isles, Sutherland, Caithness, Orkney and Shetland), and the vitrified forts elsewhere. Within each region, the population was seen as a composite of a Bronze Age sub-stratum of indigenous people together with an incoming Celtic aristocracy of fort-builders. The accepted date for the arrival of the newcomers was put, for various reasons including the presence in upper layers of broch sites of Roman finds, as around the first century BC. At this time, the main people who were on the move appeared to be coming from south-west England and France, under the growing pressure of the Romans, so given the date taken and a number of similarities in artefacts, these people were identified as the incoming Celtic element involved in the vitrified hillfort region and in the broch region too. These people, coming from the areas of the Brythonic and Gaulish languages, had to be P-Celts.[90]

Kenneth Jackson's classic analysis of the Pictish language gave support to this theory by showing that there were indeed two languages in the vitrified fort region, and that the Celtic one was of P-Celtic form. Therefore the constraints on the language of the broch region (also Pictish territory) were clear. Any Celtic language there had also to be of the P variety, and hence the absence of P-Celtic names in the broch zone was interpreted as being due to a situation where the incomers "gave up their Celtic speech almost entirely, adopting that of the Bronze Age natives, who may have constituted the bulk of the population under a Celtic aristocracy".[91]

Now, however, with the new dating that John Hedges had given us for the possible arrival of the people who became the broch-builders, taking them back to the 7th century BC, we are no longer constrained to restrict their origin to south-west England. We are back in a time of numerous population movements, and the origin of the Iron Age immigrants to Orkney becomes very open. In particular, it is perfectly feasible for them to be a Q-Celtic group, just as the original place-name list suggested.

It surely involves less hypothesis to explain the Q-Celtic place-name elements in Orkney in this way than to postulate that P-Celts arrived, built the brochs, gave up their language, and failed despite their political dominance to leave their mark on the place-names until later a whole batch of Q-Celtic place-names came in "with adventurers from the south during the later 'Scottification'".[92]

Although this latter view became widely accepted, little evidence ever seems to have been put forward to support what is, if true, a fairly major criticism of Marwick and Jakobsen's interpretations. Certainly Jakobsen, who as has already been said did not start out in search of Celtic names, was fully aware of the need to resolve the obvious question of whether they came before or after the Norse ones.

> This question would be difficult to decide from the point of view merely of language, as the linguistic forms only in exceptional cases give any guidance; but there are other means of deciding, e.g. firstly, the internal reasons: the nature of the places and names in question. A word such as *kil,* which occurs several times in Shetland place-names in sense of 'church' (Irish *ceall, cill*), must, according to its very nature, be a primitive form and originate from the Culdees . . . When a large tract of land (hill or valley) bears a Celtic name, while most of the surrounding names are of Norn origin, it is no doubt due to the fact that an

earlier designation has been adopted by the Norwegian settlers. Celtic names denoting comparatively small, insignificant places can more easily be supposed to have arisen at a later period, especially when occurring in a single instance only. The frequent occurrence of one and the same Celtic name in various places far apart in the isles is another proof of the origin of such a name.[93]

So while renewed scrutiny of Marwick and Jakobsen's work is certainly required and overdue — indeed in the light of what has been said in this chapter such study could well give new insights — their basic conclusion of a set of Celtic place-name elements, predating the Norse arrival, remains. The names are spread widely. Amongst those in Marwick's original Orkney list are: from Gaelic *ceann,* head, the farm of Cannigall near Scapa, and Cantick Head in Walls; from Gaelic *cnoc,* a hill, Knucker Hill in Westray, and the farm of Knugdale on its slope; from Gaelic *linne,* a pool, Loch Linn in Shapinsay; from Gaelic and Irish *sruth,* a stream, the Burn of Straither near Stromness; from the Brythonic root which appears in Welsh as *twyn,* headland, Twinyes in North Ronaldsay, Westray, Shapinsay and St Andrews.[94]

It will be seen that the list contains elements from both types of Insular Celtic: despite Wainwright's reductions, some of the Brythonic elements identified by Marwick do appear to be well-founded, and although their presence among a majority of Goidelic roots may only add to the complications of the situation, that is not a good enough reason to justify their removal from the list. Marwick's own words are an appropriate comment:

> It may seem staggering to some to find Cymric, Gaelic, and Irish words occurring side by side in Orkney. But Jakobsen found the same thing in Shetland, and we must accept the facts as we find them and make our theories suit them and not *vice versa.*[95]

The Viking image

The reasons for the popularity within Orkney of the Primitive Viking Model of island culture would be interesting to study. Dr Fereday, in his chapter on Lairds and Historians, observes that a focus on remoter times avoided the problem of getting too close to sensitive antecedents of powerful families. One does also wonder whether the growing 19th century bourgeoisie of Orkney was looking for suitable ancestries to match those of the lairds; certainly the modern fashion for Norse Christian names seems to have started only in the present century.[96]

The Viking image itself has also been in need of reassessment for some time, and the work of various authors makes it possible to look afresh at a concept that is beset with contradictions in its more extreme forms. How, for instance, does a savage raider double up as an industrious trader? Or have we been focusing our attention on a notorious minority to the exclusion of the peaceful majority who formed the Norwegian trading empire?

Since we readily use the word 'Viking' to describe just about any aspect of life in the Norse period over the 8th to the 12th centuries, it is worth looking at how the Norse themselves used it. In an analysis of a number of heroic episodes in the sagas, Kaaren Grimstad has noted that in each one the villain is a viking, whose major attributes are "an overweening arrogance and brutality of nature".

> The hero in each case is a Norwegian or Icelander who is on a journey abroad; hence he assumes the role of the deliverer who comes from a foreign land . . . Although the bully has the advantage in strength . . the hero possesses the intellectual advantage and is able to outwit the enemy when he is most unsuspecting.[97]

Kaaren Grimstad's interpretation of this is particularly interesting:

> The identification in these examples of the viking with the stupid berserk and villain who is tricked by the hero may at first seem surprising to the reader. According to the modern image, the viking is a fearless and ruthless seafaring warrior, who nevertheless retains a touch of the heroic splendour accorded him in the Romantic era. In the family sagas, however, vikings play several different roles: they may be heroic types, as are Björn Hítdœlakappi, Egill Skalla-Grímsson, or þórólfr Kveld-Úlfsson; they are quite often a collective group of vikings, anonymous gangs of sea-warriors who attack merchant ships and make raids along the coasts; or they can be individual villains who burn farms and steal money and women. However, an investigation by Fritz Askeberg of the two words which describe viking activity, the feminine noun *víking* in the phrase *fara í víking* 'to go on a viking expedition' and the masculine noun *víkingr,* and their distribution in the family

sagas indicates that the saga writers observed a careful
distinction in their use of the two words. The masculine
noun *víkingr* is never directly used to designate a major
hero like the three mentioned above, except when this is
historically permissible, e.g., when the character in question
belongs to the period of Icelandic settlement. The number
of such examples, however, is very small . . . Fritz
Askeberg has furthermore demonstrated that the term
víkingr never enjoyed a good reputation and generally had
a pejorative connotation.[98]

Kaaren Grimstad goes on to argue that this strong dislike of
vikings is not merely due to the Christian outlook of the writers
of the thirteenth-century family sagas: she quotes two examples
from the saga of Harald Hardråde in which viking activity is
condemned as a forbidden heathen custom. The extent to which
it was outwith the norm is also shown by the restrictions on shipbuilding set out in a section of the Gulathing Law established by
Harald Fairhair: a man building a longship had to state the
purpose of his journey, on penalty of a fine; if he failed to give
satisfaction, the neighbours had the duty to damage the ship and
remove the sail. The aim was clearly to stop viking raiding
before it occurred; the penalty for it if it did occur was
outlawry.[99]

This confirms the emerging picture of viking behaviour as far
from the norm, although it may well have been a feature of
some of the chieftains that Harald had to put down or expel. But
what is much nearer the norm for Norway is a very old pattern
of using the sea for trade, in a country where the ruggedness of
the terrain made other forms of transport for any distance
impossible. Different parts of the country had different needs
and different products to sell, and so the potential for coastal
trading is clear. Roald Morcken identified what he believed to be
a very old system of seamarks along the Norwegian coast, and
showed that a distance table had also existed, extending north as
far as the White Sea.[100]

Amongst early Norwegian seafarers was Ottar of Hálogaland,
whose home would have been near the present-day town of
Tromsø in the north of Norway. He visited Alfred the Great in
England about the year 880, and from the description given he
was a wealthy man with plenty of goods to trade, including
furs, walrus ivory, ships' ropes of walrus or seal hide,
feathers, and skins of reindeer, marten, otter and bear.[101] From
the value of a shipload of such produce, the potential for sea
trade can be seen, and also of course the potential for piracy,

just as in any other age of sea trade. But the pirates are the parasites on the host, rather than the host itself, and although day-to-day trade may seen rather mundane besides their colourful activities, the trader rather than the raider looks like the norm in Norwegian seafaring.

The one area where this may not have been the case, for a time anyway, is that around the Skagerrak and Kattegat, along the nearby coasts of present-day Norway and Sweden together with the Danish island of Sjaelland. This island, according to Alfred Smyth, was the power base of the sea-king Ragnarr *loðbrók* or Ragnar Lodbrok, sometimes regarded as legendary but, in Smyth's view, far from that since he argues that Ragnar and his sons were the instigators of the Danish assault on the British Isles that built up into the Great Army of 865. According to this picture, the Danes came later on to the British seaways than the Norwegians, possibly after pickings on the Kattegat declined as trade routes elsewhere opened up. Smyth chronicles fighting with the Norwegians in Ireland and an attack on the Norse port of Dublin, as well as attacks around the Scottish coast, including a raid on Orkney, which he suggests may have been in the late 830s or early 840s, the time when the Pictish kingdom was being fatally squeezed between the Scandinavians and the Scots.[102]

If Smyth is right, we can separate out two strands of Scandinavian contacts with Orkney. The one, predominantly trading, is with Orkney as a convenient stopping-point for trading voyages along the old route down the west side of Britain. The other comes from people who could be called Danish but who are really a mixture from the area of the Kattegat, and who would see Orkney as a good base from which to launch attacks on passing vessels and neighbouring coastal settlements.

Thus the idea of early peaceful Scandinavian settlement in Orkney is quite consistent with accounts of viking raiding at other times. There is a long tradition of ascribing an early date to the start of Scandinavian settlement in Orkney, and also of it being peaceful: the list includes Alexander Bugge and C. J. S. Marstrander as well as Hugh Marwick and J. Storer Clouston.[103]

Wainwright, however, pointed to the accounts in the sagas of vikings being in Orkney when Harald Fairhair arrived in the late ninth century, and with the earliest recorded viking raid on Britain being in 793, that seemed to set a limit to the start of the Scandinavian settlement.[104] If, however, that raid and the ones that followed were not a collective blitzkrieg launched upon Europe by the entire Norwegian coastal population, but rather the extension of a pattern of piracy by particular chieftains, then there is nothing to clash with an earlier pattern of settlement of Scandinavians in Orkney, where trading vessels could be serviced, goods exchanged, and even land bought. This pattern would continue through the ninth century, although Danish raids from the Kattegat area would cause increasing problems, as indeed they did to the kingdoms of the Picts and the Scots. Whether or not Orkney was part of the kingdom of the Picts by this time, the Pictish defeat by the Danes in 839 and their subsequent absorption by the Scots[105] would mean that Orkney was now very much on its own. An attack by the main force of Danes would be followed by a period of instability. Thus the *Orkneyinga Saga*'s account of Harald Fairhair sailing to Orkney to deal with "certain vikings whose plunderings he could no longer tolerate" fits in with this picture. It is also interesting to note that after King Harald's voyage and the subsequent deterioration in Orkney affairs following the death of Earl Sigurd, the vikings who settle in the islands are described as Danish.[106] To deal with them and to hold Orkney under the rule of law required an earl of the calibre of Torf Einar.

What we can also believe is that Harald settled a number of Norwegians in Orkney, just as the sagas said. In order to hold the islands once and for all against raiders and dissidents, he would have had to build up a structure of chieftains, loyal to him, and linked together by a network of defence plans so that any raid, from any quarter, could be beaten off. Orkney would then be a completely safe place for Norwegian ships to harbour, and for marine services and local trading to develop.

So a second wave of Norwegian settlement would have taken place in Orkney, a structured planting of specific families and retainers in specific places, and after the depredations of raiders there could well have been room for new people in several areas. After the previous period of instability, the Orcadians would have been unlikely to object.

This is, of course, just a model of the possible sequence of events, rather than a definite conclusion, and the only justification for putting forward such an untested model is that having built up a case against a previous one, a new model is needed that will fit the facts better. As an interesting example of the kind of fact it will fit, there is Hugh Marwick's reference to a story in Papa Westray of a battle having been fought long ago between the 'Danes' and the Orcadians.[107] From the arguments quoted earlier on the continuity of the Church in Papay, it seems that Norse settlement of the island was limited, and violent Norse conquest unlikely. A raid by Danes would not contradict this, given the separate characteristics that we have identified in the two Scandinavian groupings.

Again, there is the remarkable disparity between Sanday and Westray in the amount of the un-Scandinavian blood-group B, with Sanday having almost twice as much as Westray (see Table 22 in Chapter 4).[108] Sanday was a great grain-growing island, and the possibility of grain exports to Norway in saga times has been raised.[109] Westray was important to the Norse for the harbour at Pierowall, and could have had an incoming Norwegian population of traders and shipwrights, while in Sanday the indigenous people were left to get on by themselves, with a smaller admixture of Norse for administration and defence.

And in North Ronaldsay, there are the sheep which seem to be a native breed that were in Orkney when the Norse arrived. The old Orkney name for them, keero-sheep, is closely akin to the Gaelic word for 'sheep', *caora*.[110] The transfer of the word suggests peaceful contact between one group and another.

The unravelling of contact between Celtic and Norse people, though, is an extremely complex process that will take a long time to produce conclusions, and the question is not only whether or not particular contacts took place, but also where — whether in Orkney with island people, or further afield on the sea routes down the west coast of Britain. Some very interesting examples are indicated by Professor Foote and Professor Almqvist in the following chapters but they both emphasise the extent of the problems faced in this whole area of investigation.

Another labyrinth awaits us in the attempt to seek the origins of the Celtic Iron Age immigrants who became the broch-builders, but a clue worth following may be the work of J. R. C. Hamilton, who excavated at Jarlshof and Clickhimin in Shetland, and who did not join Wainwright and the other contributors to *The Northern Isles* in ascribing the broch people's arrival to the first century BC. Hamilton put it several centuries before that, and noted descriptions from the Irish epics which seemed to fit the forts of the broch-builders. He found a number of interesting references in the Irish stories — for instance, to the legendary hero Labraid Loingseach, who "smote eight towers in Tiree" and "ventured upon many of the islands of Orkney".[111] Labraid attacked strongholds in the north of the Fomorians, and from descriptions of the Fomorians, Chadwick suggested they were the broch people.[112] Any effort to identify real historical groups out of the confusing and often contradictory references in the epics will be difficult, but with increasing evidence that the broch-builders were a powerful Iron

Age warrior confederation, it is worth looking at potential zones
of contact with contemporaries, in areas such as the old west
Atlantic seaway.

In looking at the society of broch times, a survey that would
be of great interest would be one of the various seasonal ball
games like the annual Ba' held in Kirkwall. John Robertson's
excellent book on the subject shows clearly the features the
Kirkwall game has in common with those elsewhere, and with
the legend of the game's origin with a severed head bringing
fertility to its destination, the Kirkwall Ba' looks strongly like a
survival from Celtic times.[113]

The problem of Marwick and Jakobsen's list of Celtic place-
name elements is now not that of Wainwright, that they were the
wrong sort, but simply that they are of both sorts, though one
rather more than the other. If we look for the origin of the
Goidelic (Q) form in the actual Iron Age immigration that led to
the broch culture, where do we get the Brythonic (P)? One
possibility is that since Brythonic has taken shape in various
parts of Britain as the result of an encounter of a Celtic language
with an indigenous one, words in Brythonic may come from one
or the other — that is, the Brythonic words in Orkney may not
be the result of any additional Celtic group arriving, but just
survivals from the language, now lost, of the native Bronze Age
population. In this connection, there are the broad *treb* dykes
stretching across the landscape in a possible survival from the
early Iron Age (see Chapter 2), and farms called Thrave, related
to the old Brythonic word *treb,* a dwelling.[114]

And as for the men of the towers, we can sometimes come
quite near them. Hamilton, for example, follows Chadwick in
regarding the appearance of brochs in Lothian as the result of an
alliance, in Hamilton's opinion one between the northern broch
men and the local tribe, the Votadini.

> In view of the high quality of the Roman ware in the
> Torwoodlee broch it is possible that this agreement was
> made prior to the Roman withdrawal and with the
> congnizance of the army command . . . As fighting
> men or mercenaries the broch men would be posted to
> frontier regions and given land there for castle-building. On
> the northern confines of Votadinian territory we can see
> them constructing the tower at Coldoch guarding the
> highland approach to the ford across the Water of Frew on
> the Forth.[115]

With the Votadini a satellite kingdom under Roman rule, we

can indeed see the broch men being deployed southwards as auxiliaries to strengthen the frontier of the Roman empire, and the same alliance would ensure that the Romans could rely on a friendly harbour for their fleet in the north. Tactically, the arguments about being able to move rapidly from one side of Scotland to the other were as good in the Roman era as in the last two centuries, and the idea of holding the back door to Scotland through an alliance with the broch people would be a highly logical one with advantages for both parties. It is strange to think of the Orkney men setting off for Lothian, to take up their posts on the frontier of the Roman empire, holding the line of Votadini territory, and going away on a journey that would take later generations to Clontarf, to Carbisdale, or to the Somme.

Glimpses of the Votadini do appear through the general mist that obscures these times. One thread is their connection with the Romans, as a frontier kingdom, and indeed one of their rulers, around the 370s, may have been a Roman prefect. Later, we hear of them as the *Gododdin,* and some time in the 5th century, in the aftermath in Britain of the Roman departure, a group of Gododdin was deployed in North Wales to drive out Irish invaders and settle there themselves. A later force of Gododdin set out from Edinburgh around the year 600 to attack the Northumbrian kingdom of Deira; they suffered heavy defeat at Catterick, but had their story recorded in an early Welsh poem, the *Gododdin* of Aneirin.[116] The reason for following the story of the Gododdin southwards in this context is that in other Welsh sources there is the curious association of Lothian and Orkney, in the references to 'King Lot of Lothian and Orkney' as an ally of King Arthur. Whatever the basis of the Arthurian legends and whatever the identity of King Lot (possibly a mythological figure), the association of Lothian and Orkney may now not necessarily be something to be rejected out of hand, but a memory of an old alliance.

Another interesting aspect of this possible Orkney-Lothian relationship in the Roman period is in connection with the problem of the Picts. The phenomenon which one might call 'Pictishness' does seem to have a rather co-ordinated look about it, with for instance the pattern of *pit*-names in Fife and Angus falling in general on a particular type of site, in from the coast or up from the river-valleys, in sheltered and well-drained areas with good soil.[117] From the fierce description of the Picts, one might have expected them instead to come from the wilder and less accessible lands of the Highlands, where indeed the Iron Age tribal system survived fairly well intact until the post-1745 period. The East Coast, by comparison, with its fertile land, and in reach of the Roman fleet, might be expected to be more within the Roman sphere of trading. To move population groups around in the zone on the edge of empire, stabilising and strengthening some areas and undermining others, was standard Roman colonial tactics. In looking at any part of Scotland in the Roman period we have to take this factor into account, just as surely as an understanding of the rival groups in modern Lebanon requires an examination of the motives of the countries round about.

If indeed the Lothian brochs are the sign of the Roman deployment of Orcadian auxiliaries, could the various references to the Picts coming from Orkney be a hint of a similar subsequent operation further up the East Coast? This is not put forward as any kind of attempted solution to the Pictish problem, but rather as a suggestion that the problem may be even more complex than it already seems, with various partial solutions and various population groupings and movements influenced not only by inter-tribal and economic factors but also by Roman frontier strategies.

But although the Pictish phenomenon seems more complicated than ever, there is no doubt of the benefits of this general focusing on the powerful warrior-confederation of Iron Age Orkney with its chieftains of the 'high broch period'. Hitherto unrelated or unlikely scraps can take possible new significance, as for instance the old story quoted by George Marwick of Yesnaby to the effect that the Broch of Borwick in Yesnaby was the residence of a "righ" or king. The *righ* of Borwick had a dispute with the *righ* of Verran in Voystown, on the north side of the Bay of Skaill in Sandwick. They fought on a hill face called Bruntland, on a place much later occupied by the farm of East Giron. George Marwick mentions "slewchan" stones—round stones put into a stocking—and stone buttons found in the earth, and a large round steatite urn, containing bones and ashes, found in a mound on the top of the hill west of Bruntland. A large stone axe, broken, was found on top of the urn cover, he says, and the knowe was always called the Righ Knowe.[118]

A small loophole in a thick wall, giving a glimpse of a distant country and a far horizon?

Acknowledgments

This chapter has benefited greatly from the assistance of a number of people who read it in draft form at various stages, in

Four Westraymen

Poet and niece:
George Mackay Brown and Judith

The poet Ann Scott-Moncrieff

Mrs Johina Leith,
writer on traditional Orkney life

Margaret Tait, film-maker

particular William Thomson, Dr Alan Bruford, Prof. Gordon Donaldson, Dr Anna Ritchie, Dr Graham Ritchie, Dr Barbara Crawford, Dr Anthony Jackson and Dr Bente Magnus. Thanks to their kindness in taking time to go through the manuscript, I have been saved from numerous errors and omissions; the responsibility for those that remain is of course very much my own!

A Note on the Folktale Evidence

Alan Bruford

This note is based on the same material as the later part of my article 'Legends Long Since Localised or Tales Still Travelling?' (*Scottish Studies* 24 (1980), pp. 43-62). There, however, I was chiefly concerned to demonstrate the difficulty of deducing how long an orally told legend had been known in a particular place, and concluded that it was hardly ever possible to prove an association between tale and place of as much as a thousand years, or even five hundred. Here I am saying, "but if it were . . ."

The late Professor Reidar Th. Christiansen of Oslo concluded in his *Studies in Irish and Scandinavian Folktales* (Copenhagen 1959) that despite several centuries of constant contact there was little trace of direct connections between Scandinavian and Irish folktales. He was dealing, however, only with international *Märchen* ("fairy-tales") and mainly with Irish rather than Scottish Gaelic versions; some of the few parallels he did find involve the latter — not to mention the traditions of the Northern Isles. He was in fact working at much the same time on an exemplary catalogue of *The Migratory Legends* of Norway (Helsinki 1958), localised traditions *(Sagen)* of a kind whose basic patterns can also move from country to country. With the help of this and similar legends collected on this side of the North Sea by the School of Scottish Studies and others, it is now possible to look for evidence of connections between these more localised tales, though only general and tentative conclusions can yet be drawn.

Very few legends from Christiansen's list can be paralleled in Orkney or Shetland but not elsewhere in Europe. Many of Christiansen's types are known throughout much of Western Europe — 3000, Escape from the Black School; 3020, Inexperienced Use of the Black Book (Ropes of Sand); 3055, The Witch that was Hurt; 4050, "The hour has come but not the

M

man"; 5070, Midwife to the Fairies; 5075, Removing Building
Situated above the House of the Fairies; 5080, Food from the
Fairies; 5085, The Changeling; 6010, The Capture of a Fairy;
6045, Drinking Cup Stolen from the Fairies; 7015, The New Suit
[Brownie Resigns]; 7020, Vain Attempt to Escape from the Nisse
[Brownie, Hogboon]; 7060, Disputed Site for a Church. So the
fact that several of these are found in Orkney or Shetland proves
nothing.

One case where details are clearly linked to the special
Norwegian form is 6070A, Fairies Send a Message: a passer-by is
given a message from a fairy haunt to deliver at a farm (often
that a fairy child has fallen in the fire), and when he mentions it
an invisible fairy woman appears and flees, "leaving behind her
a bucket, etc." This is still known in Fetlar, formerly in Foula,
and accounts for the "fairy kit" which a family in Yell still had
recently: even the names of fairies in the message (Fivla, Tivla
etc.) are similar in Shetland and Norway, and may be seen today
on Shetland inter-island ferries! I do not know of an Orcadian
version, and elsewhere in Britain the tale takes the form 6070B,
rare in Norway: the message is "X is dead" and the response
comes from the cat by the fire, "Then I am the king of the
cats!"

Few others are as clearly related. 3080, The Finn Messenger,
where a Lapp magically brings news of home to (e.g.) a sailor at
sea, with a physical token (knife, spoon) to prove he has been in
the house, is not uncommon in Shetland, along with other tales
of "Norway Finns" (clearly magicians who can take seal or
other animal forms, not sea fairies). In Orkney the ideas of
mortal and supernatural seal-men seem to have been confused,
and the latter concept may owe more to Celtic models. At any
rate Christiansen's type 4080, The Seal Woman (who marries the
mortal who steals her seal-skin but leaves him when she gets it
back), proves to have a westerly, Atlantic distribution: the basic
plot is of course world-wide, but usually involves a swan or other
bird disguise, which indeed appears in Norse saga. The seal story
is widely known on the western and northern coasts of Ireland
and Scotland, with a variant involving a mermaid and her
"slough" or fish-tail on the east coasts, where the Atlantic grey
seal is not known; it appears in Orkney, Shetland, Faroe and
Iceland, but Christiansen can only point to a single variant for
all Norway and one for Denmark. The movement here must be
from West to East.

It should be added that stories of an affair between a seal-man
and a mortal woman (as in the ballad of *The Grey Selkie*, Child
113) seem virtually exclusive to Orkney. It was from South

Ronaldsay that I recorded a parallel to Christiansen's legend 6000, Tricking the Fairy Suitor, with a "sea-man" replacing the fairy, though in this case very similar stories of a fairy revealing the antidote to his or her own spell when asked to help with a bewitched cow have also been recorded in Gaelic; the Norwegian tale is only marginally closer. 4085, The Seahorse and the Sea-serpent, is paralleled not in the Northern Isles but in the Western, with the story of a water-horse overcome by an extraordinary bull called *Tarbh na Leòid* — apparently "Ljót's bull", rather than MacLeod's. The tale includes native Gaelic tradition — the water-horse can become a young man, and lives in a fresh-water loch — but the name of the loch, *Snigreabhad,* seems to derive from Norse **nykra-vatn,* "water-monster loch", so the belief if not the whole story may be handed down from Norse times.[119]

In general, however, it is easier to find links between the legends of the Northern Isles and Gaelic Scotland than between either and Scandinavia: not surprisingly in the case of recent tales of smuggling and illicit distilling, or those witchcraft beliefs which came in with witch presecutions from the Lowlands, but also in tales and beliefs of the Evil Eye and the taking of the "profit" or "fruit" of milk and other foodstuffs, which are far more deeply rooted. One legend (the witch gives a ship's crew a knotted string: they must untie one or two knots for a wind to take them home, but not touch the third — they eventually do and wreck the ship) has an unusual distribution. It seems to be unknown in both Ireland and Norway, but common in the Highlands and Islands — told of a Tiree witch in Barra, a Barra witch in Tiree, an Orkney witch in Caithness and vice versa, but in Shetland the witch is always in Norway — and its Baltic connections extend as far away as Finland. The associated belief in the sale of winds by wise women, like Bessie Millie of Stromness in Scott's time, probably spreads wider, but does the story descend in purely oral tradition from Aeolus' bag of winds in the *Odyssey,* or was it spread about by some Renaissance scholar's sermon? If not, we may possibly have one tradition older than either Celt or Viking.

Again, the bulk of fairy traditions seem to have moved freely across the Pentland Firth. Fairies themselves, though often (but by no means everywhere) called trows in the Northern Isles, have little in common with Norse trolls and often seem less like the grotesque cow-tailed *huldre* who are their nearest equivalent in Norway than the well-made if dangerous *sìdhichean* of Gaelic tradition. By no means all Scottish fairy legends are easy to parallel in Ireland, and sometimes their relatives may be found in

England or Wales more easily. Distribution may be affected by local circumstances. Thus the story of the fairies leaving the country forever tends to appear where there is a well-used and fairly short sea-crossing for them to make: Ulster (to England), Arran (to Ireland), the Channel coast (to France), Caithness to Orkney, Shetland to Faroe — not Norway, which perhaps would be less of a refuge from the preaching that drives them out.

The most suggestive distribution pattern, however, is that of the legend used by George Mackay Brown in his *Two Fiddlers*. Two men pass a fairy hill with light and music streaming from its open door: one, with a jar of whisky (keg of beer, basket of fish) on his back, goes in and joins the fairy dance — or if he is a musician, is asked in to play for it — and the door closes. His companion, sometimes accused of his murder, goes back a year later and drags him out protesting that he has hardly danced one reel; or sometimes he stumbles out like Rip van Winkle to find a hundred years have passed. Versions, normally localised at the nearest recognised fairy hill, are found in many Outer and Inner Hebridean islands, most parts of the Central Highlands and some further north, as well as Orkney and Shetland. There seems to be little trace of the story in Lowland Scotland, England or Ireland: but a number of versions are on record from Wales, with the difference that the dance is in the open air, on a fairy ring rather than a fairy hill, and the dancers simply vanish for a year: their mortal companion has no load, but comes out asking for the packhorses he was leading. Does the lack of Irish or Anglo-Saxon parallels (though there is a hint of a Danish one!) mean that this is a very ancient legend preserved only by P-Celts, Welsh and Pictish, and kept on because of its association with local holy places by the Gaels and Norsemen who conquered or absorbed the Picts? (The fairy hills involved may be natural mounds or hillsides, burial mounds, brochs or settlement sites in origin.) Or, since the idea of time passing faster in the other world is widespread (though sometimes claimed to be of Irish origin in Europe), do we simply conclude that some accidental factor has affected this tale's distribution?

At any rate, if the distribution of local, and therefore locally prized, legends is any guide, Orkney and even Shetland are now less part of a Norse cultural province than of a Scottish one, and there are indications that they fit in best to a pattern involving movement, either way, along the Atlantic seaboard from Ireland to Iceland.

CHAPTER 8

Pre-Viking Contacts between Orkney and Scandinavia

Peter Foote

Knowledge about early contacts between the Norsemen and the native inhabitants of what was to become the Orkney earldom, including Shetland, Orkney itself, the north mainland of Scotland, and the Western Isles, tends to be slight and confused. Yet in these regions Norsemen mingled with populations of Celtic (or pre-Celtic) strain, and Orkney can be reasonably made the hub round which the whole question of Scandinavian-Celtic relations revolves. This chapter is a review of recent studies in archaeology, language, literature and folklore, with emphasis on the natives as givers to the Norsemen rather than on the reverse.

Some introductory observations on Picts, Scots, Norsemen, chronology and Christianity

In a well-known paper, Sommerfelt[1] argued on sound phonological grounds that the Norse forms *Péttar* 'Picts' and *Péttlandsfjörðr* 'Pentland Firth' must go back to Norse name-giving not later than the seventh century. He added this to scraps of evidence adduced by earlier scholars and to some limited place-name testimony and decided that a Norse colonisation of Orkney about AD 600 should be counted a possibility. No convincing support for this thesis has so far emerged—indeed, there is conspicuous lack of evidence for direct Scandinavian contact with the British Isles in the period preceding the Viking Age.[2] What relations existed between Norway and Orkney in that period were presumably sporadic rather than intimate. Since the reappraisal by Wainwright[3] it seems generally accepted that c. 800 was the time of the major Norse settlement. Wainwright's interpretation of this period as one of conquest and subjugation has been questioned,[4] but it has been energetically supported by I. A. Crawford[5] on evidence from his excavation at the Udal, N.

Uist. Crawford does not find evidence of peaceful continuity of settlement at Buckquoy convincing, but even if it were, it might not invalidate general conclusions about the warlike character of the immigration (compare Small, 1976, on the Norse settlement of Skye).[6] It is probably also wise to bear in mind that the Norsemen—like the races they met in the British Isles—were (or rapidly became) a slave-keeping and slave-trading people. If they had the upper hand, they were more likely to export any healthy natives they did not want, or could not afford to keep, than to massacre them.

Incoming Norsemen met Picts and Dalriadic Scots. The Picts were presumably already Gaelicised to some degree,[7] and they were certainly under strong pressure from the Scots, whose church, learning and literary culture are assumed to have been hardly differentiated from those of Ireland, their original home. There are one or two suggestive details in the story of his youthful adventures told by Findan the Irishman in his monastery at Rheinau. He had been carried off from Ireland by Vikings, towards or c. 840, and escaped from them in Orkney—we cannot tell where. He was taken in by the abbot of a nearby house who had studied in Ireland and spoke his language.[8] Both the Irish links of such a community, evidently native but Columban, and its survival amid the Norse incursions are significant.

'Political' marriages between Norse and Scottish chieftains' families are well known. One might guess that it was in such circles that Celtic poetry might influence Norse verse. Among them a degree of bilingualism was probably a matter of course, and acceptance or benevolent toleration of Christianity normal. Transfer of domestic vocabulary and customs and probably of extensive folklore might equally well take place in a society of comfortably-off Norse householders, with raiding and trading as summer jobs, who had Pictish-Scottish slaves as concubines, nurses, housemaids, tutors, fishermen, stable-boys and so on. The masters were not likely to object to the Christian beliefs and practices of their servants as long as they did not interfere with their work.

'Apart from Christianity . . . the Picts gave very little to the Scandinavians' was the verdict of Wainwright (1962). In spite of advances in Pictish studies in the past twenty years, it remains difficult to detect anything that amounts to Pictish influence on the Norsemen. Limited knowledge of the Pictish languages and the meagreness of Pictish writings are well-known drawbacks, but even in decorative art, where Pictish survivals are most impressive, no similarities in Scandinavian work are judged to be the result of direct contact. It may be significant that Norse impact on central Pictland, from Fife to Buchan, seems to have been very slight,[9] but we are badly off for reliable and up-to-date information about Viking finds in Scotland.[10] Furthermore, it has been argued that Pictish art in stone continued in Shetland long after the Norse settlement, even on through the tenth century.[11] The artistic links—and they are thought to imply ecclesiastical connections—were first with Pictland proper and subsequently with Iona and Northumbria, but it seems to be an open question whether the Shetland material is evidence of an unbroken continuity or a renewal. Pictish metalwork has also been drawn more into discussion, not least since the discovery of the St Ninian's Isle treasure, but again any influence from it on Norse forms seems to be regarded as exerted through Northumbrian or Irish intermediaries.[12]

The suggestion has also been made that certain housebuilding features might have been adopted by Norsemen from Pictish-Scottish practice. The evidence is not compelling and other explanations have been offered—for example, similarities might be 'the result of Norse settlers putting a subject Pictish population to work as builders'.[13] There will doubtless be improved archaeological assessments of Pictish-Norse relations, but it is understandable that the works mentioned in the following notes are necessarily concerned with Celtic-Norse connections, as opposed to Pictish-Norse connections, because Celtic elements are much easier to define and demonstrate—though not always with much refinement, as we shall see.

Archaeology, language and folklore

In the different fields under discussion, different time-spans must be allowed. The archaeological material is drawn from the Viking Age itself, c. 800-1100 (to give it conventional limits), and more especially from the ninth and tenth century. The linguistic material may go back as far, and certainly does in some cases, but the possibility of loans lasted on into the Middle Ages, while the recorded evidence itself may be of much later date. The same is true in the field of folk-tale and folk-belief. Influence on poetry and medieval narrative, on the other hand, must be chiefly assigned to the Viking Age, but it could continue in the twelfth century and possibly longer in the Orkney realm—such continuation in the Irish Sea 'mixing area' is less likely. But it will be noted that it is often only an assumption that a given loan took place in the Viking Age itself.

Co-existence of paganism and Christianity seems more than

likely (cf. above), and can be supported by analogy from the situation that obtained in parts of England and the Isle of Man.[14] Presumably there was some proselytising by such clerical communities as were left undisturbed, but we have no record of any Celtic missionary effort in Scandinavia itself. The Celtic church undoubtedly suffered heavily from Viking incursions, and the missionary thrust in the North came from England and Hamburg-Bremen. We hear of Johannes 'the Irish' who was a missionary bishop in Iceland in the early eleventh century. He is also said to have been sent from Hamburg to Orkney, and finally died a martyr's death among pagan Slavs in Mecklenburg.[15] (As a curiosity, the nickname *skotakollr* 'Irish-pate' may be mentioned, borne by one Icelander of the tenth century, another of the eleventh, and an Orcadian of the twelfth. It is interpreted as signifying someone whose head of hair was reminiscent of the distinctive Celtic tonsure. The same name occurs twice in eleventh-century Yorkshire).[16]

The first missionary attempts in west Norway of which we can be tolerably certain came from England and not until the 940s, when a man from Glastonbury was consecrated to work there.[17] That was probably connected with efforts to promote Christianity by King Hákon Haraldsson (died 964), who had been brought up at the court of King Athelstan in England. Nevertheless, Hákon died an apostate. There seems no doubt that the tenth century was an age which saw a general Christian advance and a synthesis in some men's minds of the old and new faiths, well before the 'official' conversion of the North Atlantic Norse communities and the Norwegians themselves, which is dated as late as the 990s. Birkeli[18] has tried to show that some of the primitive stone crosses found in west and south Norway go back to such early times. He does not find the same tradition in the Faroes or the Orkney realm (apart from some slight Hebridean evidence), and draws his parallels from the south and south-west of mainland Scotland, the north of England, and the lands of the Irish sea. That tolerance and large-scale acceptance of Christianity in Orkney in the ninth and tenth centuries made some impression on Norwegians at home can hardly be doubted, but better definition of it is yet to be achieved.

A suggestion with a bearing on this problem, though in a wider Celtic context, has been made by Charlotte Blindheim.[19] A large number of 'insular' objects have been found in Norway— many more than in Denmark and Sweden—buckets, mounts of various kinds, buckles, brooches, pins, and many small weighing scales. Reliquary boxes and a thurible are among the most remarkable finds. Traditionally these objects, especially those of

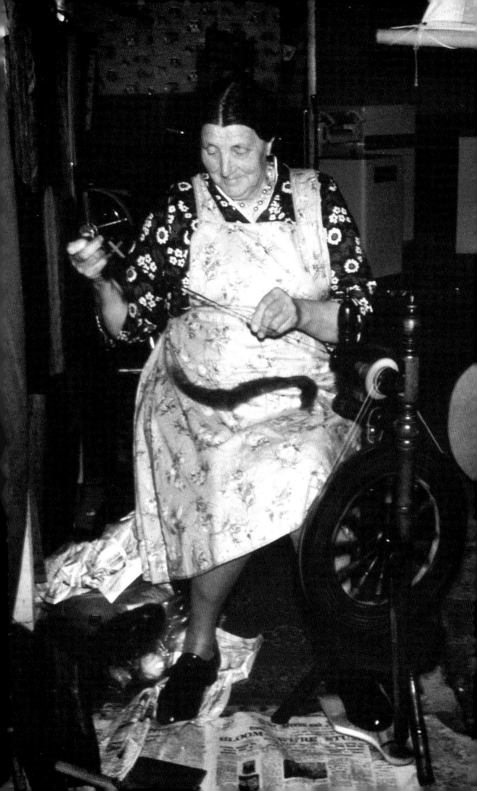

ecclesiastical provenance, have been explained as loot. Charlotte Blindheim suggests that many of the minor objects came to Norway as merchandise. Major items, on the other hand, she would prefer to see as gifts or bribes, part of the diplomacy that was necessary whether for commercial or Christian ends. The ecclesiastical objects in particular, she thinks, might point to missionary effort of Celtic origin. As she acknowledges, there are many problems. Identification of 'insular' objects is a haphazard affair; plunder, gifts and trade-goods may be the same pieces differently acquired; goods that came through commerce could follow many routes. It is tempting to think of Orcadians as middle-men, but they were not the only ones, and decisive evidence is hard to come by. (It has also been objected that undue importance has been attached to the commercial element in ninth-century western movements, at least from Denmark.[20]) Another major difficulty is deciding the precise origin of any 'insular' piece—only a few can be called specifically Irish or Scottish or Northumbrian with any confidence—and we hope that Charlotte Blindheim's call for a concerted effort on the part of a host of experts to solve the problems will meet with response. Knowing archaeologists and the pressures on them, one might hope for answers in fifty years or so.

Art and design

Acute problems of related kind beset the field of art history. Given the acknowledged strength of indigenous pre-Viking Age traditions in Scandinavia (already affected by impulses from the south) and the welter of possible influences after c. 800— Oriental, Byzantine, Baltic, Carolingian, Anglo-Carolingian, Anglo-Saxon, Irish, Pictish (many of these also variously hybrid)—it would be surprising if that were not the case. 'Priority for any local development is hard to ascertain' has been said of a particular context, but it is true over a much wider field. We may recall too that skilled craftsmen were among the travellers of the Dark Ages, willingly or unwillingly. They stood high on the list of suitable presents for exchange between great men, and were well worth buying or stealing.

It used to be thought that 'Irish' influence was paramount in the development of the tenth-century Jellinge style in Scandinavia, for example, though most scholars preferred Anglo-Saxon origins. Now the term 'Irish' is cautiously replaced by 'Hiberno-Saxon'—referring to the work, that is, of artists in Ireland, Northern England and Scotland[21]—but it is also maintained that the Jellinge style is not fundamentally dependent on any foreign art at all. At best, elements of it can be traced back to Scandinavian work of about AD 800 on which some direct, or indirect, insular influences may have been exerted.[22] The possibility of sources in much older Celtic-Germanic connections, the undeniable influence of Celtic art on Anglo-Saxon and Carolingian styles, and of these latter on Scandinavian art in their turn, have led to the conclusion that direct inspiration from Celtic territories on mainstream Norse art is improbable.[23] In the Viking colonies there is more admixture—though the convenient term 'Hiberno-Norse' used in such contexts is not always illuminating. Examples of 'colonial' co-existence may be seen on trial-pieces from Viking Dublin, which show pure Norse, pure Celtic and mixed forms side by side.[24] It is a remarkable fact that no convincing evidence of Irish influence on the notable Anglo-Scandinavian sculpture of the tenth and eleventh centuries has so far been adduced.[25]

The recognition of the 'unity' of Ireland, Northumbria and Scotland in some forms of art in this period certainly represents a more sophisticated attitude than those that previously prevailed. The arguments in favour of seeing Scandinavian art in the Viking Age as pre-eminently an indigenous development not vitally affected by shifting external influences also seems to have gained general approval. But both 'improvements' in approach make it more difficult to trace specific connections—and we are back to an appeal for co-operative effort by the Hiberno-Saxons and Scandinavians of the present day.

Better definition may occasionally be obtained from a study of minor objects (though it is proper to repeat warnings against drawing firm conclusions from archaeologists' distribution maps[26]). For example, Fanning has studied a Hiberno-Norse type of ringed pin with a plain ring and polyhedral head. From the distribution (including good examples from the Orkney earldom) and iconographic evidence he concludes that this was a Celtic form adopted by Norsemen who must at the same time have adopted its mode of use as a cloak-fastener.[27]

Words and verse

Such a link established between specific object and specific fashion is on a par with results that can be obtained from the study of loan-words—which unless associated with particular objects, techniques, customs or beliefs often have only the vaguest significance for us. In this field notable contributions have been made by Matras, ably supported by Lockwood.[28] Matras has adumbrated the notion of an 'Atlantic culture', evidenced in a number of features of farming, fishing and domestic economy in the Faroes with which terminology of Celtic origin is associated. (Sometimes the words are also reflected in Orkney or Shetland Norn, Icelandic and dialects of Norway.) Comparatively few Celtic loan-words are recognised in Old West Norse: twenty-four accepted and thirteen doubtful from Irish (understood in a wide sense), two specifically Scottish forms (of words not originally Celtic) and two more doubtful Scottish words, along with a fair number of place-names and personal names.[29] Another fifteen or so have been detected in the modern languages—chiefly in Faroese—some recognised long since, some newly demonstrated. Matras and Lockwood have been able to put terms like *sornur* 'corn-drying kiln', *blak* 'buttermilk', *slavak* 'sea-lettuce', *dunna* 'tame duck', *tarfur* 'ungelded bull', *køkja* 'couple of sheep tethered in a special way', and others, in a practical context. A few expressions of Celtic origin have probably survived because of seafaring *tabu* use. Sometimes connections can be established with Hebridean Gaelic in particular. An example is Faroese *soppur* 'wisp of hay' (also known in Shetland Norn) which not only occurs as a simplex but is also found in an idiom meaning 'to give birth', *fara á soppinn* 'go onto the (handful of) hay', directly parallel to a Gaelic expression—*air na súip* 'on the wisp of straw'—also used of a woman in childbirth.[30]

The loan place-name or place-name element **ærg(i)* has been much discussed. It is of Celtic origin and is widely found in parts of Northern England and in Scottish regions where there was Norse settlement, as well as in Orkney and Shetland. Matras has also identified it in the Faroes. The word referred to some form of summer pasturing which was presumably a novelty to the Norsemen when they met it in the west (possibly it had something to do with the degree of the shieling's dependence on the home-farm in the summer months, like distinctions made in Norway today[31]). It has recently been argued that the source of the word in Faroese was not Irish but Scots Gaelic.[32]

All these factors—along with others such as tentative recognition of veneration of St Patrick and St Brendan in the islands—have naturally led to a questioning of the traditional view of the Faroes as the home of a distinctively Norse community. Significant elements of Celtic origin, whose closest links were (not surprisingly) with Scotland and its islands, may have existed in the population from the beginning. (Permanent Norse settlement in the Faroes is thought to date from c. 800 or soon after.) It is unfortunate that we only learn some of these words from records of a thousand years later and that we are so ill informed about Faroese conditions through the Middle Ages. General conclusions about ethnic components and social circumstances can hardly be drawn from such limited testimony, but the striking Faroese evidence may possibly provide analogies that can be legitimately applied in other 'Atlantic' contexts.

'From techniques of material culture we may move to techniques of verse. The most distinctive metrical form of Viking Age Scandinavia is the scaldic *dróttkvætt*. It has inherited features—alliteration, stress, metrical syllabic length—which are common to Germanic poetry in general, but others—internal rhyme, fixed line cadence and syllable counting—which are novelties. The oldest examples known are attributed to a Norwegian poet called Bragi, who probably flourished in the second half of the ninth century. He may not have been the inventor but certain features of his practice suggest that the mode was still in an experimental stage. The question is whether the innovations are to be regarded as native developments or dependent on foreign models.

The problem has been discussed most seriously in recent years by Turville-Petre.[33] Without minimising the differences that exist between Irish and Norse forms, he still finds the strict syllable-counting and the regular cadence so notably alike in the verse of the two languages that 'it is hard to believe that they developed . . . independently'. If Bragi belonged to the latter part of the ninth century, then the possibility of Celtic influence certainly existed—it falls well within the accepted framework of Viking Age chronology—and there were certainly areas within the Orkney realm where such influence could have been exerted— and probably better there at such an early stage than in Ireland itself.

Other scholars have found it possible to reconcile the novelties with the latent possibilities of verse-making in a Germanic-Norse tradition, rather in the same way as art-historians find sources within indigenous tradition for the development of the major styles.[34] It is at least possible to adduce instances of Norse metrical borrowing later in the Viking Age: an eleventh-century development based on Latin, which produced an expanded *dróttkvætt* form; and a tenth-century development, producing a truncated form of *dróttkvætt,* based, it is suggested, on an Irish accentual metre.[35] The earliest examples of the Latin-influenced form have Hebridean and Orcadian associations and it may have been first introduced in the earldom.[36] In the metrical field the verdict at present must be that the possibility of Celtic influence is well established. Further study will affect the degree of plausibility but we can hardly hope for definitive results.

Mythology

The themes of Norse poetry that may have Celtic connections are bound up to some extent with mythology and have long attracted attention. Direct Irish-Scottish mythological influence on pagan Scandinavian religion is considered unlikely and parallels between the two are explained by much older associations, Indo-European or Celtic-Germanic. In the most authoritative survey available in English, by Turville-Petre (1964),[37] this is the accepted interpretation, for example, of the similarities between Óðinn and Balor and Lug, between Týr and Nuadu, between wars fought by Æsir against Vanir and by the Tuatha Dé Danann against the Fir Bolg and the Fomorians, and between Finn mac Cumhaill and Sigurðr the Dragon-slayer.

The prose introduction to the eddaic poem call *Rígsþula,* preserved in a fourteenth-century source, identifies the protagonist in the poem as the god called Heimdallr. In the verse itself he is named Rígr, and this has occasioned special interest because it clearly represents Irish 'king', *rí,* borrowed in the oblique case *ríg.* Other features in the poem relating to Rígr and others again in independent sources relating to Heimdallr have been found Celtic antecedents and parallels, and the composition of the poem assigned to a Hiberno-Norse milieu of the late Viking Age.[38] Once more, however, the elements that the poem and the myths have in common with Irish material are considered more likely to be survivals of much older Celtic-Germanic tradition than Viking Age loans.[39] On the other hand, the name Rígr is a specific transfer and inevitably invites speculation as to its use in the context of the poem. It must have been a well-known word, however, and one might think that the further it got from the Hiberno-Norse world, the more mystery would attach to it. Even that is far from certain, for the word occurs in the one bit of connected Irish quoted in any medieval Icelandic source, half of which says *male diarik* (sic), a phrase supposed to have been used to greet King Muirchertach of the Leather Cloaks by a Norwegian interpreter about 1100—not very successfully because it means 'May you be cursed, king'.[40] The latest word on the subject of *Rígsþula,* however, is in defence of the thesis that the poem is a learned construction of the thirteenth century and that, in spite of the introductory prose, the poet himself did not identify Rígr as Heimdallr but as Óðinn.[41] The controversy is in a state of stalemate at the moment, an unhelpful conclusion that may nevertheless bring home the extent of our ignorance and the complexity of the evidence.

More convincing evidence of immediate derivation from Irish
tales has been presented in the case of two poems, originally a
unity, called *Grógaldr* and *Fjölsvinnsmál,* composed c.1200,
doubtless in Iceland. They are considered representative of a
stage of story-telling somewhere between the mythical and the
fantastical—a development which, it is suggested, lies behind
many folk-tales.[42] The progress of such a tale and its chronology
before the recorded stage are generally unknowable, but a
terminus about 1200 and the combination attested in these poems
(and related 'entertainments'), of Irish, Romance and learned
elements, all adapted to Norse forms, might point to a twelfth-
century stage of development in Orkney, whose connections with
Ireland, Anglo-Norman England, the Mediterranean and Iceland
are all demonstrable. That of course remains a conjecture. (It
may be noted in passing that it has recently been suggested[43] that
the combination of prose and verse in Icelandic sagas, notably
where the heroes are poets, is due to the example of Earl
Rögnvaldr kali in the mid-twelfth century. The theory is that he
and his poets were inspired to report on their Mediterranean
adventures in such a mixed form by the *vidas*—troubadour
biographies—and *razos*—anecdotes explaining the circumstances
in which troubadour verse was composed—which they met in
Narbonne. Interesting parallels but not likely to be a significant
source, will probably be the general verdict.)

Among related 'entertainments' of the kind just mentioned
may be counted various groups of Icelandic sagas: sagas of
ancient times (*fornaldarsögur*), sagas of chivalry (*riddarasögur*),
and fictitious sagas (*lygisögur*). The first kind were not written
until the late thirteenth century but had oral antecedents in the
twelfth (and doubtless before that) and some of them are known
through Saxo's *Gesta Danorum* of about 1200. The second and
third groups are products of thirteenth-century translation or are
a blend of saga and folk-tale motifs and free fancy in stories
mostly put together in the fourteenth and fifteenth centuries.
Celtic material and Celtic parallels in them have long been
recognised. In the translated Romance literature it comes at
second-hand but elsewhere it must depend on a variety of literary
and oral transmission from the Celtic world, some in very
ancient times, some perhaps in the Middle Ages.[44] Tantalising
similarities between Norse and Welsh stories have been detected
which, it is suggested, could be explained by postulating a
'Hebridean saga'.[45] Irish and Norse similarities tend to reflect
separate developments of closely-related original themes.[46] The
conclusion from a study of a complex of ideas to do with re-
birth, for example, is that, although the common roots of the

Norse and Celtic manifestations may belong to the earliest period of the Dark Ages, 'we can hardly doubt that throughout this period and the Viking Age the Norse developed under literary influences from the Celtic peoples'. It was perhaps in the Hebrides that these influences were chiefly exerted—'where the two peoples seem originally to have met as friends'.[47] Perhaps not always as friends (cf. above), but certainly on more equal terms than, say, Norseman and Pict in Orkney.

Saga and history

References to Viking Age events located in Ireland, Scotland and Northern England in various kinds of sagas written two to three hundred years afterwards in Iceland are generally not treated as reliable reminiscences by modern historians, except possibly when supported by acceptably authentic scaldic verse. That attitude has been partly disregarded in recent work, for instance that of Smyth,[48] where sources are used more eclectically—some people think wildly (cf. Graham-Campbell[49] and McTurk,[50] where references to ongoing polemic will be found). Another study, by Lukman,[51] has undertaken to prove use of a specific Irish source in a group of sagas of ancient times. Prominent among these are *Sörla þáttr* and *Sörla saga sterka,* which are among the principal Norse sources for the story of Hildr and the famous 'everlasting battle' on Hoy. The Irish source in question is the so-called *Three Fragments,* annals known only in a seventeenth-century copy but perhaps originating c. 1100. Alleged parallels between names or name-elements, family relationships, events and motifs in the sagas and in the annals covering the years c. 850-70 lead to the claim that the *Three Fragments* were a source possibly known to twelfth- and thirteenth-century historians in Iceland or possibly a late medieval import there. There may of course be reminiscences of historical events in late Icelandic stories—even of ninth-century Irish events—but the strictest criteria, literary and historical, must necessarily be applied in any attempt to isolate them and to decide the manner of their survival. Certainly the hypotheses that fourteenth- or fifteenth-century Icelandic authors had independent access to an immediate Irish source—and made of it what we actually find in the sagas in question—will not stand up to scrutiny.

Postscript

When I first wrote this survey, I ended with a summary of some major points in Professor Almqvist's valuable O'Donnell Lecture of 1976, now happily reprinted in full in the following chapter. The space thus freed may be filled by reference to one or two works of interest which have appeared in the interim. The papers in the welcome re-issue in 1983 of *The Impact of the Scandinavian Invasions on the Celtic-speaking Peoples c. 800-1100 A.D.*[52] are naturally more concerned with what the title says than with the reverse, but Nora K. Chadwick's remarks (pp. 34-6) on 'mutual relations' of the Norsemen and the Irish are well worth re-reading. The fascinating papers in the 1984 *Pictish Studies*[53] mostly, and understandably, make the problems to be faced more rather than less complex, but the general reader will benefit in particular from Leslie Alcock's 'A Survey of Pictish Settlement Archaeology' and Trevor Watkins' 'Where were the Picts?'. *The Northern and Western Isles in the Viking World,*[54] published in the same year, will be well known to most readers. Papers by P. Gelling, A. Fenton, G. Fellows-Jensen, R. G. Cant, B. Fidjestøl, Hermann Pálsson and Svavar Sigmundsson all touch on aspects of archaeology, material culture, church organisation, poetry and language relevant in some degree to the topics I have touched on above, though without giving cause for any significant reappraisal of them. Finally, in an article published in 1985,[55] Rosemary Power has reconsidered Irish analogues (and brought in new material) of the famous story of Thor's visit to Útgarða-Loki in Snorri's *Prose Edda*, written c. 1220. She concludes that a Celtic source for the Icelandic tale must be accepted. When and how it was transmitted remains a matter of conjecture. Since from an Icelandic viewpoint the elements shared with the Celtic analogues appear isolated in Snorri's tale, one might be tempted to conclude that it was a late loan and in that case look on twelfth-century Orkney as the bridge. But of course we have been brought up to resist temptation.

This brief survey of a few fields of study may perhaps be enough to show that, while problems to do with Norse-Celtic relations may have become better defined in recent years, solutions to them are few and far between. Answers, especially in the most promising fields of archaeology and folklore, need years of patient labour by people with years of patient learning behind them. That is a fact seldom recognised by policy-makers, the media and the urban public. It is encouraging to think that it may be better appreciated by the people of Orkney.

The writer Bessie Skea ('Countrywoman')

The writer Christina M. Costie (centre), with her sister Bessie (left) and brother Hubert (right)

Elizabeth Miller,
proprietrix of *The Orcadian*

Ola M. Gorie
pioneered Orkney silverware

Jean Campbell, community drama
producer, took part in many plays

Ingirid Jolly,
singer and musician

CHAPTER 9

Scandinavian and Celtic Folklore Contact in the Earldom of Orkney

Bo Almqvist

In Memoriam—E. O. G. Turville-Petre

The northern parts of most European countries have not fared well in the popular imagination. They are nearly everywhere thought of as remote, isolated, and barren, and populated by silent, uncouth, and barbaric people. People also tend to look at a country from the point of view of its present capital. The fact that we are accustomed to seeing maps hanging on walls from our earliest schooldays also tends to confirm our misconception that the North is of necessity a distant prospect.

Orkney and Shetland have suffered and still suffer from popular misconceptions of this kind. In the British context they are indeed far from the capital, and looking at a map of Britain one can easily get the impression that these isles are the very end of the habitable world, a kind of Ultima Thule with nothing beyond, and in which nothing of interest is ever likely to have happened.

If we want to understand not only the history of the remote past but also the culture of the present day we must free ourselves from such misconceptions. Least of all will we be able to understand the folklore of Orkney and Shetland if we think of these isles as isolated outposts and look at them from the horizon of London or Oxford. The folklore of Orkney and Shetland is nothing less than the oral culture of these islands, and this folklore must be understood on its own terms.

Instead of being the northernmost outpost of Britain, Orkney and Shetland were for centuries southern extensions of Scandinavia, Norway in particular. But though allied with Norway, the Orkney Earldom also enjoyed a considerable degree of independence and self-government. Many of the Orkney earls were mighty rulers, holding sway over large regions of Scotland and Ireland. About Earl þorfinnr Sigurðarson the *Orkneyinga saga* says that he had in his possession not only Orkney and

Shetland but all the islands of the Hebrides, nine earldoms on the Scottish mainland, and a large part of Ireland.[1] The petty kings of Scotland, England and Ireland would then have to "look up" to Orkney, because their very existence was often dependent on the decisions that were taken, and the warlike expeditions that were planned, in the court of the Orkney earls. One must also bear in mind that the islands were in those times much more densely populated in relation to the mainland than they are now. Furthermore, travel by sea was until well into modern times so much faster and so much more comfortable than travel by land, that communications between, say, Orkney and Ireland were easier and faster than communications between, say, Kent and Oxfordshire. If we also take into account the superiority of the Viking ships over the relatively clumsy vessels the Anglo-Saxons and the Celtic peoples had at their disposal we will realize that the Orkney Earldom was a formidable naval power, backed as it also was by the forces of the whole of western Scandinavia. It would not be inaccurate to say that Orkney played a role in the North Sea similar to that played by Venice and other mighty Italian republics in the Mediterranean.

Nor was there much difference between Orkney and such southern countries in wealth and cluture. Many of the Orkney earls and their courtiers were among the most travelled men of their time. The rich literary and artistic heritage of Scandinavia was their own from the very earliest times but onwards from the 12th century, at least, they also had intimate contacts with Mediterranean culture. Poems reflecting *la gay science* of Provence were heard in the Nordic tongue in Orkney before such notes were struck in English, Irish or Welsh.[2] The building styles of the Kingdom of Jerusalem are reflected in Orcadian architecture, and the Kirkwall cathedral is still one of the most impressive churches in Britain.[3] It was built in honour of Saint Magnús, whose fame, equal almost to that of Saint Óláfr, spread all over Northern Europe, bringing pilgrims and wealth to Kirkwall.

The way in which the Orcadians themselves looked upon the rest of Britain as a kind of extension of the Norwegian naval empire, of which they formed a part, can still be clearly seen. This is why the second most northerly shire of Scotland is called Sutherland — since it is south of Caithness, which was regarded as part of Orkney proper. In a similar way the Hebrides were referred to as *Suðreyjar,* "the southern Islands", as opposed to *Norðreyjar*, Shetland and Orkney, which were also frequently referred to as *Eyjar,* "the Islands"; as if there were no other islands that merited serious consideration!

According to Old Norse sources it was Haraldr *hárfagri* who first annexed Orkney and made it a Norse dominion, at the end of the 9th century. Though there is much variety of opinion among historians and archaeologists, they now all agree, however, that the Scandinavian settlement of Shetland and Orkney took place considerably earlier, hardly later than c. 780-850.[4] The first earl is said to have been Rögnvaldr Eysteinsson, Mærajarl; the last earl of the Norse dynasty was Jón Haraldsson, who died in 1231. The succeeding Scottish earls, however, continued to owe allegiance to the King of Norway up to 1468-9. The Scandinavian language, Norn, continued to be spoken long after that. There were Norn speakers in Orkney up to the latter half of the 18th century and in Shetland there were still a few speakers alive at the beginning of the 19th century. Tens of thousands of Scandinavian words — many of which are still in common use — were recorded in Shetland and Orkney at the end of the 19th and the beginning of the 20th century, and the overwhelming majority of the place-names in the Islands are of Scandinavian origin.[5] The Norse character of Shetland and Orkney can hardly be over-rated.

Though the process of "Scottification" from the 14th century onwards did not only — as has sometimes been said — bring "dear meal and greedy ministers"[6] but also cultural elements, including folktales, legends, beliefs and customs, it is also true to say that the folklore of Orkney and Shetland is still fundamentally Scandinavian.

It is one of the greatest losses to Scandinavian folklore that the importance of Shetland and Orkney tradition was not recognized sooner and that it is still not fully appreciated. Only scattered fragments in the Norn language have been preserved, and though there has been a great deal of devotion and enthusiasm among the Orcadians and Shetlanders themselves, and though valuable collecting has recently been carried out under the auspices of The School of Scottish Studies,[7] Orkney and Shetland lore in English has not been systematically collected either. One of the pioneers, to whom special homage should be paid, was the Faroese scholar Jakob Jakobsen, who wrote a number of important articles and whose dictionary of Shetland Norn is a veritable goldmine for the study of Shetland beliefs and customs.[8] Hugh Marwick did similar work for Orkney,[9] but no injustice is done to the memory of this great man, if it is said that he was more of a philologist and less of a folklorist than Jakobsen. Some of the numerous printed collections of Shetland and Orkney tales and legends contain valuable material too,[10] but much is "fakelore", adapted, falsified and even invented by gentlemen antiquarians.

A great deal of this material is also scattered in obscure papers and periodicals and thus not easily accessible even to scholars. Systematic scholarly studies of Shetland and Orkney folklore are practically non-existent. Those which have been undertaken deal with isolated aspects of the subject. Some of the best work has been done by Scandinavian scholars. Outstanding folklorists who have understood the value of Orkney and Shetland material and who have used it for comparative purposes include Professor Dag Strömbäck in Sweden and the late Professors Knut Liestøl, Reidar Th. Christiansen and Svale Solheim in Norway. In view of what folklore studies could contribute to the understanding of the cultural history of Orkney and Shetland, it is nothing short of tragic to see how neglected the field has been. If one goes through the articles and the bibliography in Wainwright (1962), one will understand how much valuable work linguists, place-name scholars, historians, art-historians and archaeologists have done, and are in the process of doing, on Orkney and Shetland culture. But excellent though it is in these respects, the book typically enough contains next to nothing on folklore.

It would be foolish to try to repair this mistake here. Even if it were limited to the barest outlines, a survey of the Scandinavian folklore in Orkney and Shetland would fill several thick volumes, and such a work cannot profitably be written before all the material has been brought together, systematised and sifted, and before more collecting has been done. (Allow me the opportunity here to utter the usual war-cry of the folklorist about collecting: It is *not* too late! Much can still be done. Future generations will not — and ought not to — forgive us if we neglect to do our best now.)

In this paper I shall be concerned with the narrower subject of 'Scandinavian and Celtic folklore contacts in the Earldom of Orkney'. These contacts took place mainly between the 9th and the 15th centuries, though many of them, naturally, are reflected only in material collected in the last century and this. I shall, however, limit myself, with a few exceptions, to such contacts as are mirrored in sources in the Old Norse language: poems written by Orcadians, and sagas written by Icelanders but dealing with the Orkney Earldom and likely to be founded on Orkney tradition. Limited space will permit me to treat only some selected genres and examples. Before I proceed to do this, however, a few things will have to be said about the nature of the contacts between Orcadians — and henceforth I use Orcadians in the sense of inhabitants of the Earldom of Orkney, whether on the Isles of Orkney or elsewhere — and the Celts.

As we all know, the water between Orkney and the Scottish

mainland is called the Pentland Firth. This takes its name from an enigmatic people, the Picts — known to the Vikings as *péttar* — who lived on Orkney, Shetland and parts of the Scottish mainland before the arrival of the Norsemen. So little is known of the Picts that it is dangerous to assert anything about them. A few things have nevertheless been established with a fair amount of likelihood, mostly thanks to the brilliant scholarship of Professor Kenneth Jackson.[11]

It seems certain that the Picts spoke and wrote a language of their own, a non-Celtic and non-Indo-European language, which has not been deciphered. But they had also adopted a Celtic language, which in certain respects was akin to Brythonic, in others to Gaulish. To complicate matters still more, this language also seems to have contained a fair number of Goidelic loanwords — taken over from the Scottish Gaels, whose language was at this time indistinguishable from that spoken in Ireland. At the time of the arrival of the Vikings in Shetland and the Orkneys, Pictish culture in general was also in the process of being Gaelicised.

There were settlements of Gaelic-speaking monks, the so-called *papæ,* in many parts of Orkney and Shetland too. This is not only stated in the earliest Scandinavian sources, but is also well corroborated by the testimony of place-names and archaeology. The connections between the Scottish and Irish Gaels and the Norsemen in the Earldom of Orkney from the 10th century up to the late Middle Ages were close and manifold. *Orkneyinga saga,* for instance, gives a vivid picture of the different types of connection. This saga contains hundreds of Gaelic personal and place-names. Many of the personal names give ample evidence of intermarriage between the Gaels and the Norsemen, from the kings and earls down to the ordinary farmers. Thus, to give only a few examples, Earl Haraldr Maddaðarson was married to Hvarflöð (Gormflaith), daughter of Melkolmr, an Earl of Moray; and Maddaðr Melmarason (Moddan, son of Maelmuire) was married to Margrét Hákonardóttir, whose father was the Orkney Earl Hákon Pálsson; and a lady by the name of Frakökk Moddansdóttir was married to a Ljótr *niðingr* in Sutherland, and went to Orkney after her husband's death with Earl Haraldr Hákonarson, *inn slèttmáli.*[12] It is not possible here to say much more about all the marriages, treaties, banquets, feuds and wars in which the Gaels, the Norsemen, and the people who probably did not know themselves whether they were one or the other, were involved. It will suffice to say that *Orkneyinga saga,* though of course not reliable⁻ in details, gives a true overall picture of the state of affairs, except that by the very nature of its theme, it says too much about warfare and too little about trade and friendly connections. What we are likely to have had in the Orkney Earldom is thus a hybrid culture of a type similar to that which existed in the Hebrides, on the Isle of Man, and in the Irish Viking towns.

Consequently, when we speak of Celtic-Scandinavian folklore contacts in the Earldom of Orkney we are dealing on the one hand with the Orcadians, who were mainly of Norwegian origin, though there were also many Icelanders in Orkney, and on the other with the Celticised Picts and the Scottish and Irish Gaels.

Very little can be said about the relationship between Pictish and Scandinavian folklore, since the Pictish inscriptions — insofar as they can be deciphered at all — are short and factual, and the Old Norse sources are extremely reticent about the Picts. There is a fairly rich recent folklore about the Picts, taken down in the last centuries not only on Shetland and Orkney but also on the Scottish mainland and in Northern Ireland.[13] The material of this kind hitherto published is to a great extent unreliable, however, and it has not been properly studied.

Here I will limit myself to touching upon two examples of folklore about the Picts that are of special interest insofar as they occur in — or have parallels in — old Scandinavian sources.

In *Historia Norvegiæ,* a Latin history of the Norwegian kings, probably written before 1200 with English readers in mind, but in all likelihood by a Norwegian,[14] a description of Orkney is included. After having referred to the Gaelic monks, the *papæ,* the author goes on to talk about the other people who were on the Islands when the Norsemen arrived:

> Horum alteri, scilicet Peti, parvo superantes pygmæos statura instructuris urbium vespere et mane mira operantes, meridie vero cunctis viribus prorsus destituti in subterraneis domunculis præ timore latuerunt.[15]

Here we learn that the Picts, "who were hardly bigger than dwarfs in stature, worked wonders in building villages in the morning and evening, but in the middle of the day they lost their strength altogether and hid in terror in small subterranean dwellings."

This passage shows, among other things, what impression the souterrains, which were found also among the Gaels in Scotland and Ireland and are referred to elsewhere in Old Norse literature, made on the Vikings. It also shows that the Picts were no more than a memory by the time the passage was written, since it is, of course, a misconception that the souterrains were permanent living quarters.[16] Furthermore we find an early example of the process of supernaturalisation of the Picts, which has led to their equation with dwarfs and elves in later folk tradition. The most interesting of the motifs involved, however, is the idea that the Picts lost their strength in the middle of the day. I have not been able to find an exact parallel to this elsewhere. It is lacking, for instance, in Stith Thompson's *Motif-Index,*[17] where normally one seldom looks in vain. Is it only a strange coincidence, however, that the reverse idea, that the strength of certain people is increased towards the middle of the day, is found in Arthurian romance? Thus according to a French prose version of the Parceval story, Gawain's strength increased after noon, so that he never struck a knight without splitting him and his horse,[18] and Thomas Malory uses the same motif at least twice in *Le Morte d'Arthur.*[19] In view of the fact that so many of the motifs in the Arthurian romances are drawn from Celtic sources, can it be that what *Historia Norvegiæ* tells us about the Picts is actually a Celtic tradition?

The second example of folklore contacts between the Picts and the Vikings I quote from Jakob Jakobsen's article on Norse linguistic remnants on the Orkneys:

> On Rousay it is told, according to Duncan Robertson, Kirkwa, that the first Vikings who came to the Island did not dare to land, because of beings looking like elves or trolls who stood in front of them with shining spears.[20]

F. T. Wainwright, who quotes this legend — and it is about the only piece of folklore he does quote — says that it is "doubtful in age and origin" and calls it "a flimsy substitute for a genuine native tradition".[21] He is partly right in doing so, since his objective is to polemicise against scholars who have taken the passage as referring to an actual encounter between Picts and Norsemen at Rousay. But it is, of course, a misuse of folklore to try to deduce such specific facts from it, and no trained folklorist would attempt to do that any more than he would say that the passage proves that the Picts had spears, and that these were more shiny than those of the Vikings! But there is little reason to doubt that the legend, which has been recorded in many versions on the Orkneys, is an old and genuine Norse tradition. It clearly belongs to the type of story which describes how invaders are driven away by the guardian spirits of a country (Old Norse *landvættir).* The *locus classicus* in Old Icelandic literature is Snorri Sturluson's story of how the *landvættir* drove away a wizard who had taken the shape of a

whale after he had been sent out by the Danish king Haraldr
Gormsson to prepare an attack on Iceland. In this story, just as
in the Rousay legend, the failure of the attackers to land and the
army-like qualities of the *landvættir* are stressed. I have touched
on these legends and their counterparts elsewhere in Scandinavia
in another connection and have shown that they are attached in
particular to islands with steep cliffs.[22] In the case of the Rousay
story the idea that the Picts were of elvish stature was probably
welded together with a tale about *landvættir*. That may be why it
is not said that the defenders *were* elves or trolls, but that they
were "beings looking like elves or trolls".

But it is high time for us to leave the Pictish-Scandinavian
folklore contacts in the Earldom and turn to the Gaelic-
Scandinavian ones.

Heroic poems and tales are among the most outstanding Old
Norse contributions to world literature. Such poems and tales,
preserved in the *Poetic Edda* and in the so-called *fornaldarsögur,*
were written down in Iceland in the 13th and following centuries,
but were based on a much older oral tradition. Some of the
elements of this tradition were common to all the Scandinavian
countries and the Viking colonies in the west, and some also had
their roots in a tradition common to all the Germanic-speaking
peoples. But heroic tales were also a favourite literary and oral
genre among the Gaels, and among them the stories about Cú
Chulainn, Fionn Mac Cumhaill and other heroes can still be
heard from the mouths of living storytellers.

Anybody who takes the trouble to compare these literary and
oral stories in the Ulster and Fenian Cycles with those found in
Scandinavian and Germanic tradition about Sigurðr the Slayer of
Fáfnir, Helgi Hundingsbani, Ragnarr *loðbrók* etc. cannot but be
struck by the many strong similarities. The pitfalls for those who
would explain these similarities are many and varied, however.
The pattern of heroic life is similar all over the world; some
themes and motifs, such as the father-and-son combat, seem to
be a common Indo-European heritage; exchanges of tradition
may have taken place between the Celtic and the Germanic
peoples on the Continent, later to spread to Wales, Ireland and
Scotland on the one hand and to Scandinavia on the other — to
mention just some of the possibilities. Nevertheless there are a
number of instances where the similarities between Gaelic and
Scandinavian heroic tales are so close that the likeliest
explanation is direct loans in either direction; and this likelihood
is sometimes strengthened by the absence of the motifs outside
the Celtic-Scandinavian area. We should not, of course, imagine
that the Orkney Earldom was always an intermediary in the

exchange of such tales. There was also a direct Gaelic influence on West Scandinavian, especially Icelandic and Faroese, folk tradition, since some of the Scandinavian settlers on these islands came via Ireland and Scotland and had sometimes lived there and absorbed Gaelic culture. Nevertheless it is highly probable that much of the transmission took place within the borders of the Orkney Earldom. We must also bear in mind that we are dealing with oral tradition; consequently one and the same tale or motif may have been, and is indeed likely to have been, exchanged more than once, in more than one place, and at times separated by, perhaps, hundreds of years. When dealing with folklore one must rid oneself of the image of the book which is transported from one place to another — an idea that derives from the study of medieval literature. Oral tradition comes from a centre, but it spreads in streams and rivulets, as it were, flowing in many directions.

One of the heroic tales in the spread of which the Orkney Earldom is likely to have had a part is the story about how the secret of the hiding-place of the Rhine gold was lost. It is found in the Eddic poem *Atlakviða* and other Old Norse sources. These contain the motif, lacking in German versions of the story of the Rhine gold, that one of the two persons who know the secret tricks his enemies into killing the other, whereupon he triumphantly exclaims that he is now the only man alive who knows the secret and that he will never reveal it; shortly afterwards he is put to death by the enraged enemies. The same story — though the secret does not concern the hiding place of treasure but how to make a marvellous drink, mostly described as heather ale — is found in Ireland and Scotland in modern folk tradition. The northernmost examples of this legend have been recorded in Orkney and Shetland. The vast majority of the many versions, however, are in Irish or Scottish Gaelic, and there is little doubt that the form of the story involving the heather ale originated in Gaelic tradition. As I have tried to show in an article entitled 'The Viking Ale and the Rhine Gold',[23] there are nevertheless many reasons to believe that the Irish and Scottish folk legend is derived from the Old Norse heroic tale about the Rhine gold. I will not repeat all the reasons here. The one that is of most interest in the present discussion is that the episode is referred to in the poem *Háttalykill,* a *clavis metrica* illustrating a great number of different poetic measures, composed on the Orkneys in the 1140s by the Icelander Hallr þórarinsson and the Orkney Earl Rögnvaldr *kali.*[24] What share Hallr and Rögnvaldr each had in the poem's composition is not known; some scholars believe that the Earl was mainly responsible for the subject matter and the Icelander for the versification.[25] In view of the fact that the Earl is known to have been a good poet, however, I find this unlikely and feel inclined to side with those who think that Rögnvaldr and Hallr composed alternate stanzas, a theory that fits in with the fact that every poetic measure is illustrated by two stanzas, which also share the same subject matter. It may be mentioned, too, that there are examples of such poetic co-operation and competition in Provencal poetry,[26] and the Earl stayed in Narbonne on his way to Jerusalem and composed verses, showing traces of *amour courtois,* for and about an earl's daughter there.[27] Whatever the actual process of composition, *Háttalykill* could clearly never have come into being if the stories referred to in it had not already been well-known to an Orkney audience. It may also be worth mentioning that although our particular scene is not — as far as I know — found in pictorial sources in the British Isles, several other scenes included in the story of the Rhine gold are found on Manx stone crosses,[28] and if we take into account the fact that pictures from these stories are likely to have been found much more often on wall-hangings and other perishable materials than on stones, it would seem quite likely that illustrations of our particular motif were to be seen in many halls in the Earldom where Gaels and Norsemen met to celebrate, perhaps even at the wedding of Haraldr Maddaðarson and Hvarflöð Melkolmsdóttir or some similar occasion! I may also add that I have read some hundred additional versions of the heather ale legend and recorded it myself about a dozen times since I wrote my paper on it and I have found nothing to disprove, but rather a few things to confirm, my theory that it was borrowed from the Norsemen. Thus the version from Mícheál Ó Gaoithín, which I quoted from memory with certain reservations in my paper, but which I have since recorded, contains the heroic laugh, the idea of *hlæjandi skal ek deyja,* "laughing I will die", which is so prominent in *Atlamál* and other Old Norse heroic poems and tales.[29] If I am right, then, we have here an example of an Old Norse story transmitted to the Gaels through the Earldom of Orkney, to be turned into a popular legend, which then travelled back to Orkney and Shetland. Even if I should be partly or totally wrong in this assumption, however, I think I can say with a great deal of confidence that many folklore contacts between the Orcadians and the Gaels were of this intricate kind.

We do not need to go outside *Háttalykill* to find other examples of Gaelic-Scandinavian folklore contacts in the field of heroic tales. Stanzas 23a and 23b allude to the so-called Hildr legend. These stanzas illustrate a poetic measure, called *greppaminni,* in which the first four lines contain questions, the four last answers. Stanza 23a goes as follows:

> Hverr réð Hildi at næma?
> hverir daglengis berjask?
> hverir siðarla sættask?
> hverr siklingum atti?
> Heðinn réð Hildi at næma,
> Hjaðningar æ berjask,
> þeir siðarla sættask,
> saman Hildr liði atti.[30]

It appears from this that Hildr was responsible for the everlasting fight between the Hjaðningar. These allusions are fully understandable in the light of later versions of the story, told in Saxo Grammaticus's *Gesta Danorum,*[31] in Snorri Sturluson's *Edda*[32] and in *Högna þáttr* in *Flateyjarbók.*[33] As Snorri tells the story, Heðinn Hjarrandason had eloped with Hildr, a daughter of King Högni. Högni followed the elopers on his ship, finally caught up with them, and a fight — called Hjaðningavíg — which lasted the whole day, ensued. During the night Hildr resuscitated the fallen warriors on both sides, and so the fight has continued ever since, and will go on until the end of the world. In *Högna þáttr,* however, there is an addition: one of Óláfr Tryggvason's men, Ívarr *ljómi,* put an end to the fight by taking part in it and killing the warriors on both sides.

In *Háttalykill* we are not told where the fight took place, but this omission is easily explained by the compressed style of the narrative, and also by the fact that everybody was likely to know the location: the later sources all agree that the incident took place in Háey, that is to say Hoy, on the Orkneys.

Much has been written about the Hildr legend in particular, and about the so-called Everlasting Fight motif in general, by Alexander Krappe,[34] Margaret Schlauch,[35] Einar Ól. Sveinsson,[36] Gerard Murphy[37] and others.[38] The most recent contribution, perhaps, has been made by Michael Chesnutt,[39] who points to a series of close correspondences between the Hildr story and the Irish mythological tale *Cath Maige Turedh,* which may in its present form be as early as the 11th century. We are also likely to be on firmer ground before long, since Chesnutt is engaged in a detailed investigation of his text, and other forms of the Everlasting Fight motif in Old Norse sources are being studied by the Icelandic scholar Davíð Erlingsson. The matter is extremely complicated, because apart from the sources already mentioned — and an obscure allusion in Bragi Boddason's *Ragnarsdrápa,* which also refers to Hildr[40] — the motif of the resuscitating hag is found or alluded to in many Icelandic *fornaldarsögur* and similar works. There is, besides, a fair number of occurrences of the motif in Icelandic folktales.[41]

To refer to the motif as it occurs in all these sources as the Everlasting Fight — as has often been done — is in fact misleading. It would be better to call it the Resuscitating Hag, because in most versions the fight takes place only on three consecutive days, after which the hag is killed; furthermore the hag usually revives the fallen on one side only. The episode normally ends when the hero kills the hag and obtains the resuscitating ointment (or the like), whereupon he is able to bring back to life the fallen warriors on his own side.

From this it appears that the Hildr story may be regarded as a subtype within a wider complex. There can be little doubt, however, that this particular form of the motif spread to Iceland and Denmark via Orkney. Saxo Grammaticus's informants are here, as so often elsewhere, likely to have been Icelanders.

Other forms of the motif of the Resuscitating Hag, however, seem to have come to Iceland directly from the Gaels. In spite of the work in progress, it will be a long time before the spread of the motif is fully understood. One will not only have to examine all the medieval and post-medieval examples of the motif in Irish literary romances — and in Welsh and Arthurian literature — but also all the Irish and Scottish-Gaelic folktales and heroic tales in which the motif occurs.[42] This is an enormous task, since the Resuscitating Hag — unlike the Heather Ale legend, for instance — is not a single story, but a motif occurring in scores of different tale types. Because of this it has not been properly indexed and we are not in a position to say how many recorded instances of it there are in the folklore archives. I would imagine, however, that there are thousands rather than hundreds in the Archives of the Department of Irish Folklore alone. All this material will have to be classified and analysed before definite results can be arrived at. It will no doubt be found that many of these folk stories are derived from literary sources, but samplings I have made indicate that this explanation is not likely to hold true for all of them. It is quite probable that some had an oral existence that stretches back much farther than the 11th century, that is to say before *Cath Maige Turedh* and *Háttalykill* were composed.

In some Irish oral tales (and perhaps in Scottish Gaelic ones too, but this I have not investigated) one also finds the notion that only a mortal man can put an end to an "everlasting" fight in the fairy world. This motif, which is found in *Högna þáttr* (and elsewhere in Old Icelandic literature), is also likely to have been borrowed by the Norsemen from the Gaels. Within Scandinavia it does not seem to have spread outside Iceland.

These hints will have to suffice for the present. Though much is still unclear, I think we can be fairly confident that the Hildr story is an example of a Gaelic motif which spread to Scandinavia via Orkney, while other stories of the Resuscitating Hag complex exemplify a spread of Gaelic motifs to Iceland through different channels.

I shall now conclude these remarks about Gaelic and Scandinavian heroic tales with a couple of examples showing other types of connection.

It was not only the secular aristocracy in Orkney that took eagerly to such tales. The interest seems to have been just as great among the clergy. A typical representative of this class was Bjarni Kolbeinsson, who became Bishop of Orkney in 1188. He was an important man who acted as intermediary in a conflict between Bishop Jón in Caithness and the Pope, visited synods and had other official functions in Bergen and elsewhere in Norway, and who counted among his friends many cultured Icelanders, including the powerful family of the Oddaverjar.[43] Curiously enough, memories of Bjarni Kolbeinsson's father, the chieftain Kolbeinn *hrúga,* seem to have lived on in oral tradition in Orkney up to this century, for a ruin on the Isle of Wyre is called Cobbie Row's Castle.[44] The strange poem *Fornyrðadrápa* — also called *Málsháttakvæði* — has been attributed to Bjarni Kolbeinsson, and though this attribution is not entirely safe, it is, for a variety of reasons, very probable.[45]

It is not easy to say what *Fornyrðadrápa* is really about. At first glance it seems to be a hotch-potch of proverbs, proverbial sayings, and allusions to scattered incidents in heroic tales, *fornaldarsögur* and the like, very loosely strung together. A close study of the poem, however, reveals certain threads. *Fornyrðadrápa* can be characterized as a love complaint — echoes from Provence are not absent here, either. The poet was in love with a beautiful woman, who apparently left him and deceived him. The poet hints at his emotions, recalls the beauty of his beloved, complains about the unsteadfastness and fickleness of women, makes jokes about himself and expresses his desire for vengeance on the woman and her relatives, all in a curious mixture of humour and desperation. Many, if not all, of the proverbs and stories he quotes or refers to illustrate situations that are in some way or another similar to his own.

The *stef* or refrain of the poem alludes to the tragic love story between King Haraldr *hárfagri* and a Lappish girl, anonymous in *Fornyrðadrápa,* but called Snjófriðr or Snæfriðr in other Old Norse sources:

> Ekki var þat forðum farald,
> Finnan gat þó œrðan Harald,
> hánum þótti sólbjört sú,
> sliks dœmi verðr mörgum nú.[46]

Love was not a contagious disease in the old days, says the poet, nevertheless the Lappish girl made Haraldr lose his mind; he thought that she shone bright like the sun — the same thing happens to many a man now.

From the later sources (*Agrip*,[47] *Heimskringla*[48] and *Flateyjarbók*[49]) it appears that the King's madness manifested itself in two ways: he fell wildly in love with the girl at first sight (this the girl effected through a magic love potion), and exhibited boundless sorrow after her death. He sat day and night for three years watching her corpse, which, again due to magic, did not deteriorate. Though it is not quite certain, it would appear likely that Bjarni Kolbeinsson knew both these motifs.

We are dealing here with an early instance of belief in the magic power of the Lapps, a Scandinavian belief that is still found in Orkney and Shetland folklore, as well as elsewhere in Britain.[50] However, it has been demonstrated by the Norwegian folklorist Moltke Moe that the love-potion motif is of Celtic origin. Close parallels are found in Geoffrey of Monmouth's *Historia Regum Brittaniae* and its source, Nennius's *Historia Brittonum*, where the story about Hengist, the Anglo-Saxon chieftain, and Rowena, the daughter of King Vortigern, is told.[51]

The source of this part of the Snjofriðr story may then, as Moltke Moe supposes, be of Welsh origin and Geoffrey of Monmouth's or Nennius's work may have acted as intermediary. The love-potion story may, however, equally well have a Gaelic source. Possibly the love-potion motif was combined in a Gaelic tale with the motif of the inordinate love of a man for a dead woman — a motif occurring in continental legends attached to Charlemagne,[52] but which is also attested in Irish tradition.[53] I have, perhaps, complicated rather than elucidated the question of Celtic-Scandinavian contacts by leaving this problem unsolved, but the different possibilities have at least been indicated.

Let us go on to another reference to an unfortunate love affair in *Fornyrðadrápa*. In stanza 13 we read:

> Afli of deilir sízt við sjá,
> Sörli sprakk af gildri þrá,[54]

i.e. "Least of all can one try one's strength against the sea; Sörli burst from his great longing."

There are many heroes by the name of Sörli in Old Norse

literature, but none of them "burst" from love. However, Reidar Th. Christiansen has drawn attention to a ballad in Scottish Gaelic which elucidates the enigmatic lines in *Fornyrðadrápa.*[55] This ballad has been recorded fairly recently in four versions, all of them from the vicinity of Athole, a place referred to a number of times in *Orkneyinga saga* as Atjoklar, or something similar. The ballad is about a man named Seurlus, MacRigh Beirbhe (the son of the King of Bergen), who dreamed that he saw a beautiful woman with yellow tresses, with skin as white as snow, and with long, slender hands, who gave him a ring set with precious jewels. Seurlus's heart was filled with joy "as when the wind fills the sails of a fleet". When he woke up he could still feel the maiden's burning kiss on his mouth, the ring was there on his finger and he also caught a glimpse of the woman, who apparently was a mermaid, swimming away straight out into the ocean. Seurlus rushed down to the shore, threw himself into the sea and swam after her. But his strength failed him, he swooned and was carried to the shore by the waves and the wind. He was still alive, but in a short while his heart burst as well as "the ribs on both sides".

It seems likely that *Fornyrðadrápa* refers to these futile attempts of an enamoured man to pit his strength against the sea and to his "bursting". The source, however, cannot have been the Scottish ballad now preserved, which can hardly be much older than the late Middle Ages; it must rather be some earlier version of the same story.

The hero has a Scandinavian name in *Fornyrðadrápa*. Some of the motifs, such as the joy taken in seeing the sails of a fleet filling with wind and the violent reaction to grief, which latter calls to mind Egill Skallagrímsson's reaction on the death of his son Böðvarr,[56] have a Scandinavian flavour. Nevertheless other ingredients in the story, such as the dream visit from the other world, and the type of female beauty depicted, stand out as Celtic traits. Was this story originally Scandinavian or Celtic? Is not the likeliest answer that it was a product of a hybrid culture?

When dealing with the story of Snjófriðr and Haraldr *hárfagri* we have already crossed the border-line — which is not a very clear one — between heroic tales and kings' sagas. The latter is also a genre which the Gaels and the Norsemen had in common, though the Irish kings' sagas differ a great deal from the Old Norse. Apart from anything else, they are shorter and less realistic.

Orkneyinga saga, an Icelandic work based on Orkney tradition and written about 1190-1200,[57] though it deals with earls rather than kings, has many of the qualities of the Norse kings' sagas.

But it is hardly surprising that we should find Gaelic motifs in it too. Some of these belong to the field of folk beliefs, and I will touch upon a few of them in a little while. Firstly, however, I would like to draw attention to two incidents which have parallels in Irish sources.

My first example is found in chapter 5 of the saga and concerns the death of Sigurðr, the first Earl of Orkney.[58] He has been fighting with a Scottish earl named Melbrikta (Maelbrighde) in Mœrhæfi (Moray), but it has been agreed that the parties shall meet to negotiate a truce, each bringing forty men. Earl Sigurðr, who does not trust his enemy, comes with eighty men, but in order that this shall not be detected too soon, he has placed two men on each horse. As soon as Melbrikta detects the deceit a fight starts, and the Scottish earl and all his men are killed. Sigurðr cuts off their heads and attaches them to his saddle "in order to increase his own fame" *(til ágætis sér)* as the saga phrases it. But Melbrikta — who was not nick-named Melbrikta *tönn* for nothing — had a long tooth standing out of his mouth, and when Earl Sigurðr spurred his horse and galloped away triumphantly with the severed heads attached to his saddle, the tooth entered his calf and caused an infection from which he soon died.

The custom of cutting off the heads of slain enemies and carrying them around to boast about them was apparently very common among the Celts. In some of the references to this practice it is also stated more specifically that the heads were hung on the horses of the victors. Long lists of examples of this custom among the continental Celts as well as in Old Irish sources have been compiled and commented upon by H.M. and N. K. Chadwick and others.[59]

In *Orkneyinga saga,* however, the head-hunting and boasting motif has been combined with another: the head of a slain man avenges the former bearer of the head. The same combination is found in the Old Irish story about the death of King Concobhar Mac Nessa.[60] The brain of a Leinster king, Mesgegra, who had been killed by the Ulster champion Conall Cernach, had been mixed with chalk, formed into a hard ball and preserved, so that it could conveniently be boasted about on appropriate occasions. The brain was stolen, however, by a Connaught man who hated Ulster people, and as soon as he got an opportunity, he threw it at the Ulster king, Concobhar Mac Nessa. Though it entered his brain, Concobhar managed to survive for several years, but finally, when he heard the news that Christ had been crucified, he became so enraged that the ball fell out of his head; then a stream of blood gushed forth and Concobhar died. Thus the

The writer Ernest W. Marwick and his wife Janette

John D. Mackay, Headmaster of Sanday School

Leinster king avenged himself on the Ulsterman after his death. However, the Ulster king had the satisfaction of being the first Irishman to go directly to heaven: he was considered to have died a martyr's death, and was held to have been baptised in his own blood.

One need not assume that the tale about Mesgegra's brain is the direct source of the Melbrikta episode in *Orkneyinga saga,* but some such Gaelic story, perhaps in a more primitive form and without the hagiographic ingredients, seems likely to lie behind it.

Another incident in *Orkneyinga saga* to do with scorn and honour, though not with death, is connected with Earl Rögnvaldr *kali* (the joint-author of *Háttalykill).*[61] After his visit to Jerusalem he went to the river Jordan. Nothing is said about his devotions, unless the stark fact that he bathed there is significant. But we hear that he and one of his men, Sigmundr *öngull,* swam over the river, went to a place where there was some brushwood and twisted big knots in it, whereupon the Earl and Sigmundr composed some verses, the contents of which were very offensive to those who had stayed at home in Orkney instead of following the Earl on his pilgrimage. One of these men, who is not mentioned by name in the verses or described clearly enough for a case to hold up in court, but who is nevertheless likely to have recognised himself in the verses, seems to have been Sigmundr *öngull*'s step-father.

The verses stand very close to the type of calumnious poetry referred to as *níð* in Old Norse sources. More specifically, they are related to a sub-group of *níð,* called *viðáttuskáldskapr* in the Icelandic laws. This term is used about satirical poetry worded in such a way that a large group of people could be offended by it, while nobody could prove it referred to himself in particular. It is curious — and perhaps more than coincidence — that the Old Irish laws also have a name for such poetry.[62]

The twisting of knots in brushwood in order to shame an opponent, however, is the motif of most interest in this connection, since it has very close parallels in the Old Irish heroic tales about Cú Chulainn.[63] Apart from *Orkneyinga saga* this motif is found in Old Norse sources only in *Morkinskinna*[64] and in the parallel account in Snorri Sturluson's *Heimskringla,*[65] where the incident is also placed in the Holy Land, but where it is attached to the Norwegian king Sigurðr *Jórsalafari.* Louis Hammerich, who has dealt with this motif in an important article on Celtic influences on the Continent,[66] and who recognizes its Irish origins, has overlooked the instance in *Orkneyinga saga.* Finnbogi Guðmundsson, the editor of the most recent edition of the saga, takes the view that Earl Rögnvaldr tied the knots in imitation of Sigurðr *Jórsalafari*.[67] It seems to me to be just as likely that it was the passages in *Orkneyinga saga* which gave rise to the story in *Morkinskinna* and *Heimskringla*. Whatever the truth of this, the custom of twisting knots in brushwood in order to spite opponents might have spread to Norway via the Orkney Earldom. It is amazing — but typical of the mobility of the Orkney people — that they should observe Irish customs in the Holy Land!

We have already crossed the border-line between folk narrative and folk customs and beliefs. I will not have much more to say about Orcadian-Gaelic contacts in these latter fields, because the subject is both wide and poorly investigated. Nevertheless I would like to point out a few striking similarities.

Many omens of death, or apparitions occurring at or shortly after death, are common to Old Norse tradition connected with the Orkney Earldom and Irish and Scottish-Gaelic folklore.

The line in *Fornyrðadrápa* rhyming with *Sörli sprakk af gildri þrá* (discussed above) goes: *stundum þýtr í logni lá*,[68] that is to say: "A wave sometimes roars in a calm." The explanation of this saying can be found in *Orkneyinga saga,* chapter 47, in the description of how a wave suddenly and inexplicably arose in calm weather shortly before the death of Earl Magnús Erlendsson, who was to become Saint Magnús.[69] Waves as harbingers of death are frequently met with in Gaelic popular legends and beliefs.[70]

Other death omens and omens of ill-luck, for instance many of those connected with malfunctions of the body such as stumbling, sneezing and itching, are also shared by Scandinavian, Orcadian, and Gaelic tradition.[71]

The premonitions and apparitions which preceded the battle of Clontarf, some of which occurred or were seen in the Orkney Earldom, are described in great detail in *Njáls saga*.[72] Anne Holtsmark and others have drawn attention to the fact that beliefs about blood raining from heaven in anticipation of battles and deaths were common to both Celts and Norsemen.[73] In *Njáls saga* it is stated that the phenomenon was called *benregn* in other countries *(í öðrum löndum)*,[74] which indicates that the Icelanders must have met with the belief abroad. In *Eyrbyggja saga* the death of a woman from the Hebrides is foreshadowed by a rain of blood.[75] Anne Holtsmark has also thrown light on the Gaelic background of the mysterious weaving women appearing in *Darraðarljóð*,[76] a poem which, if we are to believe Walter Scott, was still known in the Norn language in Shetland in the 18th century.[77]

Among folk beliefs related to war is the special type of battle frenzy called *gjalt,* a word which occurs mainly in the phrase *verða að gjalti.* It has long been recognised that this is an Irish loan-word.[78] It occurs in *Orkneyinga saga*[79] as well as in several other Old Norse texts. In some of these other influences from Irish or Scottish-Gaelic tradition can be traced.

Certain magic practices, such as sitting under waterfalls in order to acquire secret knowledge, referred to by Bjarni Kolbeinsson in his *Jómsvíkingadrápa,* are more likely to have been taught by the Orcadians to the Gaels.[80]

While we can take it as reasonably certain that some of the beliefs I have mentioned were originally Gaelic and that the Orkney Earldom played a role in their dissemination, there are many other beliefs that the Gaels and the Scandinavians are likely to have shared before they met. But these, too, play a role in the Gaelic-Scandinavian folklore contacts. Whether the child of a mixed marriage learned a certain belief from his Norse father or his Gaelic mother, both of whom might have retained it from childhood, that belief was spread and strengthened. And when a Norseman found that a Gael believed in the same thing as he did, or *vice versa,* that must on the whole have led to a confirmation and vitalization of the belief. I would even go so far as to suggest that the common folklore heritage is part of the explanation of the unity that exists today among the peoples of the British Isles, and that the unity would be even greater, if this common heritage were properly understood.

The store of proverbs common to the Norsemen and the Gaels has a similar history. Some of these proverbs doubtless passed from the one community to the other, but a great many — probably the majority — were part of a common heritage. And even where there is no genetic relationship between the Gaelic and the Scandinavian proverbs, they often express the same values and the same type of wisdom. No doubt there is much to be learnt about the Gaelic-Scandinavian folklore contacts in the Earldom of Orkney from a close study of the Orkney proverbs in comparison with those in Scottish-Gaelic and Irish. But since only a fraction of these proverbs has been published, the full extent of any possible exchange cannot yet be properly assessed.[81]

I have unfortunately only been able to touch upon scattered examples of folklore contacts in the Earldom of Orkey. There are whole fields which I have had to ignore completely. Material folk culture, for example, with all its subdivisions — housing, settlement, land division, communication, dress, food, etc. — has been ignored. It is however fitting, while we are on the subject, that I should mention the important work done in several of these fields by a former teacher of mine, the late Åke Campbell of Uppsala.[82]

As I indicated at the beginning of my paper, I have also ignored all the contacts that can be traced only in folklore collected in recent times. There are no valid reasons for such an omission, except the limitations imposed by space and the fact that so little scholarly work has been done on recent folklore material. It was, of course, factors such as chance and the limited themes and interests of the old poets and saga writers that governed the inclusion and omission of folklore items in earlier times, and much that is only found in modern sources is likely to be just as old or older. In spite of all the work that remains to be done on folklore in the older sources, that collected in recent times is likely to yield the richest harvest in the future.

This is most obvious in the case of popular legends. Reidar Th. Christiansen was the folklorist who perhaps saw this most clearly. In several of his articles he has pointed to a series of close parallels between certain Scandinavian and Scottish-Gaelic and Irish legends, and has introduced the term North Sea legends.[83] It is not easy to account satisfactorily for these similarities. It may be that some of the motifs and legends are part of a common stock, but there can be little doubt either that the Norse and Gaelic speaking communities influenced one another, and that certain types and sub-types spread in either direction. A not inconsiderable part of this exchange is likely to have taken place in the Viking Age within and via the Earldom of Orkney. We obtain occasional glimpses of this process — in confirmation of our view — thanks to work like that done by Inger Boberg on the legend of the death of the Great Pan,[84] or by Brita Egardt[85] and Dag Strömbäck[86] on the nix in horse-shape. A study of the Seal Woman legend, which is being undertaken as a team project in the Department of Irish Folklore, also points in the same direction. But there are scores of such legends, each of them in hundreds of versions, which have hardly been touched by folklore scholars, and from which much is undoubtedly to be learnt.[87]

In the first of his O'Donnell lectures 1967-8, on Celtic and Anglo-Saxon Kingship, D. A. Binchy opened with some witty remarks about the founder of the lectures:

> The late Mr O'Donnell was convinced that the Anglo-Saxon invaders of Britain brought nothing with them but their language; everything else they simply took over from the

Celtic population. So far am I from sharing his opinion that I shall suggest . . . that one of the Insular Celtic peoples actually recast its traditional pattern of kingship after an Anglo-Saxon model. And I can only hope that as a result these venerable walls will not be haunted by Mr O'Donnell's protesting ghost.[88]

It will, I hope, have appeared that I share Professor Binchy's views and disagree with Mr O'Donnell, in so far as I do not believe that everything in Britain is Celtic. Still, I would not fulfil my duty as a folklorist unless I made some attempt to lay his ghost. It is true that it might have displeased Mr O'Donnell to hear that part of the Celtic influence on Britain consisted of stories and beliefs that the Celts had taken over from the Vikings; but I am sure that it would have pleased him and made him rest content to learn that some of the influence that the people in the Earldom of Orkney and their latter day descendants exercised, and will exercise on Britain, is a cultural legacy that they have inherited from the Celts.

Though it is high time that I concluded these scattered remarks, I would not like to do so without quoting at least one sentence in the Old Orcadian language and one in Gaelic. Since so little is preserved in Norn it is not easy to find anything appropriate, but I have finally settled on *Tara gott,* "It has been done", "It has been brought to its end".[89] The phrase is preserved as a kind of magic formula. It occurs, for instance, in a Rousay version of a popular legend about how witches sink ships — one of the North Sea legends which I mentioned before (there are versions from Iceland and the Faroe Islands).

Now we may translate the phrase into Irish: *Tá sé déanta.* I could hardly believe my eyes when I saw that this very phrase occurs in at least two Irish versions of the legend of the ship-sinking witch, in exactly the same context — as a summing-up after the magic act has been brought to its conclusion.[90]

On second thoughts, however, it is inappropriate to end a lecture on Scandinavian-Celtic folklore contacts with such an apparently clear cut example. For, as you have heard time after time, the work has *not* been done. As a matter of fact, it has hardly begun.

I am sure you will forgive me if I say that it is my fervent belief and my firm intellectual conviction that the culture of Britain would profit if all the excellent work on Celtic and Scandinavian philology done here, much of it in the University of Oxford, were complemented by more work on folklore, not least that of the Northern Isles and the Celtic-speaking peoples.

It is my hope that more academic research projects and more academic posts can be established in this field here in Oxford and elsewhere in Britain. If the institution I represent, or I personally, can give any help towards this end, we shall be more than willing to do so.

This is the advice and the promise I can offer to express my gratitude for the unusual honour that has been bestowed upon me — a Swedish folklorist with Iceland as a second homeland and Ireland as a third — with the invitation to deliver the O'Donnell Lecture for 1976.

CHAPTER 10

Pict, Norse, Celt and Lowland Scot
—A Thousand Years in the Melting Pot

William P. L. Thomson

Who are the Orcadians? — it is difficult enough to determine the proportions of Pict, Norse, Celt and Lowland Scot which make up the genetic inheritance of the present population, to say nothing of such exotic ingredients as the occasional Red Indian wife brought home from the 'Nor Wast' or English seaman who jumped ship in Orkney. But 'identity' is more complicated than that. At a very basic level, identity has little to do with race; a remarkable strand of continuity runs through all Orkney history from Neolithic times to the present day, based on the necessity of wresting a living from a bare and windswept land which only through generations of labour could be made to yield its innate fertility, and from a grey and hostile sea which brought equal rewards to those skilful enough to navigate its waters. In such an environment the impact of incomers cannot be measured simply by counting numbers. Over long periods, the Orkney way of life had a remarkable capacity for absorbing a steady stream of incomers but, on the other hand, there have been key points in history when relatively small groups have had a quite disproportionate effect. The way in which people weave their own images of the past and thereby create their own identity is also important. Do Orcadians think of themselves as members of one of the submerged sub-nations of Europe, at one time possessing their own language and political institutions, or have they come to believe that they are merely the inhabitants of a remote corner of Great Britain? These kinds of interpretations are likely to have more effect on how people think and how they act than the actual proportion of Norse blood which they may or may not have in their veins. Orkney is situated at a central point in the northern world and was open to the contrasting influences of Pictish, Irish-Hebridean and Norse culture. Its history largely consists of the working out of these different influences, but to see this in racial terms is to over-simplify what was in fact a highly complex cultural interaction, out of which emerged a society neither Scots nor Norse, but one with its own unique identity.

The relationship of the Norse immigrants to the previous Pictish population is a central theme in this book, and other chapters look in detail at the specialist evidence regarding the nature of the Pictish-Norse transition, often suggesting that the coming of the Vikings was not so violent as was at one time supposed. Here it is proposed merely to sound a cautionary note on the basis of place-names. Whatever the relationship of the Norse to the previous population, they certainly imprinted the islands with thousands of their own place-names, not just for farms, fields and minor features of the landscape which might be readily susceptible to replacement, but also for most of the main islands whose names in any normal circumstances might have been expected to persist. There is a distinct scarcity of Celtic names and, according to Wainwright's rigorous standards, there is not one single place-name which beyond doubt can be identified as pre-Norse,[1] with the one exception of the name 'Orkney' itself.[2] At face value, it seems that the Picts were totally erased from the map of Orkney.

However, just what numbers of dominant settlers are necessary to bring about place-name replacement is a highly controversial question. Despite the prevalence of Danish place-names in the north of England, it has been argued that the conquest of the Danelaw was accomplished by relatively small war-bands rather than a massive influx of new colonists.[3] The Norman Conquest of England, led by a not very remote relative of the Earls of Orkney, provides an even more obvious example of an invasion which had cultural and linguistic consequences disproportionate to the small number of invaders. The experience of Pictland itself is also relevant; at the same time as Norse was replacing the Pictish language in the north and on the fringes of the kingdom, Irish-Gaelic was replacing Brittonic-Pictish in the heartland of eastern Scotland, yet it is hardly to be supposed that the Dalriadic Scots exterminated the Picts or even outnumbered them. At that particular juncture and for reasons which are not immediately apparent, the Pictish language was peculiarly vulnerable to takeover.

What is different about Orkney is that, unlike eastern Scotland, Danelaw and post-Conquest England, no clear traces of its former inhabitants remain in its place-names. This certainly suggests that the Norse settlement of Orkney was a more thoroughgoing process. But it could be that the absence of remnant names is also due to our failure to recognise them. If the Orkney Picts had spoken an archaic non-Indo-European language, as has been suggested,[4] it is not to be expected that pre-Norse names would necessarily include recognisable Brittonic-Pictish name-elements. While the great majority of Orkney place-names are Norse, there are certain recurring elements for which no Norse explanation has yet been found, and the possibility that some of these are pre-Norse cannot be ruled out. On their arrival, the Norse may have found an unusually complicated linguistic situation; possibly both archaic Pictish and Brittonic-Pictish existed as spoken tongues, and it is even possible that Irish-Gaelic had begun to make inroads. The *Ravenna Cosmography*, written a century before the coming of the Norse, suggests that some such linguistic confusion was having an effect on place-names. Much to our loss, its puzzled author gave up all attempt to make sense of Orkney island-names, merely noting that different groups of people seemed to have alternative names for the same islands.[5] In these strange circumstances, a normal pattern of place-name development was perhaps not to be expected.[6]

Further evidence about the nature of the Pictish-Norse transition has been sought in a study of the origin of the little taxation districts known as ouncelands.[7] At first sight the system and its terminology appear to be entirely Norse and the distribution of ouncelands seems to map out the zone of Viking activity in the north and west of the British Isles. They are most clearly seen in the *urislands* of Orkney and Shetland but a similar ounceland-unit, the *tir-unga,* is to be found in the Hebrides and, less certainly, in the *treens* of the Isle of Man. However, the absence of any very clear parallels to the system in Norway itself, or in any of the lands colonised by the Norse, has led to a search for a pre-Norse origin. Hugh Marwick, despite his marked preference for a Norse explanation whenever he could find one, came to believe that the ounceland was based on the Pictish land unit known as the *davach.*[8] Other origins have been sought in the house-groupings in sixth-century Dalriada and in the obligations to provide oarsmen for royal galleys.[9] Further suggestions link the ounceland to a pre-Norse system of district chapels,[10] or else to the Shetland *scattald,* a somewhat similar type of district with socio-economic functions.[11] It has even been noted that there is a strong relationship between ouncelands and the spheres of influence of brochs in Dunrossness, Shetland,[12] although it would be difficult to replicate that relationship in most other areas. The whole question of the origin of ouncelands must be regarded as unproved, yet the balance of opinion has been that, whatever their function, they date from the pre-Norse period. If a system of district organisation could survive the coming of the Vikings, it points, not necessarily to peaceful colonisation, but at least to a takeover in circumstances which permitted the survival of Pictish institutions.

While the composition of the population as whole is a matter of conjecture, direct evidence about the earl's family can be found in saga. The brides of earls can be categorised as, first, local native aristocracy, second, more distant British royalty and, third, eminent Norwegians. Early alliances included the marriage of Groa, grand-daughter of Aud the Deep-minded, to Dungad, apparently a member of the native Caithness ruling family in exile in Norse Orkney.[13] These circumstances are sufficient to suggest that the conflicts in the north of Scotland were a good deal more complicated than a straightforward confrontation between Pict and Norse. In the next generation Grelod, daughter of Dungad and Groa, was married to Earl Thorfinn Skull-splitter,[14] and it has been suggested that this marriage brought subsequent Earls of Orkney within the *derbfine* or kinship group whose members were regarded as legitimate contenders for power.[15] Henceforth Norse Earls of Orkney, pressing their claims in Caithness, were not necessarily looked on as outsiders. Indeed there is little subsequent evidence of families identifiable as specifically native aristocracy or purely Norse; earls came to have many links with the nexus of Norwego-Celtic families inhabiting the frontier lands of Caithness and Sutherland,[16] for whom Norse-Gaelic bilingualism must have been the norm. More exalted brides were sometimes brought from more distant parts of Britain, and they included Eithne, daughter of King Cerbhall of Ossory in Ireland, wife of Hlodver Thorfinnsson[17] whose son, Earl Sigurd the Stout, was married to a daughter of Malcolm II of Scotland.[18] In contrast, the brothers, Earls Arnfinn, Havard and Ljot, were all consecutively married to Ragnhild, the sinister daughter of King Eirik Blood-axe,[19] and the strengthening of political links with Norway in the eleventh century was reflected in the marriages of Earl Thorfinn to Ingibjorg, daughter of the Norwegian nobleman, Finn Arnisson,[20] and Earl Paul Thorfinnsson to a grand-daughter of King Håkon the Good.[21]

Presumably such a marriage pattern, even at a more humble level, was not altogether typical of ordinary folk who must have been less mobile in their search for partners. Nevertheless a high degree of mobility was characteristic of the Viking Age, and there were frequent population movements involving Norway, the Hebrides, the Isle of Man and Ireland, as well as secondary emigration from the islands to Iceland. Even after what is usually thought of as the period of settlement, there were fresh infusions from Norway. In the tenth century Eirik Blood-axe and his sons periodically made Orkney their base for campaigns in Norway and in York;[22] in the eleventh century Kalf Arnisson and a sizeable following found refuge in Orkney after the killing of St Olaf at Stiklestad[23] and, at the close of the century, King Magnus Barelegs attempted to replace the earls and to set up his own Norwegian-backed regime in the islands; even in the twelfth century, Earl Rognvald Kolsson's invading force certainly included many of his fellow-countrymen, and its composition may indeed have been predominantly Norwegian.[24] No doubt many were happy to settle down with such a genial and successful leader. Immigration of individuals and smaller companies was also common; Icelanders were prominent at the court of Earl Sigurd the Stout, and the heterogeneous host which followed his raven banner at Clontarf reflected the demographic forces being brought to bear on the Orkney population. Even in the eleventh and twelfth centuries, the saga contains many casual references to individual visitors and immigrants from Iceland and the Hebrides; for example, Icelandic court poets were attracted by the patronage of Earl Thorfinn and Earl Rognvald, other Icelandic visitors included Hallvard who was present at the assassination of Earl Einar Wry-mouth,[25] and it is Holdbodi, the Hebridean, to whom the saga-writer was indebted for his account of the last hours of St Magnus.[26] Surprisingly, the saga contains fewer mentions of individual Norwegians.

The loss of Thorfinn's extensive conquests in the reign of his sons, the joint earls Paul and Erlend (c. 1070), must have reduced contacts between Orkney and the Hebrides. Orkney's political dominion was never again to extend to the west coast. The final stage in this separation was the transfer of the Hebrides to Scottish sovereignty following King Håkon's 1263 Largs expedition and, ever since that time, contacts with the Gaelic-speaking west have been few. As Hebridean and Irish connections weakened, new links were forged with both Scotland and Norway. Scots earls of the Atholl, Angus, Strathearn and Sinclair lines have been seen as the main channel for Scottish influence, but that is to over-simplify matters. The Atholl and Angus earls belonged to cadet branches of the Scottish comital families, and Earl Malise of Strathearn was in dispute with the king and was very soon deprived of his Scottish earldom. None held extensive property in Scotland, apart from Caithness, links with Norway were initially strengthened rather than weakened, and most of these earls seem to have put down their roots in Orkney.

The crucial period in the development of the new relationship with Scotland and with Norway was the long reign of Earl Harald Maddadsson.[27] His father was Earl of Atholl, closely related to the kings of the Canmore dynasty, and Harald was originally advanced as a pro-Scots candidate. However, he was raised in Orkney from the age of five and thoroughly identified with his Norse earldom, eventually aligning himself with the very rebel Scots he had been promoted to counter. The situation which Harald faced was the growth of royal power in both Scotland and Norway, where William the Lion and King Sverre were both eager to extend real control into peripheral areas and to convert the imprecise ties of the saga period into a more binding feudal relationship. Harald's ill-judged support for Norwegian rebels led to a crushing defeat of Orkney-Shetland invaders at Florvåg (1194) and, in the aftermath of the battle, he was forced to accept terms which permanently curbed the independent pretensions of the Orkney earls. In immediate post-saga times the relationship with Norway, far from weakening as is sometimes imagined, was at its most binding. However, Harald's dealings with Scotland followed a somewhat similar course, and a series of campaigns in which huge armies were brought into the north of Scotland, led by William the Lion in person, forced Harald to recognise the reality of Scottish rule in Caithness. Instead of the semi-independent Norse principality, there were now two feudal earldoms, and earls were required to perform a delicate balancing act, owing equal allegiance to the King of Norway for Orkney, and to the King of Scots for Caithness.

The development of the Norse settlements in Orkney needs to be seen, not just in its political context, but in terms of its economic circumstances. In common with other parts of Europe, the period up to 1300 was a time of population growth, an intensification of settlement, and considerable prosperity. In part, the underlying reason was climatic; it has been suggested that temperatures were at least 1°C higher than at the present day[28] and, in Orkney's cool and humid climate, a small variation might have had spectacular effects. During the terrible famine period of the 'Little Ice Age' in the seventeenth century, harvest failure occurred on average in one year out of three. In contrast, a change in temperature of the order which has been suggested might have the effect of reducing serious crop failure to about one year in twenty. This is the background to the flowering of the society described in the *Orkneyinga Saga* which produced sufficient surplus wealth to build the sophisticated medieval churches, keeps and halls now being identified by archaeologists, and indeed to finance the most ambitious project ever undertaken in Orkney — the building of St Magnus Cathedral.

In this period of growth, arable land expanded outwards from its original nucleus of *tunmal* (Old Norse, *tunvollr,* home fields) into the surrounding *townsland* which, unlike the older land, had the distinction of being held in run-rig and was liable to periodic redistribution. Round the fringes of the farming community there also developed a series of *quoys* or tiny enclosures. These originated from the management of stock, but the manuring of impounded animals enabled quoys to be temporarily cultivated as an extension of outfield, or even to be permanently settled as little hill-margin crofts outside the bounds of the older communities.

Internal division was a process greatly aided in Orkney by the odal system of land tenure whereby landed property was divisible among heirs, both male and female, the 'sister's share' being half that to which male heirs were entitled. At an early date, odal property was subject to certain restrictions designed to prevent property passing out of the family, and this probably prevented excessive fragmentation. However, by the end of the Middle Ages, all such restrictions had long since been abandoned. Even large estates seldom contained cohesive blocks of property, but consisted of a vast collection of scraps of land scattered across the parish, or even throughout the length and breadth of the islands.

The same processes of expansion and intensification of settlement can be traced in place-names. Primary Norse settlement can often be identified by *bœr*-names (Bea, Trena*by,* Se*bay*) and by *-bister, -staðir* and *-land*-names (Kirbister, Tormiston, Bigland), many of which are incontrovertibly early. The need for new names in the period of expansion was partly met by a large number of names indicative of division such as Mid-Bea, Everby, Nistigar and Isbister (respectively Middle, Upper, Lowest and East), but a further group of names are those once applied to part of the farm which now became separate holdings in their own right. These names included *-garth* (enclosure), giving rise to names such as Howsgarth and Suthirgarth, and *-akr* (field) which produced an *-igar* termination as in Thurrigar. While *-garth* and *-akr*-names mainly reflect the process of internal division, *-setter*-names tended to arise from the simultaneous process of outward expansion, and they often record a change from a pastoral to an arable land use. *Setter*-names even today are often located at no great distance from the hill, and a high proportion of them are compounded with name-elements which suggest either a marginal location or a pastoral function. Marwick discussed two related roots, *setr* a dwelling-place, and *sœtr* a shieling, and he rejected the *sœtr*-root,[29] but he was perhaps over-hasty to do so. Early forms of Shetland *setter*-names can sometimes enable a *sœtr*-root to be identified,[30] and the characteristics of many Orkney setters are consistent with peripheral pastures being brought into cultivation by a process of outward expansion.

It is often possible to measure the extent to which arable land expanded in the medieval period, at least approximately. Opportunities for growth were highly variable, hence the old *urislands* and their constituent *pennylands* became very unequal in size and value. Although they remained the basis for taxation, a new land unit, the *mark,* was used for purposes of buying, selling and renting land. Where the number of marks in the pennyland can be determined, this serves as an index of expansion. The most common situation was for a pennyland to contain four marks. However, the easily-worked machair-lands such as are found in Sanday and in other parts of the North Isles had been densely settled by the early Norse, and indeed by their predecessors, leaving little room for future expansion, hence pennylands remained small, usually containing only one mark or even less. In contrast, in parts of the Mainland where there were considerable opportunities to reclaim land from the hill, the pennyland might contain eight marks or even more.[31]

At face value, the pawning of the islands in 1468 by a Danish king short of the ready money to provide his daughter with an adequate dowry on the occasion of her marriage to James III of Scotland appears to have changed the course of Orkney history as a result of nothing more than a dynastic arrangement. However, at a more fundamental level, the impignoration was the political manifestation of changes taking place in Norway itself and in its relationship with its overseas possessions. By 1468 the period of expansion was over, and the whole structure of medieval society in the North Atlantic lands was in a state of disintegration.

In the twelfth century Orkney merchants, carrying corn to Norway, had been assured of a friendly reception[32] but, two hundred years later, they were less certain of a welcome. With the founding of the Bergen *kontor* (c. 1343), the Hanseatic merchants of the city of Lübeck came to dominate Norway's trade. The trading pattern of the Hanseatic League involved the northward transport of German grain to be exchanged for Norwegian stockfish.[33] The German merchants were themselves forbidden to trade beyond Bergen, and this prohibition extended to Orkney, the intention being that the trade of North Norway and the Atlantic colonies should be channelled through the Bergen *kontor*. It was a pattern ill-suited to Orkney's traditional exports. Whereas Shetland, which had fish to export and a need to make good a grain deficit, fitted easily into the trading pattern of the Hanse and developed a long-lasting relationship with the German merchants, Orkney's grain exports were in competition with German grain and were likely to face ruthless opposition.

Less favourable patterns of trade were compounded by the effects of the Black Death. Little is known of its consequences in Orkney, apart from the listing of Orkney in *Icelandic Annals* as being among the areas "ravaged" in 1349, but indirect evidence from later Orkney rentals suggests that the population loss may have been considerable. The economic and demographic collapse in Norway is well documented, and possibly a third of the population perished.[34] The combined effects of plague and Hanseatic domination resulted in the destruction of Norway's merchant class; there was a great reduction in the number of ships trading with Iceland, and eventually all contact was lost with the Norse colony of Greenland.

A further factor was the union of the Scandinavian kingdoms at the end of the fourteenth century which shifted the centre of gravity southwards and eastwards to Copenhagen. With Norway itself somewhat peripheral to the new power structure, Orkney now occupied a decidedly remote position, both in a physical sense and also in terms of Scandinavian priorities. Contacts across the North Sea were greatly reduced, and this led to a gradual strengthening of Orkney's trading contacts and political links with Scotland.[35]

Evidence of the depressed state of the Orkney economy is contained in the rentals of 1492[36] and 1500,[37] although by that time the worst was over and there were some signs of recovery. A feature of the 1492 rental is the large amount of land which had passed out of cultivation and was lying tenantless. More than half the arable land had been abandoned in the districts of South Sandwick, North Sandwick, Marwick, Birsay and St Andrews, while most other districts also showed substantial reductions.[38] The phenomenon of abandoned land was not confined to Orkney, but was widespread throughout northern Europe where falling grain prices led to a decline in arable farming. The situation in Orkney has close parallels with the Norwegian *ødegårder* (deserted farms) which date from the same period.[39] Difficulties in selling Orkney grain in an over-supplied

market and in the face of Hanseatic opposition are likely to have
been an important factor in the abandonment of land. But the
great extent which had passed out of cultivation suggests that
there had also been a substantial loss of population resulting
from the Black Death, or later recurrences of plague, and it is
quite in keeping with experiences elsewhere that population
recovery should have been very slow. It was with a shrunken
population and a shattered economy that Orkney passed into the
hands of Scotland.

The impignoration (pawning) of the islands in 1468, a similar
deal involving Shetland in 1469, the acquisition of the earldom
estate by the Scottish crown in 1470, and the transfer of the
Orkney see from Nidaros to the Archbishopric of St Andrews in
1472, all add up to a fundamental change in Orkney's
relationship with Scotland and Norway. At the time, it may or
may not have been seen by Denmark as reversible[40] but, at least
in retrospect, there is a strong sense that the impignoration was
merely the culmination of a long process of Scottish penetration.
Orkney earls had been inextricably involved in Scottish affairs
from the very first and they had always been susceptible to
political pressure from Scotland. Until c. 1353, and again briefly
from 1455 until 1470, Earls of Orkney had also been Earls of
Caithness, and so the earldom itself was a major vehicle of
Scottish influence. Some earls, possibly Earl Malise of Strathearn,[41] and certainly the Sinclair earls, Henry I, Henry II and
William, had been responsible for the introduction of a
numerous retinue of Scots followers and kinsmen. Many of these
incomers prospered and multiplied in Orkney and, by the early
sixteenth century, a dozen or more branches of the Sinclair
family were established as landed gentry, in addition to
innumerable lesser lines.[42]

The other main channel of Scottish influence was the church.
As early as 1320 there were complaints that the Orkney bishop
was following Scots practice in his refusal to levy the papal tax
of Peter's Pence and was consorting with "foreigners and
apostates" — namely Scots.[43] In 1369 his successor was similarly
criticised for his Scottish associates and had to promise that in
future he would surround himself with "good native men".[44] By
1450 it appears that the clergy were entirely Scots,[45] a fact which
probably reflected the great scarcity of clergy in post-Black
Death Norway. Since churchmen formed the literate part of the
population, further evidence included the adoption of the Scots
calendar as early as 1312,[46] and the appearance of the last
official document written in Norwegian in 1425[47] — forty-three
years *before* the impignoration. But national origins did not

Captain Robert Sutherland, Head of the Sea School at Stromness

A veteran of the Cape Horn run in the days of sail:
Captain David Peace, with relatives

Throwing up the Ba' at the Market Cross, Kirkwall

Two well-known figures in Orkney affairs; former MP Jo Grimond and
former Islands Councillor Alex. T. Annal

necessarily correspond to political alignment; in the last half of the century of Scandinavian rule the Scots bishops, Thomas and William Tulloch, were among the King of Denmark's most reliable supporters.

However, there is always a problem in knowing to what extent the upper strata in society — the people most readily visible in the historical record — were typical of the population at large. It may well be that Scottish influences were mainly confined to the clergy and members of the earl's retinue, and that the rural population was relatively unaffected. The last official document written in Norse may date from 1425, but nearly three hundred years later at the close of the seventeenth century, Norn still survived as a spoken language,[48] and even in the present century Hugh Marwick in his *Orkney Norn* was able to record a substantial part of its rich vocabulary.[49] An even greater continuity was preserved in the very fabric of daily life; Alexander Fenton's *Northern Isles*[50] demonstrates in enormous detail how Norse survivals continued to form the basis for the whole technology of rural life and Ernest Marwick's *The Folklore of Orkney and Shetland*[51] reveals a mental world where old habits of thought continued in story, superstition and folk-belief. The Norseness of Orkney survived, not in its earls and clergy, but in its peasant culture.

To describe the process by which Orcadians were subjected to Scottish influences, F. T. Wainwright invented the word 'Scottification.'[52] But it is important to recognise that there was an equally powerful process of 'Orknification' by means of which many incomers not only conformed in an outward way, but were completely assimilated. The Scottish Spences, Cromarties, Irvings and Browns were totally indistinguishable from the Orkney Fletts, Linklaters, Inksters and Rendalls. It is true that leading members of the Sinclair kindred moved easily between the islands and Scottish court circles but so, for that matter, had St Magnus and Sweyn Asleifsson. Nor did the Scottish origins of the Sinclairs lead to a severing of links with Norway; even after the transfer of political control to Scotland, while Lord Henry Sinclair held Orkney in tack from the King of Scots, his uncle, David Sinclair, served the King of Denmark as captain of the castle in Bergen.[53] Young Orcadians, in search of employment outside the islands, frequently engaged as labourers and household servants in Bergen and, as late as the period 1613-1650, seventy-eight people from Orkney were enrolled as citizens.[54] Of these, a substantial number had thoroughly Scottish surnames. The process of 'Orknification' had been carried to its ultimate conclusion — the Scots had become Norwegian!

Q

It is usually assumed that the pawning of the islands in 1468 ushered in a period of radical change when incoming Scots oppressed the inhabitants and destroyed their free odal institutions. But that was not the case — or at least not immediately. Under the capable and energetic rule of Lord Henry Sinclair[55] very little changed. The title of earl was gone and the Orkney revenues now had to be paid to the Scottish crown, but otherwise his relations with Scotland were essentially similar to those of his grandfather, Earl William Sinclair. The economy began to recover, abandoned land began to be re-occupied,[56] and Orkney enjoyed a period of peace in marked contrast to the turbulent conditions in the north of Scotland. Peace did not long survive Lord Henry's death at Flodden, and thereafter Sinclair struggled against Sinclair in a bitter feud culminating in the Battle of Summerdale (1528), in the aftermath of which Sir James Sinclair of Brecks briefly enjoyed more independence than earls had possessed since saga-times. As the Reformation approached, ninety years of Scottish rule had brought no major influx of immigrants and, despite several scares, there had been no real attempt to interfere with Orkney's Norse institutions or system of odal land tenure.

All that was to change, but the destruction of Orkney's traditional and distinctive society was the result of the Reformation rather than the impignoration, while its final downfall was bound up with the activities of the notorious Stewart earls, Robert and Patrick. The most immediate result of the Reformation was the dismemberment of the huge bishopric estate and the creation of a new class of immigrant landowners who were not so easily absorbed by Orkney society as the Sinclair kindred had been. Adam Bothwell, appointed Bishop of Orkney in 1559 on the eve of the Reformation, was one of the few members of the episcopate sympathetic to the reformers, but he was surrounded by a band of particularly predatory relatives, all eager for feus and pensions from the bishopric. The bishop's relatives, Bothwells, Balfours and Bellendens, were a new inter-related kindred with the well-defined characteristic that, for every member operating in Orkney, there was another, usually with a legal background, managing the necessary contacts in Edinburgh.[57] The estates they acquired from the somewhat reluctant bishop dwarfed the odal properties of the traditional gentry.[58] Orkney law, cut off from its Scandinavian roots, was withering and could simply be brushed aside; these new estates were to be held in feudal tenure without division among heirs "notwithstanding the laws and customs of the Country of Orkney to the contrary".[59]

The arrival of Robert Stewart,[60] bastard son of the late James V, further complicated the situation in Orkney. His possession of the earldom estate and what was left of the bishopric gave him a monopoly of power which aroused the enmity of the feuars of church property, many almost as newly arrived in the islands as Robert himself. Their Edinburgh connections provided an ear to government and a skilful web of oft-repeated complaints enmeshed Robert and later his son — the earls altered weights, increased taxation, made arbitrary laws, packed assizes, confiscated property, imprisoned their enemies, engaged in piracy, manipulated the currency, had treasonable dealings with Denmark and generally oppressed the inhabitants of the islands. It is a damaging catalogue, but it is worth remembering that the charges, although frequently repeated and sometimes investigated, were never proved. To some of these charges, a reasonably adequate defence could probably have been offered, but neither Robert not Patrick had an opportunity to defend themselves. When Patrick was executed in 1615, he had been condemned, not on the basis of these charges, but for his part in the recent rebellion. Many of the accusations stemmed from differences between Orkney law and Scots law — far from destroying native law, as is often supposed, Robert and Patrick laid themselves open to attack by using it. The downfall of Earl Patrick inevitably brought about the destruction of what was left of the system; even before the final capture of the Castle of Kirkwall, an Act of the Privy Council abolished "foreign laws" in Orkney and Shetland and enjoined magistrates to use "the proper laws of the kingdom".[61]

The Reformation and the era of the Stewart earls was undoubtedly the most significant period of Scottish penetration. Peter Anderson's *Robert Stewart* contains an interesting appendix listing 176 servitors of the earl whom he has been able to identify[62] and it may be imagined that other lesser people left no trace on the record. Families like Bellendens and Balfours were on a more modest scale also accompanied by their servants, kinsmen and supporters. In terms of numbers, the immigration may not have been so different from the influx which accompanied certain previous earls, but its effect was certainly greater. The new men were associated with new forms of land tenure; they were not assimilated to the traditional gentry — they replaced them.

The downfall of the Stewart earldom and the destruction of Kirkwall Castle was a moment of enormous significance. As Storer Clouston wrote, "the history of the *country* of Orkney ends, and the annals of a remote Scottish *county* begin."[63] The final rebellion on behalf of Earl Patrick had commanded a wide measure of support in Orkney but, in the long run, a system of government which depended on the dictates of an over-mighty nobleman with outdated quasi-feudal pretensions had little to commend it. In many ways, the final destruction of what was left of Orkney law was equally unregrettable; it was no longer a fully operational system of Norse law, but a confused concoction of Scots and local practices,[64] corruptly administered by earls who exploited its inconsistencies to their own advantage. What was to be regretted was not so much what these institutions were in Earl Patrick's time, or even what they had been, but what they might have become. Alone of the lands once colonised by the Norse, Orkney was unable to preserve its own political identity in the way that was possible in Iceland, Faroe and the Isle of Man.

A persistent trend from the time of Earl Patrick right through to the 1914-18 War was the concentration of land in ever fewer hands. These centuries saw the development of the landed estate, not just as an economic unit, but also as a social structure within which most Orcadians lived out their lives. This concentration of landownership in part reflected the difficulty which owners of small odal properties had in maintaining their unwritten right to their land. By the end of the Victorian Age, owner-occupiers were few and 90% of Orkney farms were tenanted.

During this long period of estate creation the nature of landownership, and even the motives for owning property, underwent a series of changes. Earl Patrick was the last to regard the islands as a feudal power-base and, after his removal, governments were slow to trust any individual with the same dangerous monopoly of power. For most of the seventeenth century the earldom estate, and sometimes the bishopric, was given out in a series of short tacks to the highest bidder. These tacksmen perhaps lacked the trappings of power which surrounded the Stewart earls, but they had even less interest in the long-term welfare of the islands. Short tacks led to notoriously bad management, the taking of quick profits, and the fossilisation of archaic agricultural practices. In the eighteenth century this system of rent-farming gave way to landowning for political motives; the Earls of Morton and their successors, the Dundas family, were preoccupied with the control of the parliamentary seat, while lesser lairds accumulated land to qualify for the vote and thereby to share the patronage which their vote might earn. Yet most Orkney estates were small, and landowning was seldom divorced from trade. Merchant-lairds had a need to dispose of the rents which they received in kind, they developed shipping interests, and were experts in selling their produce throughout northern Europe and finding profitable cargoes (not always legal ones) to supply their retail businesses.[65] Their actitivities are described in more detail in Chapter 11.

Landowners of this kind were ideally placed to benefit from the great kelp boom which for fifty years (1780-1830) dominated the economy of Orkney.[66] Orkney lairds reaped undreamt-of profits from shores rich in seaweed, a numerous and subservient tenantry, and a business acumen which enabled them to search out the most profitable outlets. When kelp collapsed in spectacular fashion, there was a brief period of depression before the agricultural advances of the mid-nineteenth century. Orkney's Agricultural Revolution (1848-1880) was a period of compressed and intense change which in a single generation re-drew the landscape, abolished common land, and revolutionised the economy.[67] At the same time, agricultural change introduced new expectations and values, in the process sweeping away a good deal of traditional folklore, language and culture. The relationship of kelp fortunes to agricultural investment was not direct; money from kelp was seldom used to improve land, but kelp profits and the fruits of eighteenth-century patronage provided Orkney landowners with army commissions and lucrative East India Company places for their sons who eventually returned to Orkney with incomes independent of their estates and sufficient capital to undertake ambitious improvements. But the fact that they had made their careers outside the islands resulted in lairds becoming a somewhat exotic species; their wealth and their Victorian upper-class habits of thought created a widening gulf between landlord and tenant. When agriculture became less profitable after 1880, and as investment declined, lairds were increasingly seen as an obstacle to further agricultural improvement. A crisis of confidence in landowning led to the break-up of big estates in the decade 1920-1930; in the course of a few years, land monopolies so lovingly built up over three centuries were demolished, and the way of life centred on the big estate was replaced by a society of 'odallers', or their modern equivalent. The nefarious feudalising of incoming Scots had never achieved change on this scale.

Chapter 13 takes up the story of how the modern Orkney identity grew out of the nineteenth-century Agricultural Revolution and the twentieth-century 'Ownership Revolution'. The new identity was built on a way of life which combined a pride in careful farming with long hours of unremitting labour for a meagre return as debts for farm-purchase were paid off and the necessary capital was accumulated to invest in stock and new farm buildings. At the same time Orkney became much more purely agricultural than it had ever been in the past; kelp-making, linen-spinning, straw-plaiting, whaling and service with the Hudson's Bay Company no longer provided diversification in the economy, shipping interests contracted to vanishing point, and the scale of fishing was greatly reduced. In the late twentieth century, further changes are already in progress; the number of agricultural holdings is now less than half the total which existed at the beginning of the century, and employment in agriculture is vastly diminished. While agriculture is likely to remain the backbone of the economy, it will never again in the foreseeable future employ more than a minority of Orcadians. Oil provides no more than a short-term palliative, and most Orcadians have a somewhat ambivalent attitude to the undoubted potential which exists for tourist development.

Orkney's recorded history began a thousand years ago with a period of population mobility and a great influx of new settlers. The society of the late twentieth century is also characterised by mobility, and it has already seen more immigration than at any single point since the Viking Age. Orkney, until about 1960, was a relatively self-contained community — indeed as it became more purely agricultural, it had been becoming more self-contained. Incomers were few, they tended to be drawn from the east and north-east of Scotland and to belong to certain well-defined categories such as ministers, doctors, teachers and civil servants. In contrast, the 1981 census revealed no less than 1,500 people born in England and Wales out of a total population of 19,040, and they were engaged in a much wider spectrum of employment. If natives sometimes grumble about the strange and unfamiliar ways of these 'New Orcadians', they can reflect that the Picts were probably none too happy about the effect of the Vikings on their old and settled community.

CHAPTER 11

The Lairds and Eighteenth-Century Orkney

R. P. Fereday

In eighteenth-century Orkney the twenty or thirty leading heritors or landed proprietors important enough to be described as lairds or landed gentry were a closely-knit local élite. Whether they be regarded as the cream or the scum of their little world, as benevolent despots or as petty tyrants, there is no doubt of their important role in economic management and social control. For better or for worse they dominated an Orcadian population which, by 1750, numbered about 23,000 people, nearly 2,000 of whom lived in the royal burgh of Kirkwall.[1]

Neither the lairds of the early eighteenth century, with their Scottish connections stretching into the past, nor the lairds at the end of the century, with their hopes of anglicization, made any claims to be Orcadian and they would have indignantly rejected any close association with the mass of the island population. Nevertheless they had links with the islands and the common folk which were in some respects stronger than in the two preceding centuries. Generations of residence and intermarriage had formed the Scottish lairds into a kindred with many roots stretching down into the lower levels of society. While lairds spent more time resident on their estates than elsewhere, they remained in contact with merchants and ministers, factors and grieves, tenants and servants.

Lairds had a shared experience of recent gains. Between 1660 and 1750 the number of heritors in Orkney had fallen from 776 to 245. Only 8 small properties had been taken into the Earldom estate; all the other 523 had been absorbed into the lairds' estates.[2] Lairds had a distinctive life-style and status. They spent summer in their two- or three-storey mansion houses, each with its walled vegetable garden sufficient to feed a large household, with mill, cornstore and landing-place nearby; they spent winter in their town houses along the Kirkwall street, living cheek by jowl with merchants and officials, mixing in social activities and exchanging hospitality.

Orcadian lairds were merchant lairds, levying rents in kind and shipping grain to Scotland, Ireland, Shetland, Norway and the Baltic. Most of them smuggled or tolerated smuggling: many were able to profit from stranded whales or shipwrecks. By the middle of the century, some of them were deriving a new and gradually increasing income from the manufacture of kelp, which they shipped mainly to the Tyne. Others profited from flax growing and spinning, especially in co-operation with Andrew Lindsay, the Kirkwall agent of the British Linen Company.[3]

Though, in the first half of the century, most lairds were inclined to Episcopalian and Jacobite sentiments, they were much more interested in island politics and personal aggrandisement. They sought to extract as much rent and labour as they could from their tenants and farm servants. They were eager to swallow up the property of the remaining udallers (i.e. freeholders) or obtain land from neighbouring lairds who were incapable or unfortunate. They strove to curb, subordinate and eventually exploit the authority of the Presbyterian ministers. Above all, except for those bound to the Earl of Morton by kinship or patronage, they hoped to reduce or evade the burden of scat payable to their feudal superior.[4]

The lairds had an ambivalent attitude to the absentee superior whose officials controlled the Earldom and Bishopric estates and the politics of county and burgh. On the one hand, the superior was the natural source of protection and patronage, a natural channel of communication with the people above. On the other hand, only a favoured few benefited much from the limited patronage available, while nearly all the lairds were irked by the scat or feu duties exacted from them. Anti-Mortonian attitudes were evident during the 1745-6 rebellion and in the long-drawn-out Pundlar Process in which a dozen lairds challenged the validity of the weights used to measure the payments to their superior.[5]

In 1766 the 14th Earl of Morton sold the Earldom estate in Orkney and Shetland to Sir Lawrence Dundas of Kerse who, in 1775, obtained a grant of the Bishopric estate from the Crown. Yet Sir Lawrence's generous patronage only whetted the appetites of recipients, and the Dundases of Kerse proved less successful than their predecessors in maintaining their hold over island politics. In the late eighteenth century and early nineteenth century the lairds reached their zenith, and between 1790 and

The house of Clestrain, Orphir, where John Rae was born

The old house of Cursetter, Firth

Westness House, Rousay

Melsetter House in the island of Hoy

Four members of the Moodie family of Melsetter: above left is Capt. James Moodie RN., the 7th laird, above right the 9th laird, Major James Moodie

A country corner: by the Brig o' Waithe, Stenness

In the town: the Double Houses, Stromness

1818 Orkney was represented in Parliament not by nominees of the absent superior but by absent lairds.[6]

A few Orcadian lairds achieved this pinnacle of influence because they were enriched by the kelp boom of 1780-1830 and because they ceased to be Orcadian. In the second half of the eighteenth century, primed by a little patronage, an increasing number of lairds' sons seized the opportunities created by Britain's colonial wars and imperial expansion. The two most successful careerists were William Honyman (1756-1825), an advocate in Edinburgh who became a Lord of Justiciary and a baronet, and John Balfour (1750-1842), who made a fortune in Madras and increased it in London. Honyman and Balfour allied with Henry Dundas of Arniston, grand master of the British patronage network, and the Dundases of Kerse did not regain a share in choosing Orkney's MP until 1818 and did not re-establish full political control until 1837.[7]

Directly or indirectly, nearly every laird in eighteenth-century Orkney was descended several times over from avaricious and enterprising Scottish settlers. Some of these Scots obtained large feus of bishopric land in the sixteenth century.[8] Other Scots acquired estates in the seventeenth century as relatives of bishops, as holders of high office in the islands or as successful merchants in the Royal Burgh of Kirkwall. All these originally Scottish families intermarried among themselves, with the ministers of the Church of Scotland and with families of Norse or Scottish descent that had been established in Orkney long before the sixteenth century.[9] About a dozen 'Scottish' families continued to be prominent landowners until the twentieth century; a dozen others were absorbed, died out or were sold up, and their places were taken by a dozen or so additional families, local or incoming, who achieved the status of lairds during the eighteenth and nineteenth centuries.

Nearly four hundred years of Orkney's history was occupied by the appearance, evolution, dilution and eventual dissolution of the lairds' estates. The eighteenth century is central to this epoch, being equidistant from the legalistic land-grab of the Reformation and the decline of landlordism in the age of democracy and bureaucracy. The lairds of the eighteenth century were quite as far removed from witchcraft and torture as from the Crofters' Commission and the Welfare State.

The Bellenden, Moodie and Balfour families, who had received lands from Bishop Bothwell in the 1560s, were all prominent in the eighteenth century. The Bellenden or Ballenden line lasted less than two centuries in Orkney, the Stenness estate

being sold by the bankrupt William Ballenden in 1744.[10]
Ballenden was vicious and improvident, but his defects of
character and his shortage of cash can be attributed partly to his
termagant mother, Christiana Crawford, whose widow's annuity
continued despite her second marriage.

Moodies of Melsetter in Walls were conspicuous in the first
half of the eighteenth century. The unscrupulous Captain James
Moodie, 6th of Melsetter, had most of the attributes of
Rashleigh Osbaldistone in Scott's *Rob Roy*. He exploited the
confusion of 1715 to become the MP for Orkney (1715-22) and it
took a very determined effort on the part of the Earl of Morton
to regain control of the parliamentary seat. Reverting to his true
colours, Moodie joined the Jacobites in exile and was last heard
of in Venice when Casanova was an impressionable youth. The
rumbustious and Hanoverian Captain James Moodie RN, 7th of
Melsetter, who displaced his nephew and namesake after a very
stormy career, was an autocratic version of Smollett's Tom
Bowling in *Roderick Random*. The old sea-dog fell mortally
wounded during an affray in Broad Street (1725) but his son,
Captain Benjamin Moodie (b. 1723, d. 1769), 8th of Melsetter,
had the satisfaction of arresting his father's enemy as a rebel in
1746 and burning the houses of Jacobite lairds who remained in
hiding.[11] The victims complained ruefully that Moodie was
"either a near relative or intimate acquaintance of every one of
us."[12]

Benjamin had thirteen children and his successor, Major
James Moodie (b.1757, d. after 1815), 9th of Melsetter, had
seven children. Launching so many young people into careers or
marriage proved very expensive, and by the early nineteenth
century the estate was burdened with debt. Benjamin Moodie
(b. 1789 or 1790, d. 1856), 10th of Melsetter, emigrated to South
Africa and soon sold the estate for £26,000 to his brother-in-law,
Robert Heddle, who had made a fortune in West Africa.[13]

Unlike the Moodies, the Balfours of Trenaby in Westray were
at a low ebb in the early decades of the eighteenth century, but
later rose to heights of power and pride. John Balfour, 1st laird
of Trenaby, only succeeded to a portion of his father's estates in
1706 and did not even own the increasingly ruinous Noltland
Castle which had been built by the first Balfour in the 1560s.
William Balfour (1719-1786), 2nd of Trenaby, after involvement
with the Jacobite raiders and the burning of Trenaby by
government troops (1746), seemed a bankrupt failure, wasting his
talents in decades of vain opposition to the Whig Earl of
Morton. However, when Sir Lawrence Dundas purchased the

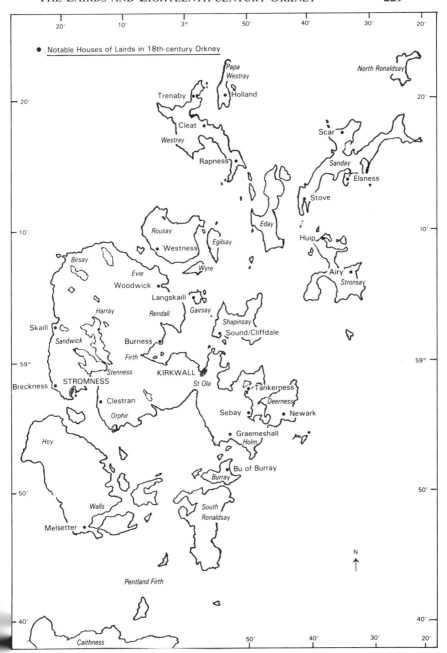

Fig. 43. Some 18th-century lairds' houses

Earldom estates (1766), William Balfour achieved a poacher to gamekeeper promotion and became the new superior's factor, first in Shetland and then in Orkney.[14]

Helped initially by the patronage of Sir Lawrence, the three sons of William Balfour were remarkably successful. John Balfour (b. 1750, d. 1842), 3rd of Trenaby, amassed a fortune in India, became a London capitalist with a house in Curzon Street, Mayfair, and a country residence near the village of Charlton, and twice represented his native islands in Parliament. Colonel Thomas Balfour (b. 1752, d. 1799) married an Earl's sister, built a Georgian house named Cliffdale at Elwick, Shapinsay, and raised two regiments of Fencibles.

David Balfour (b. 1754, d. 1813), became a Writer to the Signet in Edinburgh, a friend of General Sir John Moore, a householder in Charlotte Square and, like Walter Scott, invested in land neighbouring the Duke of Buccleuch's estate. During nearly forty years David acted as legal, commercial and political agent for first his father, and then his brothers and his nephew.

Captain William Balfour RN (b. 1781, d. 1846), 4th of Trenaby, managed his uncle John's lands and purchases in Orkney for many years before he inherited them. The Captain had fifteen children, twelve of whom became adults, yet enough of their great-uncle's money was spent in Orkney to make considerable impact. David Balfour of Balfour (b. 1811, d. 1887), 5th of Trenaby, built Balfour Castle (1847) and revolutionised farming in Shapinsay, his brother William Balfour (b. 1813, d. 1871) built Berstane House (1850), and trustees supervising John's endowments founded the Balfour Hospital in Kirkwall.[15] Most of the money for these projects had originally been derived from trade on the Coast of Coromandel or from the taxation of peasants in Tanjore. Eighteenth-century exploits and exploitation raised the family's prestige in nineteenth-century Orkney to new heights, and later Balfours did nothing in particular so very well that their decline was not apparent until the mid-twentieth century. The end came swiftly. The last laird, a convivial man who married four times, sold most of his property in the 1950s. He died childless in 1961 and his ashes were buried on the grave of his dog in the grounds of Balfour Castle, just over four hundred years after the murderous Gilbert Balfour had arrived in the islands.

The Traills, descended from trusted servants of Earls Robert and Patrick Stewart, had seven or eight branches flourishing by the eighteenth century and were by far the most numerous family group of landed gentry and Kirkwall merchants. Their importance in the Royal Burgh is revealed by a list of provosts from the late seventeenth century until the early nineteenth century.[16]

George Traill	1695-1698
David Traill	1698-1710
Andrew Young	1710-1712
David Traill	1712-1718
John Covingtrie	1718-1730
James Traill	1730-1733
George Traill	1733-1737
James Baikie	1737-1764
John Riddoch	1764-1784
William Lindsay	1784-1788
Robert Laing	1788-1792
Thomas Traill	1792-1810

Even those provosts who were not named Traill usually had close connections with the family. Thus John Covingtrie's first wife was Nicola Traill, daughter of James Traill of Westove, and James Baikie's sister Barbara married David Traill of Sabay. In 1719 there were five Traills among Provost John Covingtrie's twelve councillors, and George Traill of Hobbister was chamberlain of the Earldom estate.[17] This surfeit of Traills and the number of their town houses along Kirkwall's street provoked ribald comment.

Traills up the toon,
Traills doon the toon,
Traills in the middle.
De'il tak the Traills' guts
For strings to his fiddle.[18]

The chief estates owned by Traill lairds were Westness and Frotoft in Rousay, Tirlet in Westray, Holland in Papa Westray, Elsness in Sanday, Westove centred on Scar in Sanday, Hobbister in Sanday, Woodwick in Evie, and Sabay in Toab. Of course these lairds owned other property as well. Thus in 1727 James Traill of Woodwick also held North Ronaldsay while Traills of Elsness and Sabay both possessed lands in Stronsay.

The mansion houses of John Traill of Westness and John Traill of Elsness were among those burned in 1746 when their owners failed to appear and explain their declarations of sympathy for the Jacobite cause. The plunder of their estates and the hostility of the Earl of Morton and his officials meant that some Traills were not so prominent in public affairs during the generation after the rebellion.

In the later eighteenth century the Traills of Hobbister gained

importance by acquiring property in Caithness. After the Rev.
George Traill (b. 1719) had failed to obtain preferment from the
Earl of Morton, he became minister of Dunnet on the other side
of the Pentland Firth and purchased Castlehill.[19] His son, James
Traill (b. 1758, d. 1843) trained as an advocate, married Lady
Janet Sinclair (1784) and was appointed Sheriff-Depute of
Caithness (1788). He purchased the lands of Ratter, made many
agricultural improvements and by 1819 owed John Balfour no
less than £14,000.[20] Fortunately for Traill, the profits of the
quarries supplying Caithness flagstones to pave the expanding
cities of Britain cleared his debts, made him a rich man and
removed the need to dispose of his island property. His political
interests straddled the turbulent waters of the Firth and he
remained a close ally of the Balfours who had lent him money
and found him contracts in London. George Traill (b. 1787, d.
1871) of Hobbister, Castlehill and Ratter at first cherished his
father's friends and was MP for Orkney and Shetland (1830-35)
before he represented Caithness (1841-68).[21]

Other Traills went further afield. Lairds with small estates and
large families had every incentive to send their sons to seek
intellectual eminence in Edinburgh or fame and fortune in war
and empire. Thomas Stewart Traill of Tirlet (b. 1781, d. 1862)
became Professor of Medical Jurisprudence at Edinburgh
University and edited the 8th edition of the Encyclopaedia
Britannica: he had a lifelong interest in mineralogy and made an
important collection of fosil fish from Orkney. Patrick Traill of
Sabay rose to be a General of Artillery as well as an oft absent
freeman of the Royal Burgh of Kirkwall (1794). George William
Traill of Viera (b. 1792, d. 1847), related to the Traills of
Woodwick and Westness, had a most distinguished career in the
Bengal Civil Service surveying and taxing the 8,000 villages
scattered through the 11,000 square miles of mountainous
Kumaon.[22] A much more typical and less successful Traill
emigrant from Orkney was William Traill (b. 1751, d. 1808), a
humble Lieutenant of Marines, grateful for four months' leave
to cast his vote in the Orkney election of 1790 and ending his life
on half pay with unmarried daughters at Saltash, near
Devonport.[23]

So great was the exodus of Traills and so depressing were the
effects of falling kelp prices on small estates in the North Isles
that the family was less prominent in nineteenth-century Orkney.
The notorious exception to this rule, General Frederick William
Traill-Burroughs of Rousay and Viera (b. 1831, d. 1905), whose
conflict with the crofters reached the national press, had only the
remotest relationship to the Orkney Traills. A few of the Traills,

such as those of Woodwick and of Holland, survived to be lairds
in the twentieth century, last remnants of a family that had
scattered to the ends of the earth.

Some branches of the Stewart family had been established in
Orkney since the sixteenth century. Thus the Stewarts of Burray
traced their descent from Barbara Stewart, who as a widow had
been granted a tack of Burray and Flotta by Bishop Reid in
1550, and the Stewarts of Eday and those of Brugh (Brough in
South Ronaldsay) were descended from sons of Earl Robert
Stewart (d. 1593).[24] Towards the end of the seventeenth century
the Stewarts were literally losing ground in Orkney. Eday had
been divided between the Buchanans and the Baikies, Egilsay
went to the Douglases, and James Stewart of Graemsay sold his
island to Harry Graham of Breckness (1696) who transferred it
to his son-in-law Robert Honyman (1699).[25] Yet the Stewarts of
Burray still flourished and had been rewarded with a baronety
(1687) for services to their royal namesakes. Sir Archibald
Stewart (d. 1707), 2nd Baronet of Burray, was Steward-Principal
of the islands and one of Orkney's representatives in the Scottish
Parliament of 1702-7.[26]

Sir James Stewart, 3rd Baronet of Burray, was an Orcadian
and slightly aristocratic version of Fielding's Squire Western in
Tom Jones, except that Sir James had more arrogance and less
ability. He whole-heartedly disliked courtiers, Hanoverians and
presbyterians, especially the 14th Earl of Morton. During the
last Jacobite rebellion Sir James was such an ostentatious, if
ineffective, supporter of the Pretender that he was arrested and
sent south, his wife being taken later on board HMS *Eltham*
with Miss Flora Macdonald. Sir James died of typhus in
Southwark jail before he could be tried and convicted, so his
estate was not forfeited but passed to his relative Lord Galloway
who sold it to Sir Lawrence Dundas (1768).[27]

Other Orcadian Stewarts were also unfortunate. Robert
Stewart, nominally of Eday, lost Newark in Deerness to Bailie
John Covingtrie in 1716 complete with the family pew and tomb
in Deerness Kirk.[28] John Stewart, 3rd of Brugh, was so heavily
in debt that he had to sell his lands in Sanday to George Traill
of Hobbister for £1,666 sterling in 1733. Archibald Stewart, 4th
of Brugh, resided at Cleat, Westray, but the house was one of
those burned in 1746. Young George Stewart of Massiter, South
Ronaldsay, having very limited prospects in Orkney, embarked
on a naval career and sailed as midshipman on the *Bounty*
commanded by Captain Bligh, with fatal results. Though Stewart
was not a mutineer he failed to join Bligh in the overcrowded

launch, and later died a manacled prisoner being brought back on the ill-fated *Pandora*. He left descendants only in Tahiti.[29]

The eighteenth-century families of Grahame or Graeme, Honyman and Mackenzie all sprang from three Scots who became bishops of Orkney in the seventeenth century: George Grahame, bishop from 1615 to 1638, Andrew Honyman, 1664 to 1676, and Murdo Mackenzie, 1677 to 1688. Only the relatives of Bishop Grahame gained much land at the expense of the Church. The elder branch of the Bishop's descendants, known as the Graemes of Graemeshall in Holm, remained generally loyal to the superior and kept a little apart from the dissident lairds.

Mungo Graeme (b. c. 1707, d. 1762), 4th of Graemeshall, was a firm friend of the Earl of Morton and took no part in the Pundlar Process that challenged the validity of the weights used to measure scat payments. Patrick Graeme (b. 1739, d. 1786), 5th of Graemeshall, was a school fellow of Thomas Dundas at St Andrews and prospered when Thomas's father, Sir Lawrence Dundas, purchased the Earldom estate in Orkney (1766).[30] Patrick became Sheriff-Depute of Orkney, though he spent most summers in Edinburgh; his brother Alexander entered the Navy and his youngest brother William went into the East India Company's service but died young (1768). Alexander Graeme (b. 1741, d. 1818), 6th of Graemeshall, made the most of Sir Lawrence's patronage and ended as a one-armed Admiral, but he paid "at most, three or four fleeting visits to his estate" and the factor lived in the neglected mansion house.[31] None of the Graeme brothers married, and their lands were inherited by Alexander Sutherland, son of William Sutherland of Jamaica, the Sutherland-Graemes continuing as lairds in Holm until the estate was sold after the Second World War.

The Grahams of Breckness were descended from the youngest son of Bishop Grahame. Harry Graham, grandson of the Bishop, was a leading figure in the late seventeenth century, marrying a daughter of Bishop Honyman, representing the islands in the Scottish Parliament of 1685-6, and enlarging the house of Skaill, Sandwick. In the eighteenth century the Grahams of Breckness and Skaill were less distinguished, though Robert Graham helped undermine Mortonian power when he constituted himself a quorum of one at the Michaelmas Head Court of 1760 and enrolled five new voters, swelling the county electorate from seven to twelve.[32] In 1775 Robert's daughter Margaret married William Watt, a successful Kirkwall merchant and smuggler, who bought Breckness and Skaill from his father-in-law.[33]

Malcolm Laing, historian and brother of Samuel, the translator of *Heimskringla*

The Arctic explorer John Rae

William Balfour Baikie, explorer of the Niger River

His father, Capt. John Baikie RN, who served in the Napoleonic Wars

Four figures from the 'Golden Age' of Orkney scholarship: (above left) Duncan J. Robertson, (above right) John Mooney, (below left) J. Storer Clouston, (below right) Hugh Marwick

The Honyman family was successful in eighteenth-century
Orkney, obtained the patronage necessary for careers outside the
islands and disappeared over the horizon. Robert Honyman (b.
c. 1676, d. 1737), Presbyterian grandson of the Bishop,
purchased Graemsay in 1699 and resided at the Hall of Clestran,
in the west of Orphir, overlooking the island of Graemsay. He
was an outstandingly acquisitive laird, making many loans and
land deals, and becoming Tacksman of the Bishopric estate and
Stewart-Depute of Orkney for the Earl of Morton. Occasionally
his schemes backfired as when the Younger Captain Moodie
challenged him (vainly) to a duel (1715) or when Pirate Gow
looted the Hall of Clestran (1725).[34] His son William continued
loyal to the Mortonians but the drowning of William and his
eldest son Mungo in 1758 led not only to stories of ghosts and
hidden treasure but to a change in the family's local politics.[35] A
surviving son, Patrick, who married a Mackay of Strathy, openly
opposed the Earl of Morton politically and in the courts.[36] When
Sir Lawrence Dundas took over the Earldom estate he rewarded
Patrick's support by furthering the careers of Patrick's sons, one
of whom studied law at Edinburgh, the other entering the Navy.

In the early decades of the nineteenth century the Honyman
estate was, apart from the Earldom lands, the greatest in
Orkney, with a rental approaching £4,000 a year. This compares
with the Baikie of Tankerness and the Traill of Woodwick
estates that both had a rent roll of over £2,000 p.a. and the
Balfour, Graeme and Watt estates, each worth between £1,000
p.a. and £2,000 p.a.[37]

William Honyman (b. 1756, d. 1825) rose in the legal
profession with Gilbertian swiftness, marrying the eldest
daughter of the Lord Justice Clerk, the notorious MacQueen of
Braxfield, and adroitly switching his political allegiance from the
Dundases of Kerse to the Dundases of Arniston. By 1797
Honyman was a judge, assuming the title of Lord Armadale
from land inherited from his mother in Sutherland. In 1804 he
became a baronet.[38] His brother Robert was MP for Orkney
from 1796 to 1806 and became an admiral. William's sons
Robert and Richard were MPs for Orkney in 1806-7 and 1812-18
respectively. After William died in 1825, the second baronet sold
the Honyman estate in Orkney to John Balfour for £34,500
(1827).[39]

The Mackenzies of Groundwater, descended from Bishop
Murdo Mackenzie, were very minor landowners themselves
though related to lairds such as the Traills, Balfours and Baikies.
Murdoch Mackenzie, master of Kirkwall Grammar School (1734-

R

39), won fame as a cartographer and hydrographer. His brother James was legal agent to Sir James Stewart of Burray and was then employed by the pursuers in the Pundlar Process to support their anti-Morton arguments with a mass of historical evidence.

Among eighteenth-century lairds of Orkney the Baikies and the Feas were exceptional in having names of Norse origin, though as Baikie occurs as a place-name in Angus it is possible that the family might have been among the late medieval immigrants from Scotland. James Baikie (b. 1590, d. 1675), a merchant and provost of Kirkwall, purchased part of Tankerness in 1623 and the rest in 1630. His descendants there were important lairds throughout the eighteenth century and long after. James Baikie (b. c. 1714, d. 1764), 6th of Tankerness, married the heiress Janet Douglas in 1736 and added Egilsay and part of Rousay to his property. A leading Mortonian and Whig, he served as Provost of Kirkwall from 1737 till his death in 1764. Robert Baikie (d. 1817), 7th of Tankerness, still a minor when his father died, married Mary Balfour in 1785.[40] Since he received no favours from the Dundases of Kerse he challenged their control of the county seat and, with the help of Honyman and Balfour allies, he was elected MP in 1780, only to have his election annulled. He responded by organising an anti-smuggling campaign to embarrass Kirkwall merchants who supported his political opponents.[41]

The family survived both the philanthropy of James Baikie (b. 1786, d. 1869), 8th of Tankerness, who financed the religious and educational projects of Dr Robert Paterson, and the failure of the 9th laird to have any children. A grand-nephew, William Dover Cowan, succeeded to the estate in 1889, adopted the name Baikie and ensured that the lairds of Tankerness continued into the second half of the twentieth century.

The Feas were granted a charter to Clestran, Stronsay, by Earl Robert Stewart in 1591, but soon lived on the more valuable property of Stove, Sanday. They and branches of the family at Whitehall, Kirbister and Airy, all in Stronsay, remained lesser merchant lairds marrying all too often amongst themselves or with the multitudinous Traills, until the talents of James Fea (b. c. 1693, d. 1756), 6th of Clestran, made the family conspicuous in triumph and disaster. After studying in Edinburgh, travelling in France and acquiring Jacobite connections, Fea married the heiress Janet Buchanan (1720) when she was eleven years old or less and so gained Sound in Shapinsay and lands in Eday. Fea had the initiative to begin the manufacture of kelp in Orkney (1722) and with brilliant ingenuity captured the stranded Pirate Gow and his crew without bloodshed (1725).[42]

His later projects were unfortunate. He opposed the Earl of Morton in the Pundlar Process but in vain. By a personal visit to the camp of the Young Pretender he encouraged the Jacobites to occupy Orkney and after the ensuing fiery retribution Fea, even when he emerged from hiding, avoided his fellow lairds and lived mainly in the south.[43] Within a few years of his death in London the lands that had been acquired from Janet Buchanan were sold. Sound was bought in 1768 by Andrew Ross, the Chamberlain of the Earldom estate and Sheriff-Depute of Orkney, whose trustees sold it to Thomas Balfour of Elwick in 1784.[44] The lands in Eday were purchased by Robert Laing, merchant in Kirkwall, whose sons Malcolm Laing (b. 1763, d. 1818) and Samuel Laing (b. 1781, d. 1868) both became famous. Malcolm was MP for Orkney 1807-12, a historian and a friend of Sir Walter Scott, who called on Laing at Papdale in 1814. Samuel was Provost of Kirkwall 1820-34, a pioneer in agriculture and fishing, an archaeologist, a writer and the translator of *Heimskringla.*[45]

Janet Buchanan was not the only heiress to transfer a family estate by marriage and William Ballenden of Stenness was not the only laird to be overwhelmed by debt. The Douglases of Egilsay, the Covingtries of Newark, the Craigies of Gairsay and the Moncreiffs of Rapness, all prosperous administrative and merchant families in the seventeenth century, disappeared or declined in the course of the eighteenth century. The estates of the Douglases and Coventries passed to others by marriage; the Craigies and Moncrieffs were diminished by financial stress, sudden in the case of the Craigies and slow in the case of the Moncrieffs.

In 1736 the heiress Janet Douglas, grand-daughter of Sir Alexander Douglas of Egilsay, married James Baikie, 6th of Tankerness, in the presence of the Earl of Morton's eldest son and numerous officials.[46] This very Mortonian marriage ended the line founded by the Earl's agent in the 1660s and enhanced the importance of a new pillar of the establishment. The marriage of Elizabeth, daughter of the Rev. Thomas Covingtrie, minister in Sanday, to William Balfour of Trenaby in 1744, brought besides her dowry of land in the island a useful link with her brother, David Covingtrie, the laird of Newark in Deerness. Quite fortuitously the connection turned out to be most beneficial to the Balfours. In 1778 David Covingtrie, having no children of his own and anxious to retire, handed over his property to his sister and brother-in-law in return for an annual pension.[47] Thus an estate purchased as recently as 1716 from the profits of trade and administration was absorbed by an old established and now reviving family.

Sir William Craigie of Gairsay (d. 1712), son of Orkney's representative in Cromwell's Scottish Parliament and in Charles II's first Parliament, was himself an outstanding figure in Orkney during the last decades of the seventeenth century, representing the islands as MP in 1681 and 1689-1700. He was Stewart-Principal, Chamberlain of the Earldom Estates and Tacksman of the Bishopric lands in the years 1686 to 1691 and was knighted by King William and Queen Mary after the Glorious Revolution of 1688.[48] The terrible harvests of the 1690s affected him as well as all other land-owners (not to mention their starving tenants) and he also suffered from the destruction of Kirkwall's trade by French Privateers in the Nine Years War (1689-97) and the War of Spanish Succession (1702-13).[49] In 1700 John Traill, 2nd of Elsness, failed to pay Sir William Craigie what he owed him because "This bade years and the strick stewarts put is [us] so hard to it that they must be payed first".[50]

Perhaps Craigie was also the victim of political enmity. Sir Archibald Stewart of Burray, a Jacobite who was Tory MP for Orkney 1702-7, proceeded against Craigie for debt and in January 1703 had him imprisoned.[51] Sir William Craigie's eldest son entered the Army and was killed at Blenheim (1704), and the family never regained its former importance, though with Honyman help it lingered on. The last Craigie laird of Gairsay was William Honyman Craigie who in 1788 was described as "A weak man. A cousin of William Honyman the Sheriff to whom he sold his estate, reserving the vote."[52]

The Moncreiffs, so successful in the seventeenth century as officials and merchants in Kirkwall, went on to higher things in the south, leaving the Orkney branch to wither away. Harry Moncreiff of Rapness in Westray (bapt. 1680, d. 1749) had an elder brother and a nephew who were prosperous baronets, as well as a younger brother who became Provost Marshal General of Jamaica, yet Harry in 1726 pledged Rapness as security for a loan from a Kirkwall merchant. A generation later George Richan of Linklater, merchant in Kirkwall, became laird of Rapness, only to be drowned in 1781 taking lime out to Westray for a new house on his estate.[53]

William Richan (d. 1829) became, with a little patronage from Sir Lawrence Dundas, a lieutenant in the Royal Navy in 1781. He enjoyed big kelp profits from Rapness, had an income from his estate of Braebuster in Deerness, and supplemented his naval pay by smuggling while on convoy duties. He retired from the

Navy in 1807 after the *Norfolk,* which he commanded, was found carrying nineteen casks of illicit brandy and Geneva spirits, the guns being loaded with tobacco and tea.[54] He maintained a high style of living, vigorous law suits and increasing debts which bankrupted his heirs. His big house in Main Street, Kirkwall, built in 1824 when kelp prices were dropping, survives as a memorial to times when the going was good for lairds in Orkney. George Traill of Holland offered £8,400 for Rapness in 1830 and Braebuster was bought by Graeme Groat of Edinburgh for £2,400.[55]

Towards the end of the eighteenth century every aspect of a laird's income and prospects was affected for better or for worse by the mounting intensity of the wars with France. Kelp prices rose to such heights that, on many estates, kelp production became the main money-earner and agriculture was somewhat neglected. The traditional patterns of trade changed. Lairds became less interested in selling grain in Norway and more concerned to sell kelp on the Tyne. Wars caused more merchant ships to sail 'north about' Britain and so increased trading opportunities, colonial contact and profits from wrecks. Unfortunately, enemy privateers continued to take their toll.[56]

War on a grand scale, colonial and continental, not only stimulated even the margins of the British economy, but widened the opportunities available in government service and the colonies. By 1790, the lairds of Orkney, deserting the Dundases of Kerse, were hooked on to the imperial, military, naval, legal and political patronage networks presided over by Henry Dundas of Arniston, henchman of the Younger Pitt.[57]

Nearly all the top twenty families in Orkney had men serving in the wars or adventuring in the colonies. Some families suffered severe casualties: Captain Benjamin Moodie, 8th of Melsetter, lost four sons in India and another died after eighteen years' service as a lieutenant in the Royal Navy.[58] Most families shared the hard-won gains, which in a few cases could be considerable, as witnessed by the careers of Admirals Graeme and Honyman, General Traill, John Balfour in India and Robert Heddle in West Africa.[59] Perhaps the lawyers, Lord Armadale, Malcolm Laing and David Balfour, made the greatest gains with the least exposure to the dangers of war, the sea and tropical diseases.

The best example of a profitable military career, accomplished at no personal risk, entirely in the British Isles and largely while resident in Orkney, is that of Colonel Thomas Balfour (1752-99). When Balfour was a young man, his brother-in-law, Lord

Ligonier, allowed him to hold a commission in the 9th Regiment of Foot as a sinecure. In 1794, Balfour raised the Orkney and Shetland Fencibles to deter foreign raiders, intimidate Kirkwall's nonconformists and syphon government money into Orcadian pockets. His relatives and friends became officers and chaplain, his tenants filled the ranks and their agricultural labours were seldom interrupted by a parade or training. Shirts and transport were provided locally at huge expense. Unfortunately for the beneficiaries the regiment was inspected, declared "an island job" and disbanded.[60]

Balfour's second regiment, the North Lowland Fencibles, was required to serve in Ireland but even there he made profits and found consolation, commissioning a schoolboy son and devoting more time to an Irish mistress than to active service. Nemesis struck at him and his two sons, the younger being wounded at Cape St Vincent and the elder killed at Bergen-op-Zoom.

Marriage was in every sense a serious business in eighteenth-century Orkney since it reflected and affected the status of the partners. In the first half of the eighteenth century most lairds married daughters of fellow lairds. Ambitious young men such as James Fea of Clestran, James Baikie of Tankerness and William Balfour of Trenaby were well pleased to marry locally. In Balfour's case his wife was the daughter of a minister, but she was also sister of the Laird of Newark.[61]

Only leading figures had much chance of marrying into the Scottish aristocracy, as did the Stewarts of Burray. The match between William Ballenden of Stenness and Christiana Crawford, daughter of Alexander Crawford of Kerse, is another interesting exception to the pattern of local marriage, the lady being strong-willed and a law unto herself.

In the second half of the century the local marriage market continued to satisfy the lesser lairds of the northern isles, though their brothers and sons scattering through Britain and the empire often enjoyed a wider choice. Most male members of the wealthier families were already looking south for their wives; it became normal to think in terms of British society and neglect insular traditions. Moodies, Graemes and Honymans married south into Scotland; some Balfours went further afield. Absentee lairds and southern wives became usual rather than exceptional. The minister of Orphir commented: "The advantages of this parish are fire, water, and fine women; notwithstanding which most of the heritors reside at a distance, and leave their tenants to the mercy of the factors and under agents . . ."[62]

The most breathtakingly audacious match of this period was

the marriage of Thomas Balfour (1752-99), son of the Chamberlain of the Earldom estate, to Frances Ligonier, sister of the second Earl Ligonier.[63] It was as if a particularly charming and calculating Mr Wickham had married a Miss D'Arcy ten years older than himself. Frances' money enabled Thomas to buy the estate of Sound in Shapinsay[64] and the Ligonier connection provided him with his bloodless and profitable military career. The other Balfour brothers also married into money, David acquiring the daughter of a Glasgow businessman and John finding a well connected and wealthy young widow in Madras. The Balfour sisters of that generation still married within the islands.[65]

Another dazzlingly successful southern marriage was that of William Traill, related to the Traills of Westness, who married Mary Colebrooke in 1789. She was the eldest daughter of Sir George Colebrook, Baronet, a merchant banker and MP who was Chairman of the Court of Directors of the East India Company.[66] His wealth stemmed from West India sugar, the East India trade and a complex of manufacturing and business interests in England, Scotland and Ireland. This eighteenth-century wealth assured the career of George William Traill (1792-1847), the 'King of Kumaon', who in retirement bought most of Rousay and visited the island each summer. At his death the estate (but little money) passed to Frederick William Traill-Burroughs, a very distant relation.

Some of Orkney's eighteenth-century lairds were guilty of fornication and adultery. Patrick Traill, heir of Elsness, lived to regret fathering a child on Barbara Fea, daughter of a lesser laird, allegedly after promising her marriage. She pursued him energetically through the courts and the length of Britain, even to his ship off Spithead, seeking satisfaction or at least financial provision from a partner determined to elude her.[67] Most women who bore the illegitimate children of lairds were the wives or daughters of tenants and servants. Sir James Stewart of Burray used the salt pan house at Flotta as a warm and remote rendezvous for meetings with a young mistress from Caithness. He treated his favourite local mistress well and arranged that her daughter married a leading tenant farmer.[68]

Christiana Crawford, widow of old Captain Moodie RN, denounced the habits of the Stewarts' household "where nothing but vice and immorality is to be seen," but her own association with Hugh Ross, a strong-armed protector and man of business, was suspect. After the Rev. Keith had called her "Mr Ross's whore" Christiana, waving her riding whip, denounced the minister as he stood in his pulpit. William Ballenden, her son by a first marriage, was guilty "of a notorious Sabbath Breach and Rape . . . upon . . . Joan Gray servant woman to the Minister of Evie."[69]

Previously the Younger Captain James Moodie of Melsetter had kept a concubine, Betty Howie, who bore him three children, much to the continuing dismay of the Presbytery.[70] Probably the bad habits of this laird contributed to the downfall of the Rev. Andrew Kerr, who had already been accused of Episcopalian tendencies. When Kerr returned to Kirkwall from the South Isles "rather late and a little excited" and summoned a maid to him "it was considered expedient by the maids that both of them should attend." In the ensuing embrace and struggle Mr Kerr, Marjory Scott and Margaret Chalmers all fell down the stairs.[71]

There were occasional scandals concerning ministers later in the century such as the Rev. William Nisbet in Firth and the Rev. Thomas Lyll in Sanday, and the Presbytery attempted to depose the Rev. Francis Liddle, Orphir, not so much for drunkenness as for the heinous offence of marrying his housekeeper.[72]

The lairds, increasingly absent, showing ever more circumspection and receiving more lenient treatment from obsequious ministers, figured less prominently as sinners. An outstanding late eighteenth-century exception to the drift towards respectability and good manners was Captain Sutherland, later Lord Duffus, who leased Burray and was "the man who carried off Mrs Gen. Scot, and now keeps an Helen McBeath, sister to the McBeaths of Houna and Burwick."[73] Sutherland, who once forced the bearer of a summons to eat the document, did not confine his attentions to Helen McBeath and he was believed to have fathered three or four score children in the island.[74]

Traditional licentiousness lingered on into the nineteenth century and, in this as in other respects, the factor sometimes took on the exploitive rôle vacated by the absent, rentier laird. Thrice-married Robert Scarth, greatest of Orkney's factors, caused concern by his infidelities with tenants' wives, the sight of his stick left across the entrance to the cottage being enough to deter interruption.[75] He was waited on at the dinner table of Binscarth House by a servant girl embarrassingly recognisable as his daughter.[76] As a loyal member of the 'Auld Kirk' he was reputed to agonize on his death bed about the likelihood of unwitting incest between his numerous children in the neighbourhood.

In the 1700s the lairds of Burray, Gairsay, Brugh, Tankerness, Graemeshall and Breckness all had chaplains who were hired divinity students nicknamed Levites, employed to educate the children of the laird and his friends.[77] Given the Episcopalian sympathies of the lairds, the tutors' desire to please and become ministers, and the effect of the Patronage Act of 1712, this schooling was a two-way process which did much to tame the Presbyterian Church of Scotland and mould it to the wishes of the lairds. Intermarriage between the families of the lairds and those of the mainly Scottish ministers ensured co-operation between the lay and spiritual authorities and maintained the Scottish flavour of Orkney's ruling class.

After being tutored in Orkney older boys were sent to school and college in Scotland. James Fea, 6th of Clestran, (b. c. 1693) studied several years in Edinburgh and was then at Paris, perhaps at the Scots College there which was a notorious centre of Jacobite intrigue.[78] Patrick Graeme, 5th of Graemeshall, (b. 1739) was at school in St Andrews where the atmosphere was less Jacobite and the connections more useful. In mid-century only the feudal superior of Orkney, the 14th Earl of Morton, educated his sons partly in England, where one of them died at Westminster School in 1746.[79]

The education of the Balfours of Trenaby illustrates the range of possibilities for an old-established family which was again rising to prominence. William Balfour (b. 1719, d. 1786) and his brother Thomas (b. 1721, d. 1787) were educated first in Westray and then, in 1734, at Kirkwall Grammar School, probably because a relative, Murdoch Mackenzie, had been appointed master there.[80] In school they studied Latin, while in the streets they heard some country people, probably from the West Mainland of Orkney, speaking the old Norse language amongst themselves.[81] At home the young Jacobite gentlemen of the North Isles of Orkney, lairds of Trenaby, Clestran, Westove, Tirlet, Airie and Brugh were fond of amateur dramatics and performed Addison's tragedy *Cato* in the hall of Noltland Castle, emphasizing the theme of resistance to tyranny.[82]

When William Balfour educated his offspring he started in the traditional way, hiring a tutor in Edinburgh and furnishing a room at Trenaby with desks for his own and his neighbour's children. He urged his eldest daughter "to teach William Scott to read" (the boy being son of Balfour's grieve, Simon Scott) and instructed "that our Bairns are not to go to the Fair", i.e. the Lammas Fair at Kirkwall, which usually provided scenes of drunkenness and immorality.[83]

Balfour sent his three sons to Kirkwall Grammar School where

they were among the last generation of scholars to be taught in
the gloomy, damp classroom built by Bishop Reid in the
sixteenth century. Then all three young Balfours proceeded to
Aberdeen University. John, selected to go to India, did not
graduate but took a quick commercial course in London before
embarking on his voyage. Thomas and David completed their
degrees, then Thomas still working under Professor Traill at
Aberdeen obtained an Edinburgh medical qualification while
David began his long legal training in Edinburgh.[84]

Thomas Balfour (b. 1752, d. 1799) never used his medical
degree but married advantageously and his own sons, John
Edward Ligonier Balfour (b. 1780, d. 1799) and William Balfour
(b. 1781, d. 1846) went to Harrow. The books they purchased —
including Shakespeare and Ovid, *Robinson Crusoe* and *Tristam
Shandy,* Goldsmith's *Poems* and Burgoyne's *Plays,* Robertson's
Scotland and Cooke's *Voyages* — are a fair representation of
their parents' tastes and perhaps of their own tastes as well.[85]
Edward, nominally commissioned in the regiment of a friend
while still thirteen, showed some talent at school but, after
developing a taste for "idle dissipation and vice", was
despatched to his father's regiment in Ireland, while William
after begging that he be made "anything but a lawyer" was put
into the Royal Navy.[86]

Towards the end of the eighteenth century the daughters as
well as the sons of lairds were sent south to be educated. Thomas
Balfour of Huip (b. 1721, d. 1787) placed two of his daughters
as far away as the School for English Ladies at Bruges in 1777-8,
because he had relatives in Flanders.[87] Thomas Balfour of
Elwick (b. 1752, d. 1799) had only one daughter, Mary, who
briefly resided at a school in Edinburgh. Most of her education
was derived from her mother who made her proficient in music,
French and Italian and then put her in charge of the Cliffdale
household for most of four years. When Mary was nineteen she
married the Rev. Dr Brunton: whom she had first met in
Shapinsay as the tutor of her brother Edward: Brunton became a
professor at Edinburgh University and she became a moralising
novelist.[88]

Few of the houses built or lived in by the lairds of eighteenth-
century Orkney have survived without drastic alterations. In
Kirkwall, Tankerness House Museum, basically a seventeenth-
century building, remains much the same as it was in the days of
the Baikies. Robert Laing's house opposite 'the Tree' is a more
typical example of eighteenth-century vernacular architecture but
has two shops built in front of its ground floor. Other houses

have suffered change from internal shop developments. Richan's house, now the West End Hotel, and the present Customs and Excise building, flanked by Woolworths, have Georgian features but belong to the early nineteenth century as does Papdale House, now restored.

Skaill and Melsetter, the two finest country houses in Orkney, retain some eighteenth-century buildings, and the nineteenth-century additions harmonise well with the earlier work. The Bu of Burray is still the house used by Sir James Stewart, though oft renovated, with changed outbuildings and no colonnades. Langskaill in Gairsay remains half in ruins and half skilfully restored. Westness in Rousay, rebuilt after the burning in 1746, is little changed and a good example of a minor laird's residence. The Hall of Clestran, in Orphir, has changed much: at present it has an asbestos roof and is used for agricultural purposes.

Cliffdale, the elegant Georgian villa built by Thomas Balfour after he bought Sound (1784), partly survives in Jonah-like fashion, entirely swallowed up inside the Victorian leviathan of Balfour Castle. The intimate eighteenth-century rooms contrast strangely with the vast apartments round them. The fate of forgotten Cliffdale symbolises its inhabitants' place in history: they too have been overshadowed by their successors.

CHAPTER 12

Lairds and Historians
A Survey of Historical Literature Concerning Eighteenth-Century Orkney

R. P. Fereday

Some aspects of eighteenth-century Scotland have received more than their fair share of attention in numerous histories, biographies and novels, yet eighteenth-century Orkney has attracted comparatively little interest. There has been no surfeit of books about the Mortonian era of island history stretching from 1707, when the 11th Earl of Morton tightened his existing grip on the Northern Isles by obtaining a royal grant, until 1766, when the 14th Earl of Morton sold his estates in Orkney and Shetland. Nor has the following period, when the Earldom estate was held by the Dundases of Kerse, received much consideration.

There was an exception to the rule of literary neglect. One character in Orkney, during the eighteenth century, attracted interest in the wider world, although his career was brief and inglorious. The misguided wretch described in Daniel Defoe's *An Account of the Conduct and Proceedings of the Late John Gow* (1725) was later transformed into the improbable romantic hero of Sir Walter Scott's *The Pirate* (1822). Scott's genius and the information that he gained during his cruise round northern lighthouses in 1814 enabled him to write descriptions of island scenes that are so interesting, and comments on agricultural improvers that are so amusing, that the reader can almost forgive the ludicrous plot of the novel. Later, Allan Fea wrote *The Real Captain Cleveland* (1912), a more Orcadian and historical account of John Gow and also of James Fea, 6th of Clestran, kelp-innovator, pirate-catcher and most enterprising of Orkney's lairds.

Eighteenth-century source material has not been lacking. On the threshold of the century J. Wallace's *An Account of the Islands of Orkney* (1700) and J. Brand's *A Brief Description of Orkney, Zetland, Pightland Firth and Caithness* (1700) provide tantalising glimpses of the isles. Wallace was an Episcopalian minister who died in 1688, his account of Orkney being published by his son in 1693 and in enlarged form in 1700. We find many quaint and some important details recorded by Wallace, but these all antedate King William's reign and the lean years at the end of the century. The Rev. John Brand, a Presbyterian minister sent north in the spring of 1700 to report on and reform the ministers in Orkney, did note the decay of Kirkwall's trade and its declining population, which he might have attributed to French privateers as much as to poor harvests. Brand also touches on the grievances of Orcadian lairds against the stewards and the absentee donatories who held the Earldom and Bishopric estates from the Crown. This was to be the major theme in the history of Orkney throughout the eighteenth century.

Most private archives and many public papers have been relatively inaccessible till recent decades, but some evidence for the Mortonian period was printed at the time and has always been available. The law papers recording the lengthy *Pundlar Process,* between the Earl of Morton and the dissident lairds, were printed as the case dragged on, and some copies survived. The anti-Mortonian polemics of that indefatigable antiquarian, James Mackenzie, appeared as *The General Grievances and Oppressions of the Isles of Orkney and Shetland* (1750) and the Rev. T. Hepburn wrote *A Letter to a Gentleman from his Friend in Orkney* (1760) as a pro-Mortonian reply. The intricate legal arguments, the conflicting claims, the historical extracts quoted and the variety of Orcadian witnesses, make the *Pundlar Process* and associated works a major historical source. In sheer bulk and in width of interest the case far outstrips the more coherently presented material on the neighbouring archipelago set forth by Thomas Gifford in *An Historical Description of the Zetland Islands,* written in 1733 and printed in 1786.

Murdoch Mackenzie, elder brother of James, published *Orcades or A Geographical and Hydrographic Survey of Orkney and Lewis* (1750) on a scale of one inch to the mile. This magnificent work, several times reprinted, is a most valuable record of mid-eighteenth century Orkney, for it shows the township dykes and so reveals the extent of cultivation and the areas of common land. Since the Earl of Morton was a principal subscriber, the text which Murdoch Mackenzie wrote to accompany his maps made no mention of the Pundlar Process. He also glossed over Jacobite tendencies among the lairds, claiming that only one man had actively assisted the rebellion of 1745-6.

Some accounts of Orkney in the eighteenth century remained unpublished for more than a century. Thus Bishop Pococke's Tour, including his brief visit to Orkney in 1760, was not printed until it appeared in the *Scottish History Society* volume for 1887. More surprisingly, the Rev. George Low's *A Tour through the Islands of Orkney and Schetland in 1774* was not published until 1879 and his *Journal of a Tour through the North Isles of Orkney in 1778* only appeared in the *Old Lore Miscellany,* Vol. VIII, Part 3 (1915).

Low, born in Edzell, Forfarshire in 1747, came to Orkney in 1768 and subsequently became minister of the united parishes of Birsay and Harray in 1774. His studies in zoology, botany and archaeology included many descriptions and drawings taken from work with a microscope, and it is sad — and was certainly the cause of much distress to Low in his lifetime — that much remains unpublished. The subjects of Low's research, though including some Orkney history, kept clear of events close to his own time: he had no wish to embarrass the lairds by recalling their feuds with other families or their Jacobite connections.

After the Earl of Morton sold his estate to Sir Lawrence Dundas of Kerse there was a decade of near tranquillity, with William Balfour, formerly an outstanding opponent of Morton, employed and trusted by the Dundases. Low was careful to observe this truce between the feudal superior and the local lairds. Writing at a distance, Dr John Campbell could afford to be more critical. His *Political Survey of Great Britain* (1774) included a scholarly summary of Orkney's history in which he condemned the long-established system by which the revenues from the Earldom and the Bishopric estates were not spent in the islands but sent south to an absentee superior.

Campbell sketched out possible commercial projects that might succeed in Orkney, and James Fea, a surveyor, urged development strongly in *The Present State of the Orkney Islands Considered* (1775). Principal Gordon of the Scots College in Paris visited Orkney and his 'Remarks made on a Journey to the Orkney Islands in 1781' in *Archaeologica Scotica,* Vol. I (1782), include criticisms which suggest that he had been told some of the complaints of the lairds against their superior. A full-blooded indictment of the magistrates and councillors of Kirkwall, who were subservient to the Dundases of Kerse, was made by George Eunson in *The Ancient and Present State of Orkney* (Newcastle upon Tyne, 1788). Eunson was a former smuggler and a firebrand who had become the agent of Robert Baikie, 7th laird of Tankerness, a determined opponent of Orkney's political establishment.

Baikie was backed by a growing number of lairds who, finding that they had gained little by a change of masters, were resuming opposition to their feudal superior and his officials. The Dundases of Kerse were less successful than the Earls of Morton had been at maintaining their supremacy in the face of experienced, well-connected and resourceful opponents. Thanks to Harry Dundas of Arniston, a booming war economy, and soaring kelp prices, Orkney lairds won a share of political power. The Balfours, Honymans and Laings provided the MPs from 1790 until 1818.

These prosperous families had no desire to read of past failures and humiliations in the Mortonian era or recall more recent quarrels with the Dundases of Kerse; so the ministers who contributed to the *Statistical Account* of the early 1790s trod warily. When the old *Statistical Account* touches on eighteenth-century history the minister's aim was usually to praise the achievements of his patron's family rather than commemorate disagreeable, albeit sensational, events. The minister in Stronsay and Eday devoted four interesting pages to the development of the kelp industry since 1722, gave plenty of credit to James Fea and Thomas Balfour, but made no reference to the anti-kelp riots of 1742. Similarly, the Rev. George Barry of Shapinsay wrote flatteringly of Major Thomas Balfour's fine new house and improvements, solemnly discussed ancient history as far back as a possible visit by Agricola's fleet, but did not hint that in 1746 the Royal Navy's punitive expedition had burned the previous house after a dramatic night attack.

More information might be expected from George Barry's *History of Orkney* (1805), especially since there were living witnesses of the effects on the islands of the Jacobite rebellion. Barry, however, made no mention of the rising or its conse-quences for Orkney. He wrote of Phoenicians, Greeks, Romans; he gave twenty-five pages to the Picts and over a hundred to the Norsemen; he included only two and a half pages on the years 1707-1766, and these were merely unacknowledged extracts from the *Pundlar Process*. Even before Barry's work was published, John Balfour in London was confident that the book contained "nothing improper", i.e., there were no comments on, or criticisms of, long-established families.[1]

The lairds' conspiracy of silence was not much disturbed by the literary tourists of the early nineteenth century. P. Neill's *A Tour through some of the Islands of Orkney and Shetland* (1806) was more concerned with natural history and agricultural ideas than with the political past. The Rev. James Hall included in his *Travels in Scotland by an Unusual Route* (1807) a vivid description of Kirkwall's Lammas Fair and the enrichment of the lairds by the kelp boom, but was less able than Neill to touch on the history of the previous century.

Any outsider with strong historical interests who resided in Orkney long enough to investigate its past was bound to offend the dominant families. Such a man was Alexander Peterkin, a sheriff-substitute, who was fearless in his defence of Crown lands and the public interest against the encroachments of the lairds. He even dared to support the claims of Shetlanders to share in the election of the MP for the Northern Isles. His *Rentals of the Ancient Earldom and Bishoprick of Orkney* (1820) and his *Notes on Orkney and Zetland* (1822), though mainly concerned with earlier history, both contain the texts of documents relating to the eighteenth century. Peterkin also published in his short-lived *Orkney and Zetland Chronicle* (30 June 1825) a 'Memorial of Transactions in 1746' describing the retribution which fell on the anti-Mortonian lairds after Culloden. This interesting account is so biased in favour of the victims that their descendants could hardly complain, except in so far as they thought it inopportune for an incomer, however curious, to recall the past sufferings of leading local families.[2]

The freedom of Peterkin's comments on Orkney society, past and present, provoked a reply from the Rev. Walter Traill of Westove whose *Vindication of Orkney* (1823) was, in its Orcadian way, reminiscent of the defensive pamphlets which Shetland lairds had been writing to confound their numerous critics in the south. Traill denied that the lairds in Orkney had been or ever were tyrannical. He denounced Peterkin as a trouble-maker for mentioning the legal struggle by which the traders of Stromness had broken free from the control of the Royal Burgh of Kirkwall — "what good purpose can it serve to remind us of this unhappy affair?"

The inhibitions and prohibitions that discouraged too close an interest in the Mortonian period, or even the early years of the Dundases, continued for most of the nineteenth century. Old resentments were soothed by the passage of time; the Romantic Movement made former Jacobite connections, hitherto denied, safely admissible; the islands' weights, so long disputed, were modernised and most of the irksome feu duties were bought out; but still the lairds continued reticent about what was, for them, family history.

From 1825 until 1860 there was an almost complete absence of historical writing about the previous century. The *New Statistical Account* (1842), for instance, added very little to what had been said fifty years before. The second edition of Mackenzie's

Walter Traill Dennison,
writer and folklorist

Robert Rendall,
poet and naturalist

William Groundwater,
poet and naturalist

Evan MacGillivray,
writer and scholar

Ex-Provost George S. Robertson of Stromness

Making a Ba': Jim Harrison of Kirkwall

Islands Council Convener Edwin R. Eunson

An Orkney seafarer: John Hourie

Grievances and Oppressions, which appeared in 1836, served contemporary needs as well as antiquarian interests. The Balfours used this biased polemic as evidence in their test case with the Crown to decide the ownership of Orkney's common land: it was also useful propaganda in their negotiations about the commutation of feu duties payable to the Dundas family. Orcadian writers of historical fiction did not do much to compensate for the historians' neglect of the eighteenth century. David Vedder's *Tales and Sketches* (1832), a feeble collection of comical-historical yarns, achieved an unsurpassed level of inaccuracy. His account of the affray at Graemeshall in 1739 is a classic example of how an unscrupulous writer can mutilate and distort an already garbled folktale. Writers of fiction were not exempt from the tacit censorship of the ruling class: Vedder's worst caricatures involved families that no longer owned land in Orkney.

There is no doubt that the lairds were responsible for the post-Peterkin hiatus in historical studies. The collapse of kelp prices bankrupted some heritors, but the survivors, usually those with non-Orcadian sources of capital, remained the leaders of local society and the initiators of change. It was the lairds and their factors who supervised Orkney's long postponed and extraordinarily rapid agricultural revolution and who encouraged the development of fishing. In so far as the lairds lost some of their political power during 'The Age of Reform', they lost it to the aristocracy rather than the people. After an electoral pact in 1818, Lord Dundas shared control of the parliamentary seat with the Balfours and their friends for twenty years. In the following thirty years the Tory Balfours gave the Whig Dundases a clear run. The Earls of Zetland, as the Dundases became, controlled the seat from 1837 until after the Second Reform Act (1867) and the Ballot Act (1872), except for one costly intervention by that outstanding Shetlander and capitalist, Arthur Anderson.

At a time when the British Empire provided many profitable outlets for adventurous and combative spirits, Orkney lairds showed less interest in major or acrimonious law suits among themselves. The *modus vivendi* established between the lairds and the Earls of Zetland similarly reduced the number of legal tussles that might have revived memories of eighteenth-century struggles with a feudal superior. Those lairds not preoccupied with farming improvements or fishing projects who wished for controversy could participate in the religious turmoil of the period: others were sobered by the possibility that popular dissent might, eventually, assume political forms.

The foremost Orcadian scholar in early Victorian times was

S

Samuel Laing (d. 1868) whose pioneering translation of *Heimskringla* (1844) and archaeological writings left him little time for modern history. Virtually bankrupted by the fall in kelp prices and by his improvement projects. Laing had no wish to offend his fellow lairds unnecessarily. This was especially true of his attitude to the Balfours, to whom he sold his Shapinsay lands.

Captain William Balfour (d. 1846) had the finest family archives in Orkney, a deep interest in island history, a cultivated taste for literature, and a sister who won respect as a serious novelist. Yet he never gave the slightest encouragement to local historical studies involving the Balfours and their relatives. Taking a gloomy view of human nature, modern politics and democratic tendencies, he played the role of an Orkney Metternich or Wellington. Thanks to pragmatism, common sense and a gruff benevolence, he was fairly successful in reducing change to a minimum and damping down causes for dissension. The Captain, who generously excused the fatal consequences of an opponents' election riot (1832) to avoid a hanging trial, and who refused to call a meeting either to attack or to defend the Corn Laws on the grounds that arguments would disturb the community, was content to leave the eighteenth century in decent obscurity.

David Balfour (d. 1887) had all his father's interests and advantages, with the addition of a more cheerful disposition and even more money and leisure. His contribution to Orkney history parallels his genealogical and architectural achievements, being mainly concerned with medieval and Renaissance times to the exclusion of the eighteenth century. While his father was still alive, David had, by spending a considerable amount of time and money, convinced the heralds that the Orkney Balfours were the oldest family of that name and could rightfully claim to be Balfours of Balfour. In 1847, while planking away the medieval rigs of Shapinsay and completely modernising the landscape, he built a grand mock-Gothic monstrosity in the Scottish Baronial style to symbolise his 'feudal' lordship. It is significant that this bold statement of family pride entirely enveloped and concealed the late eighteenth-century house of Cliffdale, built by the first Balfour who purchased land in Shapinsay.

Similarly, David Balfour's *Odal Rights and Feudal Wrongs* (1860) concentrated on the sixteenth century and, intentionally or unintentionally, diverted attention from those events of the eighteenth century in which the Orkney Balfours had been involved so deeply. The book had only one paragraph referring to the *Pundlar Process* of the Mortonian era and the Earl of Morton was described simply as "the worst king stork of all the Donatories".[3] In just one of David Balfour's private notebooks, embedded among a mass of dubious information about medieval ancestors, there are a few family traditions about the events of 1746, mostly incorrect.[4]

The romantic nature of David Balfour comes out in his *Ancient Orkney Melodies* (1885), where he set down the music of thirty-six old Orkney tunes, but on the grounds that he had forgotten most of the words provided mostly new ones of his own, suitably sentimental. Despite the Victorian arangement of words and music, Balfour's collection is valuable in setting down some of the oldest Orkney melodies at a time when much was being lost.

The next age of Orkney historiography ran from the mid-1860s until the outbreak of the First World War. Compared with the preceding period there was a noticeable increase in the number of books written about the history of Orkney, and the eighteenth century was touched on now and then instead of being studiously avoided. There were more than a dozen works of importance, including very weighty volumes by Tudor, Hossack and Ruvigny, as well as articles and snippets of interest scattered through scholarly periodicals and newspapers.

This new period roughly coincided with the halcyon years of steam transport; increased emigration; the decline, though not the disappearance, of the lairds as a ruling class; and the implementation of liberal reforms. By 1865 even the North Isles of Orkney had a regular steamer service, the electric telegraph crossed the Pentland Firth in 1870, and the national railway network reached Thurso by 1873. After the Crofters' Act (1886) the lairds had lost much of their authority over their own estates: landowning became more a matter of social prestige than political or economic advantage. In every sense the lairds were losing their former power to shape history.

Contacts with the south stimulated the writing of local history. Outstanding among the visiting writers who explored the islands and their past was J. R. Tudor whose *Orkney and Shetland* (1883) is the finest survey of the Northern Isles ever written; its pages are strewn with historical information never previously published. There are a few score mistakes, almost unavoidable for a visitor writing a pioneer work, but these are minor blemishes in a book written with a freedom and scholarship that Peterkin would have admired. Among the historical documents that Tudor printed in appendices were papers relating to the

'Mutton Covenant' of 1710 imposed by Captain James Moodie Younger of Melsetter and other Episcopalian JPs on the Presbyterian ministers of the Established Church.

Professional men in Orkney, increasingly independent of the lairds, made contributions to local history that sometimes illuminated the long-neglected eighteenth century. Thus George Petrie, Sheriff Clerk and archaeologist, used documents in the Sheriff Court Records for his article 'Incidents of the '45' printed in *The Orcadian* of the 16th of January 1866.

Walter Traill Dennison (1826-1894) leased the large farm of West Brough in Sanday and through his life gathered a rich variety of folklore and information about traditional customs. By his efforts he "saved from extinction, single-handed, a whole corpus of myth, legend and historical tradition which the educated Orcadians of his time ignored, even deplored".[5] Amongst the dialect stories in his *Orcadian Sketch-Book* (1880) are two tales referring to characters and events of the Mortonian era: 'The Heuld-Horn Rumpis' concerns the immorality of Christiana Crawford, and 'Why the Hoose of Elsness Was Brunt' describes a punitive raid on John Traill of Elsness, Sanday, in 1746. The Rev. J. P. Craven's *History of the Episcopalian Church in Orkney, 1688-1882* (1883), later extended down to 1912, documented the Episcopalian tendencies of Orcadian lairds. Walter Traill of Woodwick's book *A Genealogical Account of the Traills of Orkney* (1883) briefly outlined some of the branches of that multitudinous family which had been flourishing in so many parts of eighteenth-century Orkney.

W. R. Mackintosh, editor of *The Orcadian,* furthered the development of local history both by his policy as a journalist and by his own researches. His *Glimpses of Kirkwall and its People in Olden Times* (1887) and *Curious Incidents from the Ancient Records of Kirkwall* (1892) contain interesting and informative extracts from the town's records. Most of the material that Mackintosh printed related to the eighteenth century, and some items were most revealing about feuds and factions. For instance there was evidence that Captain James Moodie, younger of Melsetter, attempted to bribe the council during the election of 1722, an account of the shooting of Captain Moodie senior in Broad Street (1725) and a record of how the Earl of Morton used the fine paid by Sir James Stewart after the affray at Graemeshall (1739) to build a new tolbooth in Kirkwall. Mackintosh was not able to print much about the last Jacobite rebellion because the incriminating records of the Town

Council together with all the minutes of the Commissioners of Supply from 1679 to 1780 had long since disappeared, presumably destroyed by the descendants of the guilty.[6]

A later collection of Mackintosh's articles appeared as *Around the Orkney Peat Fires* (1894). This ever-popular collection of folktales, now in its eighth edition, is mainly concerned with memories of the early nineteenth-century smugglers and press-gangs and Victorian versions of stories about seventeenth-century witches. It is a contribution to folklore and folklife rather than to authentic history and forms an interesting contrast to Mackintosh's earlier publications.

Orkney's historical writing in the late nineteenth century culminated in a monumental work of major importance and inexhaustible usefulness. B. H. Hossack, born in Stronsay, was enterprising enough to escape from the drudgery of teaching by marrying a young heiress. He made local history his hobby and, combining an appetite for detail with an eye for stories of human interest, he worked on Sheriff Court Records, Church Records, and old documents in the possession of solicitors. In his later years he built Craigiefield, a new house on the north of Weyland Bay with a fine view of Kirkwall, and devoted himself to writing a history of the burgh. His *Kirkwall in the Orkneys* (1900) is unique, being a well-illustrated, house-by-house history of the town, incorporating whole chapters on buildings of importance and their former occupants. Since every family of consequence in Orkney owned a town house in Kirkwall, Hossack's book contains a colossal quantity of information on Orkney families and institutions in the sixteenth, seventeenth, eighteenth and nineteenth centuries.

Such a mountain of detail with pages that range to and fro over the centuries is a collection of historical material rather than a connected history. Moreover there are some mistakes among the tens of thousands of facts. At times Hossack is misled by his authorities, such as the incorrigible David Vedder, at other times Hossack fails to mention his sources. There are some misprints. For instance, he dated his description of the Stronsay kelp riots twenty years too late.[7] Perhaps his eyesight was fading: with less than a year to live he failed to spot errors in the proofs which only he was qualified to detect.

Yet Hossack's *magnum opus* was a magnificent achievement. He collected, arranged and indexed an enormous amount of material and his style is so racy and anecdotal that nearly every part of the book can be read with enjoyment as well as profit. It remains the most important single work of local history ever written in Orkney.

The next book to be published that contained valuable information on Orkney in the eighteenth century and in other centuries was a somewhat unexpected contribution from a cosmopolitan author who privately printed one hundred and fifty copies of *The Moodie Book* (1906), mainly for subscribers in Africa and Canada. The name of the author, Melville Amadeus Henry Douglas Heddle de la Caillemotte de Massue de Ruvigny, 9th Marquis of Ruvigny and 15th Marquis of Raineval (b. 1868, d. 1921), was at least partially known in Orkney. His godmother was a Mrs Heddle of Melsetter and, through his mother, he was related to the Moodies who had built the mansion house at Melsetter in Walls.

Though invited to Orkney by Mr Middlemore, who had purchased Melsetter from the Heddles in 1898, Ruvigny was too busy to travel so far north. His genealogical researches that had produced *The Blood Royal of Great Britain* (1903) and *The Jacobite Peerage, Baronetage and Knightage* (1904) were already moving towards the climatic, fin de siècle *The Titled Nobility of Europe* (1914). Thus *The Moodie Book*'s chapters on the Orcadian branch of the family were largely based on the researches of J. G. F. Moodie Heddle who had, according to the preface, "an intimate knowledge of the history, genealogy and traditions of Orkney." Unfortunately these traditions included some highly erroneous tales about Commodore James Moodie (d. 1725) which Major James Moodie, 9th of Melsetter, had contributed to Charnock's *Naval Biographies* (1795). Ruvigny's *Moodie Book* gave these legends a new lease of life.

Information on the ramifications of Orkney's most numerous landowning family was provided by William Traill's *A Genealogical Account of the Traills of Orkney* (1883) and by Thomas W. Traill's *Genealogical Sketches: The Frotoft Branches of the Orkney Traills* (1902). The most ambitious of all the local genealogical studies was Roland St Clair's *Orcadian Families*, an undated manuscript compiled in the early decades of the twentieth century on a grand scale, now a much-used typescript in the Archivist's office at Kirkwall.

Several other historical works bearing on the eighteenth century were written in Orkney during the decade leading up to the First World War. John Smith's *The Church in Orkney* (1907) blended the information from Dr Hugh Scott's *Fasti* with the local researches of Craven and Hossack into a handy, well indexed volume giving biographical sketches of clergy and summaries of church history from the Reformation onwards. The book is entirely unoriginal, suffers from a few mistakes and omissions, but is an extremely useful work of reference giving just enough information to whet the appetite of the interested reader and make him wish to consult the original sources.[8]

The Rev. J. B. Craven wrote a well-documented *History of the Epicopalian Church in the Diocese of Caithness* (1908) and published an extended version of his *History of the Episcopalian Church in Orkney 1688-1912* (1912). John Gunn compiled and edited the saga-dominated *Orkney Book* (1909) to satisfy a need and a demand for local history in the islands' schools and amongst the people. Then, as has been mentioned, Allan Fea's *The Real Captain Cleveland* (1912) made a local historian's contribution to the story of Pirate Gow.

Orcadian scholarship in the century or so before 1914 benefited from family and county histories written in neighbouring parts of Scotland. As early as 1829 Robert Mackay had written a *History of the House and Clan Mackay* including interesting snippets of information on *Le Prince Charles* and its cargo of gold captured in 1746. James Dennistoun's *Memoirs of Sir Robert Strange Knight and his Brother-in-Law Andrew Lumisden* (1855) provided tantalising glimpses of some Jacobites with Orcadian connections. The first work of any consequence on Orkney's nearest neighbour was J. T. Calder's *History of Caithness* (1861). This was intended "merely as a sketch or outline" since "neither the public records of the county nor yet family papers, afforded sufficient materials" for a full account.[9] Calder's death (1864) in Shapinsay, where his brother Marcus was factor for David Balfour, delayed a revised version of his book, but this was eventually printed, with additions by others, in 1887. Meanwhile John Henderson's *Caithness Family History* (1884) excited the interest of Orcadians since it recorded many links between the gentry on either side of the Pentland Firth.

Three articles by Alexander Gunn in the *Northern Ensign* of 24 September, 8 and 15 October, 1895, improved on Calder's brief references to the northern campaign of 1746 and mentioned that "a gentleman of the name of Balfour" was present at the rebel rally on Spittal Hill. This clue, indicating that it was William Balfour who carried the Orkney lairds' letter to Lord Macleod, is all the more valuable since the incriminating records in Kirkwall were destroyed, probably before the eighteenth century ended.

It is infuriating to think that Calder, writing thirty-five years earlier than Gunn, would have been inhibited by his brother's links with the Balfours from dwelling on their ancestor's treasonable involvement in the Highlanders' raid on the islands and their recruiting in Caithness.

William Frazer's *The Earls of Cromartie* (1876) printed Lord

Macleod's own narrative of the northern campaign for the first time. Further details of the same expedition and of the closing debacle at Drummoy and Dunrobin on the 15th of April 1746 appeared in William Frazer's *The Sutherland Book* (1892). The *Old Lore Miscellany of Orkney Shetland Caithness and Sutherland,* from 1907 onwards, contained the occasional article relevant to Orkney in the eighteenth century. For instance, when the Rev. George Low's *Tour Through the North Isles and Part of the Mainland of Orkney in 1778* came to light it was printed in the *Old Lore Miscellany,* Volume VIII, part three (1915).

Despite the academic depression described by Marinell Ash's *The Strange Death of Scottish History* (1980) there was enough historical activity in Scotland to provide occasional additions to the knowledge of eighteenth-century Orkney. The Society of Antiquaries' journal *Notes and Queries* contained only snippets of information about Orkney in the Mortonian era and after, but towards the close of the nineteenth century the *Scottish History Society*'s publications began to make significant contributions. Bishop Pococke's *Tours in Scotland, 1747, 1750 and 1760,* edited by D. W. Kemp (1887), included glimpses of northern Episcopalians. The Rev. Robert Forbes' *The Lyon in Mourning,* edited by Henry Paton (1895-6), contained a valuable account of the experiences of the Episcopalian minister for Thurso and his friends after their capture at the Bu of Burray by Benjamin Moodie's marines. *The Letter Books of John Steuart, Bailie of Inverness,* edited by W. Mackay (1915), touched on the trading activities of Sir James Stewart of Burray. The *Scottish Historical Review,* founded in 1903, did not neglect the north and in 1914 W. R. Scott contributed an article on 'The Trade of Orkney in the Eighteenth Century'.

Progress made in editing or calendaring state papers and other collections began to bring to light material of interest to Orcadians. Thus the *Albemarle Papers,* edited by C. S. Terry (1902), printed several references to the Young Pretender's hopes of reaching Orkney under the assumed name of Sinclair. This did much to explain the continued presence of troops in Orkney after the rebellion ended in 1746.

Between the two world wars the writing of local history in Orkney was dominated by the activities of the Orkney Antquarian Society founded in 1922. Among the outstanding members were A. W. Johnston and the imaginative J. Storer Clouston (b. 1870, d. 1950). These descendants of minor landed families were matched by the pious and meticulous John Mooney (b. 1862, d. 1950), managing director of Garden's Stores, and Dr

Hugh Marwick, Headmaster of Kirkwall Grammar School (1914-29) and Director of Education (1929-1946). These leading local historians and other members of the society who contributed to the *Proceedings of the Orkney Antiquarian Society* (1922-1939) maintained a praiseworthy standard, concentrating their efforts on the medieval period rather than on later centuries. However, the society's bias in this respect was never so pronounced as that of the Old Lore Miscellanies produced by the Viking Society for Northern Research.

J. Storer Clouston, the most prolific Orcadian writer of his generation, earned the time and the money which he devoted to historical research by writing ephemeral novels. The early ones imitated R. L. Stevenson, while the later ones had some of the virtues and all of the failings of works by P. G. Wodehouse. Despite or because of these profitable flights of fancy, Clouston was able to contribute weighty, well-researched articles to the *Scottish Historical Review,* the *Old Lore Miscellany,* the *Proceedings of the Orkney Antiquarian Society,* and other journals. His strong interest in Norse times sufficiently appears in his brilliantly-written *History of Orkney* (1932). The book has 328 pages on the centuries dominated by the Norse and Scottish Earls and ended by the death of Earl Patrick in 1615, but there are only thirty-two pages devoted to the seventeenth century and then a final chapter of a mere twelve pages entitled 'The Last Two Centuries'.

In Clouston's view the history of the island community faded into insignificance once political independence was lost. Thus his painstaking search through, for instance, the Sheriff Court Records of Orkney, was a quest for information about place-names and land tenure that might preserve traces of Norse settlement patterns or medieval tax systems. Yet he did make one major contibution to the study of eighteenth-century Orkney. He collected the Orcadian articles scattered through the numerous volumes of the old *Statistical Account* (1791-99) and published them in his *Orkney Parishes* (1927) complete with introductory notes on the early history of each parish.

Dr Hugh Marwick was primarily concerned with Norse times, the Orkney Norn language and place-names, but he wrote several articles relevant to the eighteenth century. One of these, dealing with Patrick Fea of Airy (one-time agent of Sir James Stewart of Burray) was entitled 'An Orkney Jacobite Farmer' and appeared in the *Journal of the Orkney Agricultural Discussion Society* (1930). Other articles were printed in the *Proceedings of the Orkney Antiquarian Society*. Thus 'The Feas of Clestran' (1931) untangled the complicated genealogy of that important family;

'Two Orkney Eighteenth Century Inventories' (1934) revealed the domestic arrangements and agricultural ideas of Sir James Stewart of Burray; and 'Orkney Weights and Measures in the 18th Century' (1939) was a useful introduction for anyone trying to make sense of the Pundlar Process.

The greatest contribution that Dr Marwick made to eighteenth-century studies was his *Merchant Lairds of Long Ago* (1936, 1939) a two-volume study of Orcadian life and conditions in the early eighteenth century, based on the Traill Papers. He transcribed and edited over one hundred and fifty letters, and quoted extensively from scores of related documents and records. He gave a masterly description of farming in Orkney 1700-1730, the decline of the udallers, the terms of tenancies, teinds, the old weights and surviving farm accounts. His survey of trade and traders included the historical background, the commodities involved, the merchant ships and boats employed, the charter party agreements, loading arrangements, bounties and debentures, the ports of destination, profits and examples of well-documented voyages to Norway, the Baltic and Holland.

After the Second World War Dr Marwick used his retirement to produce *Place-names of Rousay* (1947), a scholarly guidebook called *Orkney* (1951) and his indispensable *Orkney Farm Names* (1952). Eventually he, his surviving colleagues from the defunct Orkney Antiquarian Society and some younger men, decided they must revive the idea of a local history society. They felt that they must act because those Orkney estates that had not disappeared after the First World War were being sold off in the early 1950s and there was a danger that the estate records and family papers would be destroyed. The Orkney Record and Antiquarian Society was formed to preserve historical material and to publish, from time to time, volumes of an *Orkney Miscellany*.

The four volumes of *Orkney Miscellany* that appeared between 1952 and 1957 contained a much higher proportion of articles dealing with the eighteenth century, especially that century's later decades, than had been the case in the *Proceedings of the Orkney Antiquarian Society*. This change in the emphasis of local studies reflected the date of the collections deposited with the society for preservation. The lairds were a nearly extinct species and their papers were a vast but endangered historical heritage.

P. N. Sutherland Graeme, the last laird of Holm, contributed articles on 'The Parliamentary Representation of Orkney and Shetland 1754-1900' (1953) and on 'George Eunson—Orkney's 18th Century Firebrand' (1957), based on the Graemeshall and other papers. W. S. Hewison, a journalist from a Westray family, gave a well-documented illustration of 'Smuggling in Eighteenth Century Orkney' (1956) based on the Skaill Papers. Other documents from the same collection relating the business concerns of two Orkney merchants were edited by Evan MacGillivray, County Librarian, under the title 'Letters of Thomas Balfour to William Watt, 1784-87' (1957). The Rev. V. G. Pogue used Orkney Church Records to write one article on 'Schools in the Cairston Presbytery in the Eighteenth Century' (1956) and another on 'The Case of the Rev. Jas. Tyrie' (1957), describing an unfortunate minister caught in the political cross-fire of 1745.

The most significant influence on Orcadian literature and local studies during the twenty-five years from 1952 to 1977 emanated from Ernest W. Marwick (b. 1915, d. 1977). An extraordinarily scrupulous and responsible journalist, he dedicated most of his working life to exploring and protecting Orkney's heritage.

> He was more than a scholar: woven into his immense knowledge of Orkney in all its aspects were threads of sensibility and poetry without which learning is so much dry dust.[10]

His main interests were folklore and folklife, and his masterpiece *The Folklore of Orkney and Shetland* (1975) is of value to any student of human nature or Orkney's past. Most of his historical writing was about the nineteenth and early twentieth centuries.[11] He was not attracted to the eighteenth century, a period when Orkney was dominated by local lairds and their absentee superiors. Yet he was always ready to assist and advise anyone who wished to discover more about the exploiting class and their politics. Nothing connected with Orkney was alien to him. Perhaps the most important of his own writings on the period is his monograph about *Robert Strange, Kirkwall Artist* (1964) which managed to add fresh information as well as providing a readable summary of material hard to come by in the islands.

The work of Ernest Marwick in recording and popularising local history and encouraging Orcadian writers was all the more necessary because the Orkney Record and Antiquarian Society had begun to falter. After 1957 the society produced no further volumes of *Orkney Miscellany,* although sixteen years later the name was used again for a volume produced by the County Library to print the papers read by foreign scholars and Eric Linklater at the King Håkon Conference.

The most obvious reason for the inactivity of the *Orkney Record and Antiquarian Society* was that Orkney's television station at Netherbutton came into service on the 22nd of December 1958. Social life and leisure pursuits were affected dramatically. Perhaps Ernest Marwick's continued and increased activity as journalist and broadcaster may be attributed to his refusal to acquire a television set himself.

A more serious cause for the decline of the Society was the shortage of new talent. Older members of the society were dying off and the ranks of the younger generation had been thinned by emigration. For fifty years Orkney had prided itself on exporting professors, and by the 1960s the 'brain drain' was at its peak. Never before or since had university entry been so easy. There were innumerable well-paid careers in Britain and the wider world awaiting talented Orcadians. By 1961 the population of the islands had fallen to 18,650 and, though the number of professional posts in Orkney was slowly increasing, there was much less demand for talent than in the booming cities of Britain.

The sheer quality of the articles published by the Antiquarian Society (1922-1939) and the Record and Antiquarian Society (1952-7) tended to inhibit potential contributors — the five articles in *Orkney Miscellany* Volume IV (1957) were contributed by three men. The surviving members felt that *Orkney Miscellany* should only continue if and when a sufficient number of original and scholarly articles were forthcoming. Perhaps they were also conscious that they stood at a crossroads in the progress of historical writing and were somewhat diffident and uncertain about which route to take. On the one hand there was an increasing demand for reminiscences and detailed description of the vanishing rural past. As tractors replaced horses there was increasing nostalgia for the old way of life as described by John Firth's *Reminiscences of an Orkney Parish* (1920). W. R. Mackintosh's *Round the Orkney Peat Fires* (1894) reached its seventh edition in 1967, with more to come. On the other hand the writing of history was becoming more professional, university-based, recondite and esoteric. The pseudo-scientific trends, the search for statistics, the call for quantification, above all the increase in jargon, widened the gap between 'the experts' and amateur scholars.

The cultural vacuum created when the Record and Antiquarian Society lapsed into inactivity was partly filled by various professional men working beyond the call of duty. Ernest Marwick showed the same inexhaustible patience and helpfulness to parish writers attempting an article for *The Orcadian* as to visiting scholars of international standing. Evan MacGillivray, the County Librarian, did everything possible to enlarge the county archives and see that they were properly housed. He also organised a conference in 1968 on the five hundredth anniversary of the impignoration of Orkney. John Shearer, Director of Education, assisted by the headmasters of Stromness and Sanday schools, William Groundwater and John D. Mackay respectively, edited a *New Orkney Book* (1966), a concise introduction to island studies. The following year J. A. Troup and F. Eunson's *Stromness* (1967) sketched the history of that burgh on its one hundredth and fiftieth anniversary. Extensions to the library, conferences and publications all cost money. The Orkney County Council was generous because of the prosperity of island farming and the fact that in the late sixties and most of the seventies over eighty per cent of local expenditure was covered by central government grants.

Although, between 1957 and the mid-1970s, there was little research into the history of Orkney's eighteenth-century lairds, the prospect of further progress was ensured by Evan MacGillivray, who rescued and preserved the Balfour Papers. If he had not intervened to save the 50,000 documents mouldering in the attics of a castle about to be sold, it is quite probable that the whole accumulation of papers would have been burned in heaps. The ledgers and papers in the estate office were destroyed by the last factor before vacating his post. Fortunately, J. R. Wards of Edmonstone, Shapinsay, took the initiative to save some fine estate plans from the factor's holocaust, and the Johnstons of Orphir House possessed a one-volume summary of the nineteenth-century ledgers that had been destroyed.

The addition of the Balfour Papers to the already impressive county archives made Orkney a paradise for anyone interested in the local gentry of the eighteenth and nineteenth centuries. About a quarter of the Balfour Papers, perhaps more, date from the eighteenth century and include several thousand family letters. In the course of the 1970s, workers from the Scottish Record Office and then Orkney's own archivists produced outline catalogues of the Balfour Papers, Sheriff Court Records, Orkney Church Records and the other collections in Kirkwall. The materials were there: it only remained for researchers and writers to exploit their opportunity.

Until local historians could sketch some coherent pattern of events in the history of eighteenth-century Orkney, national historians could not be blamed for neglecting the islands in that period. No local study had been written in Orkney, prior to 1980, to compare with Alistair and Henrietta Tayler's *Jacobites*

of Aberdeenshire and Banffshire in the '45 (1928) or Sir James
Fergusson's *Argyll in the Forty-Five* (1951). Consequently, even
the numerous books dealing with the Jacobite rebellions ignored
Orkney's political tensions, the Jacobite raid, Moodie's revenge
and the Earl of Morton's activities in France. All the works
recommended by W. Fergusson in *Scotland: 1689 to the Present*
(1968), pages 425-7, and more recent publications such as D.
Daiches' *Charles Edward Stuart* (1973) or B. Lenman's
important and wide-ranging book on *The Jacobite Risings in
Britain* (1980), virtually omit Orcadian affairs.

The distortion that resulted from an honest ignorance of the
existence, let alone the structure, of Orcadian politics in the
eightenth century is well illustrated by R. J. Adam's article on
'The Northern Campaign' in *History To-day* (June, 1958). This
summarised the efforts of Duncan Forbes of Culloden, touched
on the attitude of northern chiefs and clans, and was brief to the
point of obscurity about the campaign and the final defeat at
Dunrobin. No mention was made of the Jacobites' occupation of
Caithness or of their expedition to Orkney and its consequences.
Yet twenty-two years later Bruce Lenman called this article the
best modern account of the northern campaign.[12]

The continued absence of any outline of eighteenth-century
politics was not deplored or even noticed by writers of Scottish
history, but I attempted to remedy the deficiency for the first
half of the eighteenth century by researching and writing *Orkney
Feuds and the '45*. The book examined the quarrels of some
lairds and their relations with successive Earls of Morton. The
first six chapters covered significant characters and episodes in
the generation before the last Jacobite rebellion: the six
remaining chapters described the impact of the rising on Orkney
and the consequences of the Earl's wartime visit to France.

Fortunately for local historians in Orkney there were some
books written during the last two decades that, while primarily
concerned with Scottish history, offered new ideas and
stimulating examples to Orcadian academics. Such a book was
J. S. Gibson's *Ships of the '45* (1967): a splendid account of a
hitherto neglected aspect of the campaign. Mr Gibson was able
to achieve this enthralling story of naval operations in northern
waters by skilful use of French sources and naval records as well
as the Jacobite narratives. A small but original contribution
to the history of the same campaign and its aftermath was made
by Göran Behre's article 'Sweden and the Rising of 1745' in *The
Scottish Historical Review* (1972) which discussed possible
Swedish participation and the escape of thirteen Jacobites from
Scotland to Norway. In another article in the same journal 'Two

Swedish Expeditions to Rescue Prince Charles' (1980), Behre mentioned how a Swedish vessel lay for eight weeks at Stronsay and how Patrick Fea of Airy preferred to lie low in the islands rather than to escape into exile.

Scotland in the Age of Improvement: Essays in Scottish History in the Eighteenth Century (1970) contained a number of useful articles, the best being John M. Simpson's 'Who Steered the Gravy Train, 1707-66?' This penetrating study of Scottish politicians and the Westminster spoils system is instructive reading for anyone studying the Orkney lairds' expectations of patronage from the Earl of Morton or Sir Lawrence Dundas.

Alexander Fenton's *The Northern Isles: Orkney and Shetland* (1978) was a massive, encyclopaedic and definitive study of folklife, based on many years' research in museums, archives and the islands. Over six hundred pages of well-illustrated text on every aspect of working peoples' lives and nearly a hundred pages of references, bibliography, index and glossary made this book a mine of information for historians of the eighteenth and many other centuries.

The proliferation and expansion of record offices throughout Britain has been an added encouragement to local historians in Orkney as elsewhere. Apart from the Royal Archives at Windsor, the Public Record Office in London and the Scottish Record Office in Edinburgh (which possesses the Morton Muniments), the repository that contains the most interesting collection of documents relating to eighteenth-century Orkney is the North Riding Record Office at Northallerton, which houses the Zetland (Dundas) Archives.

The appointment of an archivist for Orkney helped two Sixth Year pupils at Kirkwall Grammar School make useful contributions to local studies. Sylvia Gow's *James Moodie Younger of Melsetter* (1976) was based on ten letters from Moodie to his uncle that had survived in the Sheriff Court Records. Jane Ross's *Orkney and the Earls of Morton, 1643-1707* (1977) showed how and why the Mortonian grip on Orkney fluctuated before the grant of 1707.

During the 1970s W. P. L. Thomson, Headmaster of Kirkwall Grammar School, emerged as an amateur historian with professional skills. He provided the modern introduction to Orkney's section of Sir John Sinclair's *The Statistical Account of Scotland, 1791-9, Vol. XIX, Orkney and Shetland* (1978), and wrote a definitive monograph on *Kelp-Making in Orkney* (1983). His major work *The Little General and the Rousay Crofters* (1981), a classic description of conflict on an Orkney estate in the nineteenth century, included a survey of the earlier history of the estates on Rousay.

Another development was that Mr Thomson undertook to edit a new journal for the Orkney Heritage Society. The first volume of *Orkney Heritage* appeared in 1981 and the eighteenth century was well represented. Ian MacInnes, Rector of Stromness Academy, wrote 'The Alexander Graham Case: The Royal Burgh of Kirkwall and the Unfree Traders of Stromness'. This test case, of interest to every merchant in Scotland, revealed the contradictions of the Act of Union, which had guaranteed the rights of the Royal Burghs of Scotland and yet promised that merchants of the whole United Kingdom were to enjoy the same trading privileges. The victory of the Stromness traders virtually ended the privileges of Kirkwall and other Royal Burghs and opened the way to free trade.

I followed my *Orkney Feuds and the '45* (1980) with an article on 'William Balfour After the '45: His Relations with the Earl of Morton and Sir Lawrence Dundas, 1747-69'. This explored the circumstances in which Morton sold the Earldom estates to the eighteenth century's most notorious war profiteer.[13] W. P. L. Thomson's own contribution to *Orkney Heritage* Volume One was 'Common Land in Orkney' which gave a lucid explanation of a complicated subject. He concentrated on the dramatic changes in the nineteenth century, but also described early encroachments, the first attempts at division and the changes in the management of commons after the abolition of heritable jurisdiction had ended the Baillie Courts and the Country Acts.

It is now over fifty years since Storer Clouston wrote his *History of Orkney,* and over a hundred and eighty years since George Barry published the first book with that title. William Thomson's new *History of Orkney,* due to appear in 1987, will be a landmark in modern historical research on Orkney and is eagerly awaited.

An understanding of the lairds of the eighteenth and adjacent centuries will be a necessary part of any new historical survey. For better or for worse they controlled local society. While they and their descendants were a power in the land they exacted, all too often, an obsequious respect. Their merits were lauded and their sins concealed by writers who were their relatives, their dependants or their guests. In a more democratic age local writers have been free to depict the lairds in a less flattering light as arrogant, selfish, oppressive exploiters of the people. The ultimate insult is to ignore them as alien in origin, unrelated to their tenants, interested mainly in southern affairs and irrelevant, except as parasites, to the enduring, gradually evolving, folklife of Orkney. This last view is mistaken. The lairds were an active element in Orcadian society, managing the economy and exercising social control. Benevolent or malevolent, the lairds are too important, interesting and well documented to be neglected by historians.

CHAPTER 13

Who are the Orcadians?

Ronald Miller

The Founding Fathers of Orkney, the Norsemen and their predecessors, have received a generous share of scholarly attention, but the extent of subsequent intrusions, which over the last seven centuries may well have exceeded that of the Norse, has not been studied in detail. The principality of Orkney and the kingdom of Scotland being so close physically, it is not surprising that Norse jarls, with ambitions to extend their rule, should have married influential Scots and that finally (1231) a Scottish family should have succeeded to the Jarldom. Bishops, too, came from the south and in 1472 the see was transferred from Nidaros to St Andrews.

Both temporal and spiritual rule in the islands thus became wholly Scots, and we can imagine how officials and their servants, and adventurers, must have flocked into Orkney. Their typically Scots names feature in the documents of the period, but in no way can we ascertain their exact numbers. Scots influence strengthened with the transfer of the islands to the Scottish crown and reached catastrophic level with the Stewart earls, Robert and Patrick, when to Scottish rule was added the displacement of odallers in favour of Scottish superiors (in the feudal sense). Several of the Scots families who at the time distinguished themselves in the acquisition of other people's land remained prominent thereafter, and some are represented at the present day. Most kept their links with Scotland, often married there and thus further enlarged the Scottish fraction in the Orcadian genetic stock. But again, this cannot be quantified, though we can have recourse to indirect evidence.

The Court Book for Orkney and Shetland of 1614-15 records among its cases patronymics like Eriksone and Johnsdochter in Shetland, but not a single such Norse name figures for Orkney, where all the personal names are either typical Scots, like Cromartie, Craigie, Stewart, or are derived from Orkney place-names like Hackland, Corrigal, Halcro. Since it is a

Scottish custom to name a farmer after his land rather than his father, we cannot be sure that all of these men with Orkney township names are in fact native Orcadians.

Come the Agricultural Revolution, spearheaded by the principal landowner, the Earl of Zetland, and followed by Balfours, Grahams, Traills and other lairds of lesser degree, another influence began to operate. This was the gradual evolution of Orkney agriculture away from subsistence to a market economy. Agricultural improvements originated in the south, and to accelerate change to their profit the lairds brought in factors, grieves, and probably workers skilled in the new techniques, as well as giving tenancies of the newly-enclosed farms to incomers whose expertise qualified them to find the new, inflated, rents. The next step in this process, and perhaps the major instalment in the economic revolution, was the introduction of regular steam navigation in 1833. Apart from general convenience, this had the prime effect of making possible the export of cattle, something that was hopelessly risky in sailing ships. Since the climate and soils of Orkney make grass the optimum crop, farmers were now able to move away from their former uneconomic dependence on grain, a crop that was frequently ruined by inclement weather. The transition to the present emphasis on cattle was accompanied by mechanisation and a rash of new building which created a considerable service industry often initiated or run by incomers. As the scientific element in agriculture waxed and government intervened with regulations, advice, subsidies and the like, a considerable bureaucracy developed — recently estimated at one individual for every 12 farms — and most of them were incomers. This older bureaucracy, however, has now been more than matched by the elaboration of governmental intervention, both central and local, in recent times, and again the majority of the functionaries are incomers, as are most of the medicals, veterinaries, clergy and schoolteachers.

But the land was not the only attraction to incomers. Fishing activity was desultory until last century, when a considerable herring fishing developed. But the Scottish boats 'followed' the herring, starting on the west coast, passing to Shetland, then Orkney, Wick and so on down to Lowestoft eventually. In Stronsay, which was the principal Orkney centre, immigrant families from the Fair Isle are still recognised, while Burray had strong links with Wick, bringing in Caithness people to match the earlier settlers who had suffered Clearance from Sutherland.

But the geographical position brought yet another distinctly outlandish contribution to the genes of Orkney. The Hudson's

Bay Company engaged large numbers of young men for minimum contracts of five years. Inevitably a new race developed — Orcadian × Indian (mostly Cree), and while on the one hand many Hudson's Bay Orcadians settled in Canada, some of those who returned brought Indian wives and/or their children. Only family histories could estimate how much Cree blood is in Orkney, for since the Cree partner was female, personal name clues do not exist.

The twentieth century has probably seen as great an influx of new blood as at any time, largely through war. True, the Napoleonic Wars brought a few incomers — we know that an Irish veteran gave his name to Finstown and a Corporal Downie to the Mortification[1] of that name in Stromness — but it was in the two World Wars that the input was most striking. Not only did some Orcadians serving in the south bring back spouses, but since Scapa Flow was a major naval anchorage in both wars, large numbers of servicemen were posted to the defence of Orkney in general and the Flow in particular. Such was the threat from the air in the Second War that the Orkney garrison outnumbered the residents by two to one. The effect on the genetic stock is incalculable.

Finally, the deterioration of the quality of life in the industrialised south — 80% urban — and the relatively unspoilt state of Orkney has of recent years attracted many settlers, whose numbers are officially estimated at 100 per year, born in England and Wales.

We can learn a great deal about recent immigration to Orkney from the national census, which records place of birth, but this rich mine of information has not yet been worked. However, even a cursory glance is enlightening. Before the First World War, the 1911 census showed that 92% of the population was native-born; in 1961, the last year for which this information was given, the percentage was 87%. At that time, then, 13% or almost one in seven of the population of Orkney was non-native. In 1911, 211 people, or 0.8% of the population were born in England and Wales; in 1971 there were 505, or 2.9% of the population. In 1911, 110 people were born outwith the UK; in 1971 there were 195. Within Scotland, the principal places of origin were in 1971, Edinburgh — 293 persons, Aberdeen 279, Glasgow 204, Shetland 218 and Caithness 115. Other counties contributed, but less than 100 each. It is not suggested, of course, that all the incomers recorded in the census became settlers; only a study of the census enumerators' books over a series of decades could determine this.

But if it is worth asking "Who are the Orcadians?" the same

question in the singular must also be valid, viz. "Who is an Orcadian?" Most Orcadians believe that this is much more than a matter of being born in the County, or of Orcadian parents, or having x years of residence. Such criteria may be sufficient to determine whether a man, be he black, brown or yellow, can acquire British nationality or a variant thereof, but the requirements for the title 'Orcadian' are much more subtle. Orcadians have been called a 'Peculiar People' and there is much truth in this, for they have a peculiarly strong individuality. In England, Yorkshire people and the Cornish, for example, regard themselves as Something Else. So it is with Orkney, and this feeling of being distinctly different stems from a unique physical and historical ambience.

Life on a small island sets one apart not only literally but also mentally. Most human beings feel a curious reaction, which cannot be articulated, to living on, or even visiting, a small island. With the exception of the Mainland, none of the islands comprising Orkney is too big for all the inhabitants to know, or know of, all the others. This generates a wonderful sense of community, expecially in contrast with a similar-size group set in the continuum of, say, the millions in the English plain. The small total population of Orkney — a mere 18,000, less than the combined student total for the universities of Edinburgh and Glasgow — also confers a certain distinctiveness.

But there is also a community of cultural background. There is a general belief that Orcadians are descended from Vikings. However mistaken this may be, it has a unifying effect, though happily not so intoxicating as to lead to the excesses of Up-Helly-Aa. On a more mundane level, the rack-renting lairds of great-grandfather's day inculcated the virtues of hard work and the ability to see a task through, be it ever so distasteful or wearying. Certain other islands of Scotland, with a different background, have been described as placing a high value on leisure. Idleness is not counted a virtue in Orkney. Not that Orcadians are so virtuous: punitive rents, paid in kind, often yielded the laird bad meal (which he exported to Shetland or Norway) and butter so outstandingly foul that it served only to grease carriage wheels. A notable Orcadian of the eighteenth century, James Fea, wrote that Orcadians are 'quick in discerning their interest and indefatigable in the pursuit of it.' Nowadays, presumably, he would say they were go-getters, but he would, we hope, be meaning they were full of get-up-and-go. The Hudson's Bay Company valued Orcadians because they were literate, numerate, docile but tough, conscientious and above all poor, so that they could be engaged for small wages. They also had the reputation of being clannish and reserved. One Canadian writer called them 'the slyest set of men under the sun.'

In a later generation, another unifying factor appeared. Crippling taxation on big landowners after the 1914-18 war led to the sale of land to its occupiers and though the average farm was small and all the virtues listed above were still necessary to remain viable, nearly everyone became a 'peerie laird,' master of all he surveyed up to his boundary fences, and motivated to take advantage of the new and remunerative ideas the government agricultural advisers were offering. Thus while the rest of the country was four-fifths urban, full of wage-earners often doing dull and even meaningless work and building the Bedlam which is our modern industrialised society, Orcadians shared independent owner-occupier status, were self-employed and concerned with real things, the land, the sea, the weather, plants and animals. For a more eloquent expression of this, read George Mackay Brown. They shared, moreover, the same annual cycle of events and work on both land and sea and thus developed a fellowship and an almost classless society. As a local man wrote:

> The solitudes of land and sea assuage
> My quenchless thirst for freedom unconfined;
> With independent heart and mind
> Hold I my heritage.[2]

But if there is a common background in culture, way of life and standard of values, there is also a unifying influence in the physical environment. Orcadians share in the delights of insularity but deplore in chorus the high cost of transport. They delight in the high summer weather, the simmer dim, the pure crystal-clear air off the sea, the sky full of larks and the scent of clover and meadow-sweet, and they respect each other for the phlegm with which they endure the purgatory which is the winter weather. A deep fellow-feeling is generated by recollections of how sea-sick they have all been in the mail-boat.

Such then, or something like it, is the experience and outlook which characterises the Orcadian, and one who is born into, or comes in and accepts such attitudes and standards, merges into the communal life and is recognised as an Orcadian, even though, after 40 years, he retains his Lowland, Cockney, or American accent. On the other hand one who believes — and shows — that he brings and subscribes to different and to him superior standards remains an outsider, though normally he would receive the basic courtesies. New Orcadians come in all shapes and guises, from A to Z — A for Adams, a family founded by one who came ashore from his Aberdeen ship and stayed, to Z for Zawadski, a family founded by a Polish officer who was so integrated into the community that a ship had to be chartered to take the Mainland mourners to his funeral in his home island.

It has to be confessed, however, that this essay is written by one who is at best a Senior Citizen and at worst, Past It. He is by birth and upbringing an Orcadian with a background of farmers, fishermen and rural craftsmen — blacksmith, boat-builder, cooper — and he could well be charged with nostalgic misconception or, more kindly, with being grossly out of date. Both of these may well be true and he would be the first to point out that the long evolution of man and his relationship to the land and sea in Orkney is still proceeding. Television, of course, is eroding local characteristics in Orkney as elsewhere, as are other influences from the south. Orkney farmers, for long fiercely independent, now rattle the begging bowl with the best, and national subsidies on cattle, sheep, fences, lime and transport are enthusiastically accepted. The growth of the services and of officialdom, mostly centred in Kirkwall, forming of it a bigger proportion of the population of Orkney than ever before, has multiplied the numbers of wage-earners, many living in subsidised housing. Features of urbanised industrialised life are appearing, such as juvenile delinquency and strikes, previously almost unknown in Orkney. It has to be recognised, therefore, that there are tendencies, often generated by outside influences, as in the past, that may well erode what were the essential Orcadian characteristics. It could be that the time is approaching when the answer to "Who are the Orcadians?" will be "Who?"

Appendix A
The Environment of Early Man in Orkney

Elaine R. Bullard

Analysis of pollen from Sandwick and The Loons on the Mainland indicates that the Orkney landscape was open and rather barren between 14,000 and 10,000 years ago (bp, or before present), consisting of open grassland and heath. This became better developed during the climatic warming of the so-called Allerød Interstadial period, with grasses, sedge, juniper, willow, saxifrages, sorrel and crowberry being important constituents of the flora. The remnants of the tundra flora, which characterised the islands as the Pleistocene ice finally retreated, persist on the tops of the highest Hoy hills today and which probably covered all hill tops in Orkney all through the warm Boreal period and up to the commencement of blanket peat c. 3400 bp. (The initiation of blanket peat in Orkney also appears later than in the rest of Scotland.)

The climax pine forest of mainland Scotland never seems to have reached Orkney, possibly because the Pentland Firth was a too efficient barrier, but the birch/hazel scrub, which probably appeared first well before the Boreal, seemed to reach a climax corresponding to that in Scotland. Except that hazel was more abundant, it seems to have had roughly the same components as the remnant in Berriedale today, and this type of scrubby woodland can be found in parts of Europe within a wide band of temperature range and wind exposure although all may be in areas of relatively high rainfall or humidity. Recent studies have shown that the trees in Berriedale have a perfectly normal rate of growth, indicting that their restriction is not due to climatic conditions alone.

Whether it was man or climate that caused the birch/hazel scrub to decline is uncertain, although present opinion inclines to the former. Certain pollen studies indicate a largely treeless landscape since at least 4,300 bp. The dating of a settlement at the Knap of Howar to 4,800 bp puts the erection of these earliest known domestic buildings in Orkney very close indeed to the sudden decline of the birch/hazel scrub around 5,000 bp, as dated from samples taken in the West Mainland. Possibly the transition from birch/hazel scrub occurred in two phases, with woody species disappearing first whilst tall herb and fern communities remained, followed by grazing and the change to pasture vegetation. Certainly it all took place over a short period of time. The presence of tree remains found preserved in peat below sea-level has not yet been satisfactorily explained.

The birch/hazel scrub declined less rapidly in more sheltered sites and sufficient pockets survived throughout the Neolithic period to permit some regeneration in the early part of the Bronze Age; the Berriedale wood in Hoy is a pocket which still survives. Only if the tree decline in Orkney could be proved to have begun before the arrival of man, could it be attributed entirely to a change in the climate, especially an increase in strength and frequency of westerly gales.

Other evidence frequently quoted for increase in winds, not only in Orkney but in other offshore islands around Scotland, is the appearance of depositions of sand, sometimes under Neolithic settlements but also in loch sediments near such settlements. At least five are quoted, but in one a few Neolithic sherds were found under the sand. Once the presence of Neolithic man before the deposition of sand is indicated it immediately opens the possibility that man himself was responsible for sand movement, by the removal or damage of vegetation covering stable dunes; and although blown sand will itself kill trees (badly disturbed dunes may take 50-100 years to 'settle down') it could also be inferred that if early Neolithic man had the ability to destroy dune vegetation how much more would he be likely to destroy trees, especially for fuel in the absence of peat and in the period before domestic stock made dried dung available? (He also used seaweed, but any available woodland must have been a far superior source of fuel.)

Of course, there is ample evidence for climatic changes over the greater part of Scotland and all the earlier changes in vegetation must have been caused by natural agency. So far, there is less evidence for pre-5000 bp climatic changes in the extreme north and west, particularly the islands, and it seems likely that all the fluctuations were less marked, just as on the mainland of Scotland they were less marked than in England and Europe. Once the critical 5000 bp age is reached the possible intervention of Neolithic man becomes a possibility, even in the lack of archaeological remains as old as this. The apparent 'gap' is very short and a non-expert could postulate the possibility of early Neolithic man being completely nomadic, living off the shore and such fruits and nuts as were available, using the scrub for shelter and fuel, perhaps carelessly, until later settlers brought in domestic livestock, crop husbandry and the need to settle, and leave artefacts and evidence of settlements. By then most of the scrub was gone and building with stone became essential.

The evidence that by burning and by extremely heavy grazing, late Neolithic man was at least partially responsible for the initiation of blanket peat, is indisputable. The almost complete removal of trees, disturbance of dune systems, and blanket peat initiation, are more or less irreversible or self-perpetuating. Loss of trees, however scrubby, does itself cause a deterioration of climate almost anywhere in the world, and once the tree species fall below certain numbers (or are banished from islands altogether) tree regeneration becomes impossible through lack of seed, even if all grazing and burning ceases. Blanket peat quickly makes fertile soils infertile, well-drained soils waterlogged and unsuitable for a natural return of trees or even of dwarf shrub tundra. Once sand deserts are initiated they become very difficult to reclaim.

Within historic times in Orkney several changes in agricultural practice have profoundly influenced the appearance of the landscape. The use of leys and of methods to stabilise sand changed the North Isles considerably, although some marked sand movement still occurs and could probably be halted. Leys and semi-permanent pasture including wild white clover brought almost all hill pasturing to an end and took sheep off cliff faces (resulting in a big increase in woodrush). Many other changes are taking place at present; these are controlled in the sense that they are carried out for a definite purpose, even if all may not agree; Neolithic man seems to have had little control over the results of his actions and may have hastened his own decline by allowing himself to be grazed out. The early blanket peat period has a dearth of archaeological remains.

A guess based on the available evidence indicates a pre-5000 bc Orkney with a lot of open water, marsh and fen; a dense, probably almost impenetratable scrub of hazel and birch and a few other tree species, especially willows, twisted with wild rose and honeysuckle and a jungle-like undergrowth of ferns, herbs and sedges, completely ungrazed, even by rodents, on all low land and on the lower slopes of hills, (something like the more unspoiled parts of the Burren in the west of Ireland today). And even the higher parts of the hills and their tops would have had some kin with the open limestone pavement of the Burren, for the soils would have been extremely thin but base-rich and the tundra dwarf shrubs would have included an abundance of

Mountain Avens. Like the Burren, it was probably very attractive and 'green' and not at all an inhospitable land.

One thing, still unproven, and only indicated by negative evidence, is the suggested absence of all land mammals. So far, all the land mammals known to be in Orkney now or in the past are either known introductions or highly probable introductions, and land carnivores are conspicuously absent. If this is so, and pollen analysis is highly indicative of it, the Pentland Firth or some other barrier existed at an early date.

That climatic changes, even very slight, do bring about other changes can be seen in recent events in Orkney. The north and west Highlands had a marked amelioration of climate around the middle of the last century; the subsequent deterioration has probably been the cause of a decrease of Mountain Avens in Hoy, and by the known increase of the Oyster Plant. The former likes base-rich conditions which have been leached out by the slightly increased rainfall over the last 100 years, while the Oyster Plant must have cool summers! But generally the effects of such changes are not very marked and do not last long. The effects of man's actions usually are marked and usually persist. The fact that apples etc. were frequently planted by the big houses in the 19th century may indicate the 'warm' period.

Appendix B
St Findan and the Pictish-Norse Transition

Introductory Note William P. L. Thomson

In Chapter 8 Professor Peter Foote refers briefly to the important evidence about conditions in early Norse Orkney contained in the biography of an obscure Irish saint, St Findan. The 'Vita Findani' appeared in print as long ago as 1887[1] but its significance, and indeed its very existence, seems to have escaped the notice of historians. The 1887 edition was printed in the original Latin and is now somewhat inaccessible; no translation has hitherto appeared. It has been thought useful to include the *Life* as an appendix because of the light it sheds on a theme crucial to this book — the Pictish-Norse transition.

When we make use of any saint's *Life,* it is important to come to some conclusion about its reliability as historical evidence. Findan's *Life* is not just a catalogue of carbon-copy miracles, and in fact it is not particularly miraculous. Like any saint's *Life,* it contains the obligatory miracle, but that was an incident which might not have been regarded as supernatural by someone with more knowledge of maritime survival techniques than Findan's cloistered biographer. Findan's *Life* also has the great merit of being more or less contemporary. He was admitted to holy orders in 851 AD and is believed to have died in 878 AD, his whole religious life being spent on the Continent. His biographer, believed to be a fellow-Irishman since he occasionally uses Irish words, was personally acquainted with Findan and, it has been suggested, may have lodged for a time in his cell.[2] The biography was probably written in the latter part of the ninth century, and Findan's youthful adventures in Orkney can be dated no later than the decade 840-850 AD. In general, the *Life* may be considered likely to contain useful historical material.

The first section consists of a very believable description of Viking slave raids and slave trading in Ireland, but the story becomes important to us when Findan eluded his captors in Orkney as he was being transported back to Norway. Escaping from an uninhabited island, Findan found chance benefactors who took him to a bishop whose seat was nearby (*tunc illi susceptum eum ad vicinae civitatis duxerunt episcopum*). Since the *Life* describes Orkney as lying next to the land of the Picts (*iuxta Pictorum gentem*), it was clearly not regarded as part of Pictland, and so must already have been under Norse control, as indeed we would expect by that date. The presence of a bishop and a monastic house a generation or more after the first arrival of the Norse hardly squares with the traditional image of bloodthirsty raiders who obliterated all traces of Christianity. It suggests conquest and settlement by Norwegians in circumstances which permitted the survival of Pictish institutions. However, an element of doubt remains since the *Life* does not make it clear how far Findan was taken before he reached the bishop's residence. The bishop was apparently located in Orkney but, even if he was not, the presence of a monastic house anywhere in the north of Scotland at that date is highly significant.

The Findan story also provides a little information on language. We are told that the bishop, although not himself an Irishman, had been educated in Ireland and was therefore able to converse with Findan. Apparently the bishop was unable to communicate in his own language, and this suggests that he was a native Pict. Since the whole question of the language spoken by the Northern Picts is a highly contentious issue,[3] this reference is interesting. Whatever language it was, it was apparently incomprehensible to a mid-ninth century Irishman.

The bishop's Irish connections point to links between the church in Orkney and the Columban-Irish brand of Christianity. While a previous generation would have expected such a connection, recent authorities have been at pains to stress the very pronounced Northumbrian influences to be found in the pre-Norse church in Orkney.[4] The bishop's Irish affiliations are perhaps a useful counterbalance; Irish and Northumbrian influences were not altogether mutually exclusive.

Beyond that we may, if we wish, enter the realms of speculation (but we should be very clear that that is what we are doing). The temptation to engage in some fascinating detective works is irresistible — where was Findan's desert island, and where was the seat of this interesting bishop? The *Life* provides a surprising number of clues:

1. The island was situated in Orkney and in a convenient place for a Viking ship to take shelter while waiting for suitable conditions for a voyage to Norway.
2. It was "at one point surrounded by a great sea, and in another fringed by a small bay".

3. Part of its coast had caves and clefts in the rock which provided Findan with a hiding-place.
4. The island was uninhabited but was opposite land which could be seen to be peopled.
5. It was hazardous, but not impossible, to escape from the island without a boat.
6. The neighbouring island may have contained the seat of a bishop.

It has recently been suggested on quite different grounds that Pictish Orkney may indeed have had a resident bishop and that the most likely location of his seat was in Papa Westray[5] where the pre-Norse dedications to St Boniface and St Tredwell, and the extensive nature of the former site,[6] suggest an ecclesiastical centre of some importance. Such a place was ideally situated to serve both Orkney and Shetland, possibly having links with other west coast ecclesiastical sites such as Birsay, St Ninian's Isle and Papil. So, if there was a bishop in Orkney in Findan's day, perhaps we should look for him in Papa Westray. Interestingly, Hugh Marwick on the basis of place-name evidence (which some people would nowadays discount) suggested that the *papae* might have been left relatively undisturbed by the Norse invaders.[7]

The *Life* describes how Findan's captors on their homeward voyage to Norway arrived in Orkney where they waited for a fair wind for the North Sea crossing. There must have been many similar occasions in the Viking Age. In the meantime they travelled "here and there" among the islands, but it might be expected that the general direction of their wanderings was northwards in readiness for the next leg to Shetland; possibly they intended to follow the route west of Shetland which was often used as a means of avoiding the hazards of the Pentland Firth and the Sumburgh Roost.[8] In these circumstances it would not be surprising to find the Viking ship in the vicinity of Papa Westray.

The Holm of Papay fulfils the requirements for Findan's desert island. The description of his island as open on one side to the ocean and on the other fringed by a small bay might fit several places in Orkney, but it is certainly an exact description of the holm. The small bay, South Wick, between the holm and the main island is an excellent harbour where modern fishing boats can lie at their moorings. It was just the kind of place where a viking ship en route to Shetland might shelter. But we do not need just to guess that the *vík* was a likely harbour for Viking ships — we know that it was. On the west side of the inlet lies the farm of Skennist (Old Norse *skeiða-naust*) which takes its name from the place where a *skeið*, a fast-sailing type of longship, could be drawn up.[9]

With a newly-captured slave to exercise, it was a sensible precaution to put him ashore on the holm rather than on the settled side of the bay. The low cliffs on the exposed east side of the island provide the kind of terrain necessary for the location of Findan's hiding-place. Escape from the holm after the departure of the Vikings would not have been easy — it would have been a memorable experience, but it would not have been impossible. With local knowledge, it is relatively easy to reach

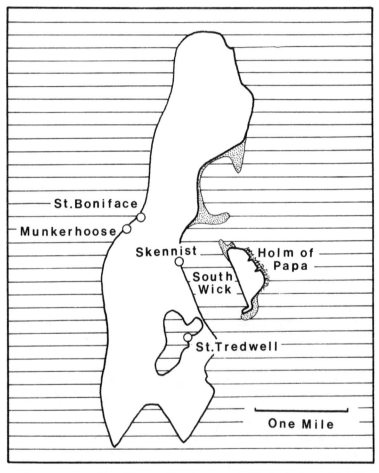

Fig. 44. The Holm of Papay (Papa) — was it Findan's desert island?

the holm at low tide although there often appears to be a fair expanse of water. At one time horses were grazed on the holm, and it was possible to drive them across the channel. A desperate man could certainly escape. The miracle which his biographer describes whereby Findan's clothing became rigid, enabling him to float on the water, suggests that the practically-minded saint had improvised an air-filled float from his own garments, and was so able to reach the main island by a combination of swimming and wading. We may then imagine him being looked after by the bishop and the hospitable monks on the St Boniface site.

One would have to admit that his search for three days before he climbed a hill and discovered human habitation seems hardly likely in Papa Westray, but it would be almost equally difficult to imagine that this statement could be literally true in any other part of Orkney. The purpose of hagiography was to emphasise the suffering and endurance of the subject; an element of exaggeration was invariably a feature of a saint's *Life*.

The author of this note would be the first to recognise that the identification of the Holm of Papay as Findan's desert island is far from certain, yet it seems to fit the bill remarkably well. The linking of the Findan story with the archaeological remains on the St Boniface site is an exciting possibility. But if this remains doubtful, the main point of the story is clear; the 'Vita Findani' provides acceptable historical evidence pointing to the survival of a Christian community in Orkney as late as the period 840-850 AD.

References

1. O. Holder-Egger, 1887, 'Vita Findani', *Monumenta Germanicae Historica* XV 1, pp. 502-506.
2. O. Holder-Egger, *op.cit.,* p. 502.
3. K. H. Jackson, 'The Pictish Language', in F. T. Wainwright, *The Problem of the Picts* (1955), pp, 129-160.
4. R. G. Lamb, forth., 'The Eighth-Century Pictish Church of Orkney' (Orkney: Brochs to Viking Age Conference, 1986).
5. R. G. Lamb, forth., *op.cit.*
6. R. G. Lamb, *The Archaeological Sites on Papa Westray and Westray* (1983), pp. 18-19; William P. L. Thomson, *History of Orkney* (1987), Ch. 1.
7. H. Marwick, 'Antiquarian Notes on Papa Westray', *Proceedings of the Orkney Antiquarian Society* III (1924-5).
8. Barbara E. Crawford, 'Papa Stour: Continuity, Survival and Change in One Shetland Island', In Alexander Fenton and Hermann Pálsson, *The Northern and Western Isles in the Viking World* (1984), p. 40.
9. H. Marwick, *Orkney Farm Names* (1952), p. 46.

The Life of Saint Findan

translated from the Latin by Christine J. Omand

Some were chosen and predestined by almighty God for eternal life before the world began and these, in His ineffable compassion, He is accustomed to guide into more perfect ways of life by the various means springing from the purest fountain of His mercy.

Also I thought it not inglorious to write a short composition in praise of a remarkable man who gave our times examples to imitate. Both we who read them often and also future generations will find something useful for personal improvement.

I shall now, therefore, try, God willing, to explain in detail how a man called Findan, of Scottish[1] race and a native of the Leinster [*Laginensis*] region, reached perfection of life, though frequently afflicted with temptations and troubles.

To begin: Foreigners called Norsemen [*Nordmanni*] had captured Findan's sister, along with other women during raids on that Scottish[1] island [*Scottiae insulae*] called Ireland. His father then gave his son Findan some money and ordered him to buy his sister back and return her to her father.

Eager to fulfil his father's orders and with his loyal heart full of brotherly love, he set out with some companions and an interpreter, but was soon captured on the journey by the pagans.

He was put in chains and taken without delay to their ships, which lay on the shore nearby. That day and the following night, he remained bound in fetters, without food or drink. In the morning, when the Norsemen went into council, some of the more reasonable men with, I believe, a kindness inspired by God, suggested that those who had come there to ransom others, should not have been held by force, and so in this way he was freed. In short, our most holy Lord knew that His servant, living still the life of the laity, would later serve Him most devotedly in all things; and so He deigned to free him from the hands of his enemies. Similarly, when a crowd of the same enemy chased him as he ran into a house and hid behind a door, none of them could find him although they were running round about him in all directions.

I do not think I should fail to mention how it came about that he undertook a journey abroad and tried very laudably to complete it. In that same province of Leinster, a great quarrel arose between two chieftains. Findan's father was a soldier of one chieftain and he killed a man from the other side. Hearing

284

this, the chieftain of the other side, exceedingly angry, immediately went to Findan's father's house accompanied by a large army, intending to destroy all his property and himself with fire and sword. Coming by night, they surrounded the house with arms and, throwing fire at the roof, murdered Findan's father as he came outside. Findan was staying at another house and they beset him similarly with flames, but were unable to seize him as he courageously defended himself in front of the door; obviously protected by divine grace, he escaped, only slightly injured, through the flames and the enemy. They killed his brother who had been in the same house. Following this, great hostility and inexorable strife arose between the two races.

After a short interval of time, however, due to the mediation of certain trusted men, a considerable sum of money was given to Findan and his men and peace was resumed on both sides. In that same year, however, Findan's enemies feared that the grief for his father would rekindle in his heart and vengeance would fall on them. At the same time they wished to be rid of him entirely, and so they plotted secretly to trick him in this way. Having decided on a plan, they prepared a banquet at a place on the seashore. After Findan had been invited here, the Norsemen came and, as agreed with his enemies, seized him from the middle of the guests, bound him very tightly in chains and took him away with them. Then, according to custom, his Norse master, not wishing to return to his homeland, sold him to another, who sold him to a third, who in turn sold him to a fourth. This last master, longing to see his native land again, gathered his companions together and took Findan and others with him into captivity. Then, when they had sailed half-way across the sea, they happened to meet a fleet from their native country. A man from these ships boarded the ship Findan was on and asked about the nature of the island and how they had fared there. On that ship, however, was one whose brother had been killed by the man who asked the questions; he immediately recognised and killed him. When his companions saw this, they got ready for battle and a long and fierce struggle between the two ships followed. While this struggle was going on, Findan, though held in chains, stood up, eager to bring help to his master and his companions. Several of the other ships, however, intervened and came between those who fought and in this way Findan's ship moved back, out of harm's way.

Then his master remembered the devotion he had shown in wishing to bring him help, even in chains, and he wanted to reward such loyalty. Soon, therefore, he removed the chains and foresaw that Findan would be an asset to him.

After these events, they came to certain islands called Orkney [*Orcades*] next to the land of the Picts. They therefore disembarked, recuperated, travelled here and there over the islands and waited for a fair wind. When Findan observed their dissoluteness, he began to explore places on the islands and to worry about his safety and escape. Finding therefore a huge rock in a remote region, he set about hiding himself under it at once. The sea normally came up to this rock as the tide rose, so he did not know what to do or where to turn. On one side the sea pressed him; on the other side he was tormented by fear of the enemy as they ran to and fro about him, walked on top of the rock under which he lay hidden, and called for him by name from every quarter. And so, preferring to endure the rage of the sea rather than fall into the hands of men surpassing all monsters in ferocity, he scorned the massive waves and remained in that place without food, that day and the following night. Next day, however, the enemy stayed in another part of the island. There was also a recession of the tide which had touched the cave's entrance and sometimes, driven by a gust of wind, had forced a wave right into the cave. Findan therefore stood up and, creeping through the thorny places in fear of the heathens, examined everything most carefully with his hands and began to find a way out. He thought, moreover, that the land around him was inhabited by people. In fact, seeing the end of the island, he realised that in one part it was surrounded by a great sea, and in another part fringed by a small bay.

So, having lost all his bodily strength, and too overwhelmed by sickness brought on by imprisonment and hunger, he did not dare to entrust himself to the water. His troubles increased and for three days on end he stayed there, wandering through the island looking for a way out, sustained only by plants and water. At last, at the dawn of the third day, he caught sight of sea-monsters and huge-bodied dolphins playing and rolling about near the shore. He was overcome with divine tranquillity and pondered over these things with a quiet mind. Tearfully he poured out these words from the bottom of his heart: "God, you have created both these dumb animals and me, a man; you have given them the sea to move through, and me the earth on which to plant safe footsteps. Help me now in my distress with your accustomed compassion. From this hour, I dedicate my body and soul to your service and I shall never turn my mind back to worldly allurements. I shall seek you at the thresholds of the Apostles. I shall undertake a journey abroad, never to return to my native land. From this time I shall serve you with all my strength and following you, I do not wish to look behind me."

Armed with this firmness of faith, therefore, though fully clothed, he jumped into the water. I am about to tell of marvellous things: divine compassion immediately made his clothes so stiff that, held up by them, he could not sink. His clothes seemed to float and he was carried along to land like this, through the waves, unharmed. He climbed up to the top of the hills, hoping to be able to see houses or smoke coming from dwellings, and he had again spent two days on a sparse diet of plants, when at dawn on the third day, he suddenly saw men walking in the distance. On seeing them, his heart leapt with joy and he had no hesitation in approaching them, though they were strangers. They came to his aid and took him to a bishop whose seat was nearby. This man had been instructed in the study of letters in Ireland and was quite skilled in the knowledge of this language. Findan stayed with him for two years, enjoying the many benefits of his kindness and generosity. But, remembering his promise, he gathered his companions and, with the permission of the bishop, prepared to go to the Gallic countries. First he headed for the shrine of Martin, then, travelling through Franconia, Alemannia and Langobardia, at last arrived at Rome after a weary journey on foot.

Returning from there, he went to a certain nobleman in Alemannia, with whom he stayed in clerical office for four years, each year making progress in the virtue of abstinence and always setting new examples. Then the superior at his monastery, called Rinaugia, received him into holy orders in 851 AD.[2] Every year for five years, he climbed the staircase of virtue and eventually, inflamed with a greater desire for improvement, shut himself up in a very confined place and completely subjugated his body by unheard-of abstinence.

1. Findan is called 'Scottish' and Ireland a 'Scottish' island because of the Irish origin of the Scots.
2. This is the date accepted as correct by scholars.

Appendix C
An Orkney Family Story

Alex T. Annal

(All Orkney families at one time knew about the lives of the generations before them. Today few have the opportunity to learn, and certainly very few indeed have such a systematic knowledge of their forefathers as does Alex. Annal of Brecks and Myres in South Ronaldsay. He has shown how the Annals originated from the arrival in Orkney around the year 1550 of the Rev. James Annand, from Annandale in Dumfries, one of the two commissioners for the planting of kirks who travelled around Orkney to carry out the work of the Reformation. There were several Annals with Governor William Tomison of the Hudson's Bay Company at Edmonton, Alberta, including one of Alex. Annal's great-grandfathers. Another of his great-grandfathers was for a time a harpooner at the whaling in Davis Straits.)

The other night while watching the TV there flashed across the screen a picture of Tynemouth in Northumberland; there was the mile-long breakwater where I often had a Sunday evening stroll, the old castle, the Grand Hotel, and the house where I stayed at Kenners Dean — and, most of all, the twenty-foot-high statue facing the sea where I had read so often on the stone plinth the inscription: "This monument was erected by the people of Tynemouth in honour of a noble citizen of this town, Admiral Collingwood, who commanded the battleship *Saint of Trinidad* at the naval battle of Trafalgar."

My grandfather often told me about this ship because from the age of four years he was reared by his uncle Jackie Flett who served as an officer under Admiral Collingwood on board the *Saint of Trinidad* and was there at the Battle of Trafalgar. When Jackie returned home after Napoleon was defeated his speech was very flamboyant and 'Englified' with what he described as 'the King's English', and naturally my grandfather adopted the same style. I can still remember him talking always very proper while all the rest of the family spoke Orcadian dialect.

The *Saint of Trinidad* was a very strong vessel, the pride of the French fleet, but was captured by the British and sailed against the French at Trafalgar. It is not so long ago since this battleship ended her days on the sands of Florida. During the 1930s, my cousin Captain James Young, while on a voyage along the coast of Florida, saw a huge hulk of a wooden ship beached up on the sands and on her transom in huge gold letters was her name, *Saint of Trinidad*. It was of great interest to Captain Young to see this vessel intact one hundred and thirty years after his great-grandfather had served aboard her at Trafalgar.

Jackie Flett bought a little croft, about 12 acres, in the Hollan district of South Ronaldsay, and continued to farm and live there until his wife died in 1860. When Jackie thought he would marry again, however, the lady of his choice was in Flotta, so Jackie sold his farm and went to stay with his wife in that island. Jackie was quite an old man by this time; however, his wife bore him quite a family, and I understand that some of his descendants are still in Flotta. He died in Stromness well up in his nineties.

A small dry gloup at Ham Geo is known as Jackie Flett's Hole: that was where he hid from the press gang, but he was cornered there by Scott the Sheriff Officer and Lawrightman Donald Tomison of Halcro. (The press gang were compelled to find a certain number of men, or have to serve the King themselves.)

Appendix D

Orkney Blood Group Samples

Observed numbers and gene frequencies for all red cell antigens, enzymes and serum proteins from four major regions of Orkney, and Orkney tables.

Symbols used in tabulation

North Isles = NI   South Isles = SI
West Mainland = WM   East Mainland = EM

ABO Blood Group System Observed numbers					
	NI	WM	EM	SI	TOTAL
A_1	23	38	26	30	117
A_2	8	9	3	2	22
B	32	16	10	7	65
A_1B	1	4	0	0	5
A_2B	4	2	0	1	7
O	59	51	34	38	182
Total	127	120	73	78	398

Gene frequencies (%)					
	NI	WM	EM	SI	TOTAL
p_1	10.02	19.40	19.95	21.70	16.84
p_2	5.55	5.88	2.78	2.73	4.74
q	15.88	9.63	7.19	5.29	10.24
r	68.55	65.09	70.08	70.28	68.18
Total	100	100	100	100	100

P Blood Group System						
	NI	WM	EM	SI	TOTAL	
P_1	40.70	52.57	53.18	54.71	48.95	%
$P_2 + p$	59.30	47.43	46.82	45.29	51.05	
No. tested	128	120	73	78	399	

Lutheran				
	NI	WM	EM	SI	TOTAL
Lu^a	2.37	4.69	5.64	3.26	3.83
Lu^b	97.63	95.31	94.36	96.74	96.17
Total	128	120	73	78	399

Kell				
	NI	WM	EM	SI	TOTAL
K	4.29	1.25	2.05	3.84	2.88
k	95.71	98.75	97.95	96.16	97.12
No. tested	128	120	73	78	399

Kp^a				
	NI	WM	EM	SI	TOTAL
Kp^a	0	2.08	0.68	1.28	1.00
Kp^b	100	97.92	99.32	98.72	99.00
No. tested	128	120	73	78	399

Duffy				
	NI	WM	EM	SI	TOTAL
Fy^a	57.39	41.12	52.12	46.15	49.32
Fy^b	42.61	58.88	47.88	58.55	50.68
No. tested	115	107	71	78	371

Kidd				
	NI	WM	EM	SI	TOTAL
JK^a	insuff.	56.82	48.59	43.33	48.46
JK^b	data	43.18	51.41	56.67	51.54
No. tested		66	71	75	227

Adenosine Deaminase Variation				
	NI	WM	EM	SI	TOTAL
ADA^1	96.59	94.54	97.89	93.51	95.50
ADA^2	3.41	5.46	2.11	6.49	4.50
No. tested	88	199	71	77	355

Acid Phosphatase					
	NI	WM	EM	SI	TOTAL
P[a]	32.11	34.87	28.78	36.53	33.20
P[b]	61.39	59.24	69.19	59.63	61.83
P[c]	6.50	5.88	2.04	3.84	4.95
No. tested	123	119	73	78	393

6-Phosphogluconate Dehydrogenase					
	NI	WM	EM	SI	TOTAL
PGD^A	97.66	99.16	98.63	98.10	98.37
PGD^C	2.34	0.84	1.37	1.90	1.63
No. tested	128	119	73	79	399

Adenylate Kinase					
	NI	WM	EM	SI	TOTAL
AK^1	96.88	94.12	100	92.31	95.72
AK^2	3.12	5.88	0.00	7.69	4.28
No. tested	128	119	72	78	397

Haptoglobin					
	NI	WM	EM	SI	TOTAL
Hp^1	40.70	44.91	36.98	50.64	43.23
Hp^2	59.30	55.09	63.02	49.36	56.77
No. tested	129	118	73	79	399

Phosphoglucomutase					
	NI	WM	EM	SI	TOTAL
PGM^1	72.80	77.31	76.71	76.28	75.57
PGM^2	27.20	22.69	23.29	23.72	24.43
No. tested	125	119	73	78	395

MNSs Blood Group System *Observed numbers*					
	NI	WM	EM	SI	TOTAL
MSMS	4	9	2	4	19
MSMs	22	13	11	10	56
MsMs	17	13	18	6	54
MSNS	0	1	0	2	3
MNSs	30	22	12	23	87
MsNs	40	44	22	16	122
NSNS	0	0	0	0	0
NSNs	4	0	2	4	10
NsNs	11	18	6	13	48
Total	128	120	73	78	399

Gene frequencies (%)					
	NI	WM	EM	SI	TOTAL
MS	21.83	22.29	16.43	25.84	21.83
Ms	39.10	34.79	49.33	26.08	37.07
NS	3.17	0.62	3.43	5.57	2.86
Ns	35.90	42.29	30.81	42.51	38.24
Total	100	99.99	100	100	100

Orkney (total) Rhesus System		
	Number observed	Number expected
R_1R_1	70	72.58
$R_1^wR_1$	5	4.27
R_1R_z	0	1.56
R_1R_2	62	56.10
R_1r	132	131.75
$R_1^wR_1^w$	0	0.08
$R_1^wR_z$	0	0.04
$R_1^wR_2$	3	1.64
R_1^wr	2	3.95
R_1^ur	2	1.92
$r'r$	1	0.96
R_1^ur'', R_2^ur', $R_1^uR_2^u$	0	0.04
R_2R_z	2	0.60
R_2R_2	9	10.33
R_2r	42	47.48
R_2^ur	1	1.08
$r''r$	2	2.19
R_or	2	1.92
rr	64	60.53
Total	399	399.02

Gene frequencies (%)	
CDe	41.72
C^wDe	1.25
Cde	0.31
CD^ue	0.62
CDE	0.46
cDE	15.03
cdE	0.70
cD^uE	0.35
cDe	0.61
cde	38.95
	100

Orkney (South Isles) Rhesus System		
	Number observed	Number expected
R_1R_1	22	16.12
R_1r	19	26.07
R_1R_2	7	11.38
R_2R_2	3	2.00
R_2r	12	9.62
$r'r'$	0	0.03
$r'r$	1	1.23
rr	14	11.54
Total	78	77.99

Gene frequencies (%)	
CDe	43.45
cDE	16.03
Cde	2.06
cde	38.46
	100

Orkney (East Mainland) Rhesus System		
	Number observed	Number expected
R_1R_1	6	8.56
$R_1{}^wR_1$	2	2.39
R_1R_2	16	11.99
R_1r	20	18.49
$R_1{}^wR_1{}^w$	0	0.17
$R_1{}^wR_2$	3	1.67
$R_1{}^wr$	2	2.58
R_2R_2	0	4.13
R_2r	14	11.33
$R_2{}^uR_2{}^u$	0	0.05
$R_2{}^ur$	1	0.81
$r''r''$	0	0.01
$r''r$	1	0.81
rr	8	9.99
Total	73	72.98

Gene frequencies (%)	
CDe	34.25
C^wDe	4.79
cDE	20.98
cdE	1.50
cD^uE	1.50
cde	36.98
	100

Orkney (West Mainland) Rhesus System		
	Number observed	Number expected
R_1R_1	21	19.24
R_1R_2	14	13.70
R_1R_z	0	0.74
R_1r	36	40.62
$R_1^wR_1^w$	0	0.02
$R_1^wR_1$	3	1.20
$R_1^wR_2$	0	0.41
$R_1^wR_z$	0	0.02
R_1^wr	0	1.34
$R_1^uR_1^u$	0	0.05
R_1^ur	2	2.11
R_2R_2	5	2.16
R_2R_z	1	0.25
R_2r	8	14.29
R_zR_z	0	0.01
R_or	2	1.61
rr	28	22.21
Total	120	119.98

Gene frequencies (%)	
CDe	38.05
C^wDe	1.25
CD^ue	2.05
cDE	13.40
CDE	0.77
cDe	1.46
cde	43.02
	100

Orkney (North Isles) Rhesus System		
	Number observed	Number expected
R_1R_1	21	29.52
R_1R_z	0	1.00
R_1R_2	25	18.02
R_1r	57	45.65
R_2R_2	1	2.48
R_2R_z	1	0.29
R_2r	8	11.80
$r''r''$	0	0.04
$r''r$	1	1.52
R_zR_z	0	0.01
rr	14	17.65
Total	128	127.98

Gene frequencies (%)	
Cde	48.02
cDE	12.43
cdE	1.60
CDE	0.81
cde	37.13
	99.99

Notes and References

Foreword

Robert Rendall, *Orkney Shore* (Kirkwall: The Kirkwall Press, 1973).
R. T. Johnston, *Stenwick Days* (Stromness: The Orkney Press, 1984).
Gregory Bateson, *Steps to an Ecology of Mind* (Paladin edition, 1973).
Richard E. Leakey, *The Making of Mankind* (London: Michael Joseph, 1981).
John Shearer, William Groundwater and John D. Mackay (eds.), *The New Orkney Book* (Edinburgh and London: Nelson, 1966).

Chapter 1

1 A. W. Brøgger, *Det norske folk i oldtiden*, quoted by Charlotte Blindheim, 'Norwegian Viking Age Archaeology Today', *Norwegian Archaeological Review* 15: 1-2 (1982), p.3.
2 Robert Rendall, *Country Sonnets* (Kirkwall, 1947).
3 George Mackay Brown, 'What is an Orcadian?' in *The Storm* (Kirkwall, 1954).
4 John Gunn (ed.), *The Orkney Book* (London and Edinburgh: Nelson, 1909).
5 G. Goudie, *The Celtic and Scandinavian Antiquities of Shetland* (Edinburgh and London: Blackwood, 1904); D. P. Capper, *The Vikings of Britain* (London: Allen and Unwin, 1937).
6 A. W. Brøgger, *Ancient Emigrants* (Oxford: Clarendon, 1929).
7 *Historia Norvegiae*, ed. G. Storm, in *Monumenta Historica Norvegiae* (Oslo, 1880), pp.69-124, referred to in F. T. Wainwright, *The Northern Isles* (Edinburgh and London: Nelson, 1962).
8 Hugh Marwick, *Orkney* (London: Robert Hale, 1951), p.37.
9 *ibid.*, ch.20.
10 *ibid.*, p.271.
11 F. T. Wainwright, *op.cit.* in note 7, pp.161-2.
12 *ibid.*, p.116.
13 *ibid.*, pp.111, 101 and 157.
14 *ibid.*, pp.103-7.
15 A. Ritchie, 'Pict and Norseman in Northern Scotland', *Scottish Archaeological Forum* 6 (1974), pp.23-36.
16 V. G. Childe, *Skara Brae, A Pictish Village in Orkney* (London: Kegan Paul, Trench, Trubner, 1931).
17 F. T. Wainwright, 'The Picts and the Problem' in F. T. Wainwright (ed.), *The Problem of the Picts* (Edinburgh and London: Nelson, 1955), repub. The Melven Press 1980, p.13.
18 Hugh Marwick, *op.cit.* in note 8; Eric Linklater, *Orkney and Shetland* (London: Robert Hale, 1965); John Shearer, William Groundwater and John

D. Mackay (eds.), *The New Orkney Book* (Edinburgh and London: Nelson, 1966); Patrick Bailey, *Orkney* (Newton Abbot: David and Charles, 1971); Ronald Miller, *Orkney* (London: Batsford, 1976). Ronald Miller has also edited the Orkney entries for The Third Statistical Account of Scotland, Vol. XX A, *The County of Orkney* (Edinburgh: Scottish Academic Press, 1985).

19 A. Fenton, *The Northern Isles: Orkney and Shetland* (Edinburgh: John Donald, 1978).

20 Quoted by A. O. Anderson, *Early Sources of Scottish History* (Edinburgh, 1922), Vol. 1, pp.330-1.

21 D. Forsythe, *Urban-Rural Migration, Change and Conflict in an Orkney Island Community,* North Sea Oil Panel Occasional Paper No. 14 (Social Science Research Council, 1982).

22 *ibid.*

23 *ibid.*

Chapter 2

1 J. W. Hedges, *Isbister, a Chambered Tomb in Orkney* (Oxford, 1983); *Tomb of the Eagles* (London, 1984).

2 Guardianship sites open to the public, described in A. Ritchie and J. N. G. Ritchie, *The Ancient Monuments of Orkney* (Edinburgh, 1978).

3 V. G. Childe, *Skara Brae. A Pictish Village in Orkney* (Edinburgh, 1931); *D. V. Clarke, The Neolithic Village at Skara Brae, Excavations 1972-73, an Interim Report* (Edinburgh, 1976); D. V. Clarke, 'Excavations at Skara Brae: a summary account' in C. Burgess and R. Miket (eds), *Settlement and Economy in the Third and Second Millennia BC* (Oxford, 1976), pp.233-50; V. G. Childe and W. G. Grant, 'A Stone Age settlement at the Braes of Rinyo, Rousay, Orkney', PSAS 73 (1938-39), pp.6-31; V. G. Childe and W. ' G. Grant (A Stone Age settlement at the Braes of Rinyo, Rousay, Orkney (second report)' PSAS 81 (1946-48), pp.16-42; D. V. Clarke, 'Links of Noltland' in CBA (Scottish Regional Group), *Discovery and Excavation in Scotland* (1980), p.25; D. V. Clarke and N. Sharples, 'Settlements and subsistence in the third millennium BC' in C. Renfrew (ed.), *The Prehistory of Orkney* (Edinburgh, 1985), pp.54-82.

4 A. Ritchie, 'Excavation of a Neolithic farmstead at Knap of Howar, Papa Westray, Orkney', PSAS 113 (1983), pp.40-121; 'The First Settlers' in C. Renfrew (1985), *op.cit.* (note 3).

5 A. Ritchie and J. N. G. Ritchie (1978), *op.cit.* (note 2), p.27.

6 C. Renfrew, *Investigations in Orkney* (London, 1979).

7 One of many sites, excavated and unexcavated, which are worth visiting although not officially open to the public.

8 J. W. Hedges (1983), *op.cit.* (note 1); (1984), *op.cit.* (note 1).

9 A. S. Henshall, *The Chambered Tombs of Scotland. Vol. 1* (Edinburgh, 1963).

10 J. W. Hedges (1983), *op.cit* (note 1); (1984), *op.cit.* (note 1).

11 J. N. G. Ritchie, 'The Stones of Stenness, Orkney', PSAS 107 (1975-76), pp.1-60.

12 J. W. Hedges, 'Excavation of two Orcadian burnt mounds at Liddle and Beaquoy', PSAS 106 (1974-75), pp.39-98.

13 J. W. Hedges, 'Gordon Parry's West Burra Survey', *Glasgow Archaeological Journal* 11 (1984), pp.41-60; 'Tougs, Burra Isle, Shetland', *Glasgow Archaeological Journal* (forth.).

300

14 D. L. Clarke, *Beaker Pottery of Great Britain and Ireland. Vol. 2,* (Cambridge, 1970), p.520; A. S. Henshall (1963), *op.cit.* (note 9), p.110; Anna Ritchie, pers.comm.

15 G. Petrie, 'Notice of a barrow at Huntiscarth in the parish of Harray, recently opened', PSAS 3 (1857-60), p.195.

16 M. E. Hedges, 'The excavation of the Knowes of Quoyscottie, Orkney; a cemetery of the first millennium BC', PSAS 108 (1976-77), pp.130-55.

17 W. G. Grant, 'Excavation of Bronze Age burial mounds at Quandale, Rousay, Orkney', PSAS 77 (1936-37), pp.72-84; J. N. G. Ritchie and A. Ritchie, 'Excavation of a barrow at Queenafjold, Twatt, Orkney', PSAS 105 (1972-74), pp.33-40.

18 J. W. Hedges, 'The Broch Period' in C. Renfrew (1985), *op.cit.* (note 3), pp.150-175.

19 J. W. Hedges and B. J. Bell, 'That tower of Scottish prehistory — the broch', *Antiquity* 54 (1980), pp.87-94; J. W. Hedges (1985), *op.cit.* (note 18); J. W. Hedges, *Bu, Gurness and the Brochs of Orkney* (Oxford, forth.).

20 J. W. Hedges and B. J. Bell (1980), *op.cit.* (note 19); J. W. Hedges (1985), *op.cit.* (note 18); J. W. Hedges (forth.), *op.cit.* (note 19); C. Renfrew (1979), *op.cit.* (note 6); N. Sharples, 'Excavations at Pierowall Quarry, Westray, Orkney', PSAS 114 (1984), pp.75-126.

21 C. S. T. Calder, 'Excavations of Iron Age dwellings on the Calf of Eday in Orkney', PSAS 73 (1938-39), pp.167-85.

22 W. Traill, 'Notice of excavations at Stenabreck and Howmae in North Ronaldsay, Orkney', PSAS 19 (1884-85), pp.14-33; J. Traill, 'Notes on the further excavations at Howmae', 1889, PSAS 24 (1889-90), pp.451-61.

23 S. P. Carter *et al.,* 'Interim report on the structures at Howe, Stromness, Orkney', *Glasgow Archaeological Journal* 11 (1984), pp.61-73.

24 J. W. Hedges and B. J. Bell, 'The Broch of Lingro, St Ola, Orkney', (forth.).

25 Raymond Lamb, pers. comm.

26 J. W. Hedges, 'Short cists recently excavated at Lower Ellibister and other locations in Orkney', PSAS 110 (1978-80), pp.44-71.

27 A. Ritchie, 'Orkney in the Pictish Kingdom' in C. Renfrew (1985), *op.cit.* (note 3).

28 J. N. G. Ritchie, 'Two new Pictish symbol stones from Orkney', PSAS 101 (1968-69), pp.130-33; A. Ritchie (1985), *op.cit.* (note 27).

29 F. T. Wainwright (ed.), *The Problem of the Picts* (Edinburgh, 1955).

30 A. Ritchie, 'Excavation of Pictish and Viking Age farmsteads at Buckquoy, Orkney', PSAS 108 (1976-77), pp.174-227.

31 J. W. Hedges, 'Trial excavations on Pictish and Viking settlements at Saevar Howe, Birsay, Orkney', *Glasgow Archaeological Journal* 10 (1983), pp.73-124; J. W. Hedges (forth.), *op.cit.* (note 19).

32 J. W. Hedges and B. J. Bell, 'The Howe', *Current Archaeology* 7 (1980), pp.48-51.

33 R. G. Lamb, *Iron Age Promontory Forts in the Northern Isles* (Oxford, 1980).

34 F. T. Wainwright, 'The Scandinavian Settlement' in F. T. Wainwright, *The Northern Isles* (Edinburgh, 1962), pp.117-62.

35 S. Cruden, 'Earl Thorfinn the Mighty and the Brough of Birsay' in K. Eldjarn (ed.), *The Third Viking Congress* (Edinburgh, 1958), pp.156-62; 'Excavations at Birsay' in A. Small (ed.), *The Fourth Viking Congress* (Edinburgh, 1965), pp.23-31.

36 R. G. Lamb, 'Coastal settlements of the North', *Scottish Archaeological Forum* 5 (1973), pp.76-98; 'The Burri Stacks of Culswick, Shetland and other paired stack settlements', PSAS 107 (1975-1976), pp.144-54.

301

37 J. W. Hedges (1980), *op.cit.* (note 26).
38 S. Greig, *Viking Antiquities in Scotland* (Oslo, 1940) (= H. Shetelig (ed.), *Viking Antiquities in Great Britain and Ireland. Part II.)*
39 F. T. Wainwright (1962), *op.cit.* (note 34).
40 J. Hedges, *op.cit.* (note 31); A. Ritchie, 'Pict and Norseman in northern Scotland', *Scottish Archaeological Forum* 6 (1974), pp.23-36, A. Ritchie, *op.cit.* (note 30).
41 A. Ritchie, *op.cit.* (note 30).
42 C. D. Morris, 'Viking Orkney' in C. Renfrew, *op.cit.* (note 4), pp.210-42.
43 A. Thorsteinsson, 'The Viking burial place at Pierowall, Westray, Orkney' in B. Niclasen (ed.), *Fifth Viking Congress* (Torshavn, 1968), pp.150-73; A. Ritchie, 'Westness, Rousay' in A. Ritchie (ed.), *Field Guide to the Prehistoric Society Summer Conference in the Orkney Islands* (Edinburgh, 1982); A. Ritchie, *op.cit.* (note 30); C. D. Morris, 'Birsay, Orkney; 'small sites' excavation and survey', *Universities of Durham and Newcastle upon Tyne Archaeological Reports,* 1978, pp.11-19; J. W. Hedges, *op.cit.* (note 19).
44 C. Burgess, 'Meldon Bridge: A neolithic defended promontory complex near Peebles' in C. Burgess and R. Miket, *op.cit.* (note 3).
45 J. W. Hedges (forth.), *op.cit.* (note 19).
46 N. T. Moar, 'Two pollen diagrams from Mainland, Orkney', *New Phytologist* 68 (1969), pp.201-8; T. H. Keatinge and J. H. Dickson, 'Mid Flandrian changes in vegetation on mainland Orkney', *New Phytologist* 82, pp.585-612; D. A. Davidson, R. L. Jones and C. Renfrew, 'Palaeo-environmental reconstruction and evaluation; a case study from Orkney', *Transactions of the Institute of British Geographers* (1976), pp.346-61; R. L. Jones, 'Appendix 3. Environment — pollen' in J. W. Hedges (1975), *op.cit.* (note 12), pp.84-88; D. Bartlett, 'Analysis of pollen from neighbouring locations' in J. W. Hedges (1983), *op.cit.* (note 1), pp.177-84.
47 W. G. Watt, Article 18 (Submerged forest in Bay of Skaill), *Edinburgh Philosophical Journal* 3 (1820), p.100; W. Traill, 'On submarine forests and other remains of indigenous wood in Orkney', *Transactions of the Botanical Society of Edinburgh* 9 (1868), p.146.
48 J. W. Hedges (1983), *op.cit.* (note 1); (1984), *op.cit.* (note 1).
49 M. I. Platt, 'Report on the animal bones' in J. G. Callander and W. G. Grant: 'Hower, a prehistoric structure on Papa Westray, Orkney', PSAS 71 (1936-37), pp.317-321; A. Ritchie (1983), *op.cit.* (note 4); A. Ritchie (1985) *op.cit.* (note 27); D. M. S. Watson, 'The animal bones from Skara Brae' in V. G. Childe (1931), *op.cit.* (note 3); pp.198-204; D. V. Clarke (1976), *op.cit.* (note 3).
50 N. Fojut, 'Towards a geography of Shetland brochs', *Glasgow Archaeological Journal* 9 (1982), pp.38-59.
51 J. W. Hedges (forth.), *op.cit.* (note 19).
52 N. Sharples (1984), *op.cit.* (note 20).
53 C. Renfrew (1979), *op.cit.* (note 6); J. W. Hedges (1983), *op.cit.* (note 1); J. W. Hedges (1984), *op.cit.* (note 1).
54 G. S. Maxwell, '*Casus Belli:* Native pressures and Roman policy', *Scottish Archaeological Forum* 7 (1975), pp.31-49.
55 A. Ritchie (1985), *op.cit.* (note 27).

Chapter 3

1　J. Thurnam, unpublished records with museum collection.

2　J. Garson, 'On the osteology of the ancient inhabitants of the Orkney Islands', *Journal of the Anthropological Institute* 13 (1883), pp.54-86; W. Turner, 'A contribution to the craniology of the people of Scotland. Part II', *Transactions of the Royal Society of Edinburgh* 51 (1915), pp.171-255.

3　A. Low, 'Some cist burials in Orkney', PSAS 3 (1928-9), pp.377-383; 'A short cist at West Puldrite in the parish of Evie and Rendall, Orkney', PSAS 3 (1928-9); A. Robinson, in V. G. Childe, 'Final report on the operations at Skara Brae', PSA S 65 (1930-31), pp.27-77.

4　A. Low, 'A long stalled chambered cairn or mausoleum (Rousay type) near Midhowe, Rousay, Orkney', PSAS 8 (1934), pp.320-50.

5　J. T. Chesterman, 'Investigation of the human bones from Quanterness', in C. Renfrew (ed.), *Investigations in Orkney*, Society of Antiquaries of London Research Report no. 38 (1979), pp.97-111.

6　J. W. Hedges, 'An archaeodemographical perspective on Isbister', *Scottish Archaeological Review* 1 (1982), pp.5-20; *Isbister, a Chambered Tomb in Orkney* (Oxford, 1983).

7　D. R. Brothwell, in preparation.

8　R. W. Reid, 'Remains of Saint Magnus and Saint Rognvald, entombed in Saint Magnus Cathedral, Kirkwall, Orkney', *Biometrika* 18 (1926), pp.118-150.

9　D. R. Brothwell, 'On a mycoform stone structure in Orkney and its relevance to possible further interpretations of so-called souterrains', *Bulletin of the Institute of Archaeology* 14 (1977), pp.179-190.

10　For a review of these, see D. R. Brothwell, *Digging up Bones* (British Museum (Nat. Hist.), 1982).

11　A. C. Berry, 'The use of non-metrical variations of the cranium in the study of Scandinavian population movements', *American Journal of Physical Anthropology* 40 (1974), pp.345-358.

12　G. Lamb, *Orkney Surnames* (Edinburgh: Paul Harris, 1981).

The reference sources of data in Table 2 are:-
E. M. B. Clements and K. G. Pickett, 'Stature of Scotsmen aged 18 to 40 years in 1941', *British Journal of Social Medicine* 6 (1952), pp.245-252; R. W. Reid, *op.cit.* in note 8; P. C. Mahalanobis, 'A statistical study of certain anthropometric measurements from Sweden', *Biometrika* 22 (1930), pp.94-108; J. Pálsson and I. Schwidetzky, 'Anthropological characters of urban and rural populations of Iceland', *Homo* 24 (1973), pp.154-162.

13　W. A. Marshall, 'The relation of variation in children's growth rates to seasonal climatic variations', *Annals of Human Biology* 2 (1975), pp.243-250.

14　E. R. Bransby, 'The Seasonal Growth of Children', *Medical Officer* 73 (1945), pp.149, 157, 165; W. A. Marshall, 'The evaluation of growth rate in height over periods of less than one year'. *Archives of Disease in Childhood* 46 (1971), pp.414-420.

15　G. F. Black, *The Surnames of Scotland. Their Origin, Meaning and History* (New York: New York Public Library, 1962).

16　A. Sandison, 'Surnames found in Shetland in 1804 and 1954', *The Genealogists' Magazine* 15 (1968), pp.500-504.

17　See for instance:- R. S. Barclay, *The Population of Orkney, 1755-1961* (Kirkwall, 1965); A. J. Boyce, V. M. L. Holdsworth and D. R. Brothwell, 'Demographic and genetic studies in the Orkney Islands', in D. F. Roberts and E. Sunderland (eds.), *Genetic Variation in Britain* (London: Taylor and

Francis, 1973), pp.109-128; D. F. Roberts, M. H. Roberts and J. A. Cowie, 'Inbreeding levels in Orkney islanders', *Journal of Biosocial Science* 11 (1979), pp.391-395; E. R. Brennan, 'Kinship, demography, social and geographical characteristics of mate choice on Sanday, Orkney islands', *American Journal of Physical Anthropology* 55 (1981), pp.129-138.

18 H. R. Jones, 'A spatial analysis of human fertility in Scotland', *Scottish Geographical Magazine* 91 (1975), pp.102-113.

19 D. F. Roberts *et al., op.cit.* in note 17.

20 E. R. Brennan, *op.cit.* in note 17.

21 A. J. Boyce *et al., op.cit.* in note 17; E. R. Brennan, *op.cit.* in note 17; E. R. Brennan, P. W. Leslie and Bennett Dyke, 'Mate choice and genetic structure, Sanday, Orkney Islands, Scotland', *Human Biology* 54 (1982), pp.477-489.

22 A. J. Boyce *et al., op.cit.* in note 17.

23 D. Suter, 'Hair colour in the Faroe and Orkney Islands', *Annals of Human Biology* 6 (1979), pp.89-93. John Beddoe's book is *The Races of Man* (Bristol: Arrowsmith, 1885) and John Gray's paper 'Memoir on the pigmentation survey of Scotland', *Journal of the Royal Anthropological Institute* 37 (1907), pp.375-401.

24 D. Suter, *op.cit.* in note 23; J. Pálsson and I. Schwidetzky, 'Icelanders and Irish. Contribution to the problem of the origin of the settlers of Iceland', *Homo* 26 (1975), pp.163-170. The Fischer and Saller hair colour table is described in E. Fischer and K. Saller, 'Eine Neue Haar farbentafel', *Anthropologischer Anzeiger* 5 (1928), pp.238-244.

25 J. Grieve and G. M. Mowat, 'Records of eye colours for British populations and a description of a new eye-colour scale', *Annals of Eugenics* 13 (1946), pp.161-171.

26 V. M. L. Muir, *Biological Relationships of Orkney Islanders with Neighbouring Populations,* University of Surrey, unpublished Ph.D. thesis.

27 A. J. Boyce *et al., op.cit.* in note 17; V. M. L. Muir, *op.cit.* in note 26; R. G. Harvey and D. Suter, 'Digital dermatoglyphics of the Faroese', *American Journal of Physical Anthropology* 61 (1983), pp.337-

28 V. M. L. Muir, *op.cit.* in note 26.

29 R. A. Fisher and G. L. Taylor, 'Scandinavian influence in Scottish ethnology', *Nature* 145 (1940), p.590.

30 J. Steffensen, 'The physical anthropology of the Vikings', *Journal of the Royal Anthropological Institute* 83 (1953), pp.86-97.

31 V. M. L. Muir, *op.cit.*

32 M. M. Izatt, 'The Gm(1) and Gm(2) factors in Scotland', in D. F. Roberts and E. Sunderland, *op.cit.* in note 17.

33 D. Tills, J. van den Branden, V. R. Clements and A. E. Mourant, 'The world distribution of electrophoretic variants of the red cell enzyme adenylate kinase', *Human Heredity* 20 (1970), pp.517-522.

34 D. Tills, J. van den Branden, V. R. Clements and A. E. Mourant, 'The distribution in Man of genetic variations of 6-phosphogluconate dehydrogenase', *Human Heredity* 20 (1970), pp.523-529.

35 D. Tills, V. Muir, A. Warlow, D. A. Hopkinson, P. A. Lorkin, M. A. F. El-Hasmi and H. Lehmann, 'The occurrence of Hbe Saskatoon in Scotland', *Human Genetics* 33 (1976), pp.179-180.

36 S. G. Welch and G. W. Mears, 'Genetic variants of human indophenol oxidase in the Westray Island of the Orkneys', *Human Heredity* 22 (1972), pp.38-41.

37 S. G. Welch, 'A local Orkney polymorphism', in D. F. Roberts and E. Sunderland, *op.cit.* in note 17.

38 R. Kherumian and R. W. Pickford, *Heredité et Frequence des Dyschromatopsies* (Paris: Frères, 1959).
39 The Norwegian figure is from work by Schiotz.
40 R. H. Post, '"Colorblindness" distribution in Britain, France and Japan: a review, with notes on selection relaxation', *Eugenics Quarterly* 10 (1963), pp.110-118.
41 V. M. L. Muir, *op.cit.*
42 E. Sunderland, 'The testing of phenylthiocarbamide in selected populations in the United Kingdom', *Eugenics Review* 58 (196), pp.143-148.
43 V. M. L. Muir, *op.cit.*
44 G. M. Howe, *Man, Environment and Disease in Britain* (Newton Abbot: David and Charles, 1972).
45 R. J. Berry, 'Genetic factors in the aetiology of multiple sclerosis', *Acta Neurologica Scandinavica* 45 (1969), pp.459-483.
46 D. F. Roberts *et al., op.cit.* in note 17.
47 V. M. L. Muir, 'Tylosis in the Orkney Islands', *Journal of Biosocial Science* 10 (1978), pp.1-6.

Chapter 4

1 The comparative gene frequencies in this table are taken from R. J. Berry and J. L. Johnston, *The Natural History of Shetland* (London: Collins, 1980), pp.62-3.
2 E. S. Brown, 'Distribution of the ABO and Rhesus (D) blood groups in the north of Scotland', *Heredity* 20 (1965), pp.289-303; A. J. Boyce, V. M. L. Holdsworth and D. R. Brothwell, 'Demographic and genetic studies in the Orkney Islands', in D. F. Roberts and E. Sunderland (eds.), *Genetic Variation in Britain* (London: Taylor and Francis, 1973), pp.109-128.
3 T. Allan and B. Lewis, quoted as personal communication (1969) in A. E. Mourant, A. C. Kopec and K. Domaniewska-Sobczak, *The Distribution of Human Blood Group and Other Polymorphisms* (Oxford: University Press, 1976), p.806.
4 R. A. Fisher and G. L. Taylor, 'Scandinavian influence in Scottish ethnology', *Nature* 145 (1940), p.590; J. Steffensen, 'The physical anthropology of the Vikings', *J.Roy.Anthrop.Inst.* 83 (1953), pp.86-87; A. J. Boyce *et al., op.cit.*
5 A. W. F. Edwards, 'Distances between populations on the basis of gene frequencies', *Biometrics* 27 (1971), pp.873.881.
6 M. Nei, 'Genetic distance between populations', *Amer. Naturalist* 106 (1972), pp.283-292.
7 L. D. Sanghvi, 'Comparison of genetical and morphological methods for a study of biological differences', *Amer.J.Phys.Anthrop.* 11 (1953), pp.385-404.
8 The systems used were those for the MN, P, Kell, Duffy and Rhesus D blood groups, the haptoglobin types of the serum, the adenylate kinase red cell enzyme types, and ABH and PTC tasting ability. The Orkney figures for this last were reported by E. Sutherland, 'The tasting of phenylthiocarbamide in selected populations in the United Kingdom', *Eugenics Rev.* 58 (1966), pp.143-8.
9 The systems used were: haplotypes of the MNSs and rhesus blood group systems; allele frequencies of the ABO (differentiating the A_1 A_2 subtypes,

P, Kidd, Duffy, Kell and Lutheran blood-groups, of the enzymes adenylate deaminase, 6-phosphogluconate dehydrogenase, adenylate kinase, acid phosphatase, and phosphoglucomutase locus 1, and the serum proteins haptoglobin and transferrin; the monomorphic systems malate and lactic dehydrogenase and phosphoglucomutase locus 2 were omitted. There are unfortunately too few local data for the HLA types for their inclusion in this distance analysis.

10 H. C. Harpending and T. Jenkins, 'Genetic distance among southern African populations', in M. H. Crawford and P. L. Workman (eds.), *Methods and Theories of Anthropological Genetics* (Albuquerque: University of New Mexico Press, 1973), pp.177-199.

Chapter 5

1 D. Suter, 'Hair colour in the Faroe and Orkney Islands', *Annals of Human Biology* 6 (1979), pp.89-93.
Diana Suter, Robin G. Harvey, Mogens Hauge, Peter Hinderson and Jørgen Cohn, 'Anthropological and genetic studies of the Faroese', *Fróðskaparrit* (Annal. societ. scient. Faeroensis) 27 (1979), pp.57-74.
R. G. Harvey, 'The morphology of the hypothenar radial arch: a study of hypothenar patterns in the Faroe Islands population', *Annals of Human Biology* 9 (1982), pp.103-111.
R. G. Harvey and D. Suter, 'Intra-population variability in the Faroe Islands', *Anthropos* (Brno) 22 (1982), pp.107-115.
R. G. Harvey and D. Suter, 'Digital dermatoglyphics of the Faroe Islanders', *American Journal of Physical Anthropology* 61 (1983), pp.337-345.
R. G. Harvey and D. Suter, 'Migration in the Faroe Islands', *Journal of Human Evolution* 13 (1984), pp.311-317.
R. G. Harvey, 'Palmar dermatoglyphics of the Faroe Islanders', *Annals of Human Biology* 13 (1986), pp.397-401.

2 J. Jóhansen, 'Cereal cultivation in Mykines, Faroe Islands AD 600', *Geological Survey of Denmark. Yearbook 1978* (København, 1979), pp.93-103.

3 The references given by Prof. Roberts include A. W. F. Edwards, 'Distances between populations on the basis of gene frequencies', *Biometrics* 27 (1971), pp.873-881. Examples of genetic maps of the United Kingdom from comparisons based on a few selected genetic markers of the blood, for example ABO and Rhesus groups, can be found in A. C. Kopeć, *The Distribution of the blood groups in the United Kingdom* (London: Oxford University Press, 1970).

4 D. Tills R. G. Harvey, A. Warlow, A. C. Kopeć, D. suter, M. Hauge, H. J. Simonsen and A. Marin, 'Blood groups, serum proteins and enzymes of the Faroe Islanders', *Journal of Human Evolution* 14 (1985), pp.725-738.

5 E. A. Thompson, 'Estimation of the migration history from current genetic data; application to the Faroe Islands', in A. J. Boyce (ed.), *Migration and Mobility*, Symposia of the Society for the Study of Human Biology Vol. 23 (1984), pp.123-142.

6 A. E. Mourant, A. C. Kopeć and K. Domaniewska-Sobczak, *The distribution of the human blood groups and other polymorphisms* (Oxford University Press, 1976), p.65.

7 V. M. L. Muir, 'Biological relatonships of Orkney Islanders with neighbouring populations', unpublished Ph.D. thesis, University of Surrey, 1977.
8 D. Suter, *op.cit.* (1979) in note 1.
9 V. M. L. Muir, *op.cit.* in note 7.

Chapter 6

1 J. R. Cowie, *Shetland and its Inhabitants* (Aberdeen: Lewis, Smith and Son, 1871).
2 Census of Scotland, 1971 (Edinburgh: HMSO).
3 A. Edmonston, *A View of the Ancient and Present State of the Zetland Islands* (Edinburgh: Ballantyne, 1809).
4 A. T. Cluness (ed.), *The Shetland Book* (Lerwick: Zetland Education Committee, 1967), p.82.
5 *ibid.,* p.87 and p.90.
6 *ibid.,* p.84.
7 A. T. Cluness, *The Shetland Isles* (London: Robert Hale, 1951), p.161.
8 *ibid.,* pp.160-1.
9 George S. Robertson, *Reminiscences of an Orkney Nonagenarian* (Stromness, 1977), p.23.
10 *Orkneyinga Saga,* c.52.
11 J. Wallace, *An Account of the Islands of Orkney* (1700).
12 Alex Comfort, *The Biology of Senescence* (New York: Elsevier), 3rd edition (1979).
13 John Graunt, *Natural and Political Observations upon the Bills of Mortality* (London: Tho. Roycroft, 1662).
14 Sigismund Peller, *Quantitative Research in Human Biology and Medicine* (Bristol: John Wright & Sons, 1967).
15 W. R. Macdonell, 'On the expectation of life in ancient Rome, and in the provinces of Hispania and Lusitania, and Africa', *Biometrika* 9 (1913), pp.366-377.
16 Sir John Sinclair, *The Statistical Account of Scotland* (Edinburgh, 1793).
17 *ibid.*
18 James Fea, *The Present State of the Orkney Islands Considered* (Holyroodhouse, 1775).
19 James Fea, *Considerations on the Fisheries in the Scotch Islands* (London: 1787).
20 William P. L. Thomson, *Kelp-making in Orkney* (Stromness: The Orkney Press, 1983).
21 *ibid.*
22 *The Statistical Account of the Orkney Islands* (Edinburgh and London: Blackwood, 1842).
23 George MacGregor Jnr., *Descriptive Notes on Orkney* (1893).
24 J. D. Durand, 'The view of historical demography', in Brian Spooner (ed.), *Population growth: anthropological implications* (Cambridge, Mass.: MIT Press, 1972); G. Masnick and S. H. Katz, 'Trends in fertility in a North Alaskan community', Third Int. Symp. on Circumpolar Health, Yellowknife (1974).

25 S. H. Katz, 'Anthropological perspectives on ageing', *Annals, American Academy of Political and Social Sciences* 438 (1978), pp.1-12.

26 R. S. Barclay, *The population of Orkney 1755-1961* (Kirkwall: W. R. Mackintosh, 1965).

27 R. S. Barclay in John Shearer, William Groundwater and John D. Mackay (eds.), *The New Orkney Book* (Edinburgh and London: Nelson, 1966).

28 See for instance Diana Forsythe, *Urban-Rural Migration, Change and Conflict in an Orkney Island Community* (1982), and Ronald Miller, *Orkney* (London, 1976).

29 *ibid.* Also see J. R. Coull, 'Population trends and structures on the island of Westray, Orkney', *Scottish Studies* 10, pp.69-77.

30 Ronald Miller and Susan Luther-Davies, *Eday and Hoy* (1968).

31 V. G. Childe, *Skara Brae: a Pictish Village in Orkney* (Edinburgh, 1931).

32 Colin Renfrew, *Investigations in Orkney* (London, 1979).

33 Ronald Miller, *Orkney* (London, 1976), p.66.

34 Eric Linklater, *Orkney and Shetland* (London: Robert Hale, 1971).

35 E. J. Bowers, 'Observations on the modal age at death in the Orkney Islands', unpublished M.A. thesis, University of Pennsylvania (1975); 'Patterns of adult mortality in Orkney', unpublished Ph.D. thesis, University of Pennsylvania (1983).

36 The England and Wales figures are reported by Comfort, *op.cit.* in note 12.

37 E. A. Murphy, 'Genetics of longevity in man', in E. L. Schneider (ed.), *The Genetics of Ageing* (New York: Plenum Press, 1978).

38 Karl Pearson, 'Contributions to the mathematical theory of evolution. II Skew variation in homogeneous material', *Philosophical Transactions of the Royal Society of London* (Series A) 186 (1895), pp.343-414.

39 *ibid.*

40 G. Acsadi and J. Nemeskeri, *History of human life span and mortality* (Budapest: Akademiai Kiado, 1970).

41 P. L. Panum, 'Observations made during the epidemic of measles on the Faroe Islands in the year 1846', transl. from the Danish by A. S. Hatcher (New York: Delta Omega Society, 1940), p.26.

42 R. J. Berry and V. M. L. Muir, 'The natural history of man in Shetland', *J. Biosoc. Sci.* 7 (1975), pp.319-344.

43 R. H. MacArthur and J. H. Connell, *The Biology of Populations* (New York: Wiley, 1966).

44 Charles E. King, 'The evolution of lifespan', in Hugh Dingle and Joseph P. Hegmann (eds.), *Evolution and Genetics of Life Histories* (New York: Springer-Verlag, 1982).

45 J. F. Fries and L. M. Carpo, *Vitality and ageing, implications of the rectangular curve* (San Francisco: W. H. Freeman, 1981).

46 W. S. Laughlin, 'Aleuts: ecosystem, holocene history and Siberian origin', *Science,* N.Y. 189 (1975), pp.507-515.

47 V. A. Bolshakov, S. I. Brook and V. I. Kozlov, *Specific Features of the Statistical Studies of Longevity* (New York: Second U.S.-U.S.S.R. Symposium on Longevity, 1982).

48 R. B. Mazes and R. W. Mathisen, 'Lack of unusual longevity in Vilcabamba, Ecuador', *Hum. Biol.* 54 (1982), pp.517-524.

Chapter 7

POAS—Proceedings of the Orkney Antiquarian Society.
PSAS—Proceedings of the Society of Antiquaries of Scotland.

1 Rev. George Low, *A Description of Orkney* (1773), unpublished MSS. quoted in Hugh Marwick, '"A Description of Orkney"', POAS II (1923-24), p.52.

2 J. Storer Clouston, 'Tradition and Fact', POAS IV (1925-26), p.14.

3 *ibid.,* p.13.

4 Ernest W. Marwick, *The Folklore of Orkney and Shetland* (London, 1975), p.81. Although Marwick does not here mention the Shetlander by name, it is almost certain to have been the remarkable Laurence Williamson of Mid Yell.

5 Sir Walter Scott, *The Pirate,* note to Chapter II.

6 W. B. Yeats (ed.), *Fairy and Folk Tales of the Irish Peasantry* (1888), repr. along with *Irish Fairy Tales* as *Fairy and Folk Tales of Ireland* (London, 1979), p.4.

7 Lady Wentworth in Brian Vesey Fitzgerald (ed.), *The Book of the Horse* (Nicholson and Watson, 1946), p.141. The point is developed in George Ewart Evans, *The Horse in the Furrow* (London: Faber, 1960), ch.13.

8 Plato, *Phaedrus* transl. Walter Hamilton (Harmondsworth: Penguin, 1973), p.96.

9 J. Storer Clouston *op.cit.* in note 2, p.10.

10 *ibid.,* pp.12-13.

11 *Orkneyinga Saga,* transl. Hermann Pálsson and Paul Edwards (London, 1978), c.4, p.30.

12 F. T. Wainwright, 'The Scandinavian Settlement' in F. T. Wainwright (ed.), *The Northern Isles* (Edinburgh, 1962), p.128.

13 Hugh Marwick, 'Celtic Place-names in Orkney', PSAS 57 (1922-23), p.251. It should be noted that Marwick was referring to this idea in order to argue against it.

14 F. T. Wainwright, *op.cit.* in note 12, p.162.

15 Walter Traill Dennison, *Orkney Folklore and Traditions,* edited with an introduction by Ernest W. Marwick (Kirkwall, 1961), p.22.

16 *ibid.,* p.23.

17 Tor Åge Bringsværd, *Phantoms and Fairies* (Oslo, 1979), p.72.

18 *ibid.,* p.73.

19 Ernest W. Marwick, *op.cit.* in note 4, p.24.

20 Walter Traill Dennison, *op.cit.* in note 15, p.22.

21 From an interview recorded on 12.3.69 and retained in the Ernest W. Marwick Tape Collection (M7) in Orkney County Library.

22 Gordon Donaldson, 'The Scots Settlement in Shetland' in Donald J. Withrington (ed.), *Shetland and the Outside World 1469-1969* (Oxford, 1983), p.13.

23 T. M. Y. Manson, 'Historical problems of Shetland to the end of the old earldom', in W. Douglas Simpson (ed.), *The Viking Congress . . . Lerwick, July 1950* (Edinburgh and London: Oliver & Boyd, 1954), pp.58-83.

24 For stories and descriptions of trows in Orkney and Shetland, see Ernest M. Marwick, *op.cit.* in note 4, ch.2.

25 Sir Walter Scott, *Northern Lights,* ed. William F. Laughlan (Hawick: Byways, 1982), p.36. Scott's journal of his voyage north with the Commissioners for the Northern Lighthouse Service was originally published in Lockhart's *Memoirs of the Life of Sir Walter Scott, Bart.,* and

the voyage produced much raw material for Scott's subsequent second novel, *The Pirate*.

26 Ernest W. Marwick, 'Creatures of Orkney Legend and their Norse Ancestry', *Norveg Folkelivsgransking* 15 (1972), p.181.

27 For modern Norwegian words, Einar Haugen's *Norwegian-English Dictionary* (Oslo and Madison, Wisconsin) is used.

28 For Old Norse Norwegian, the dictionary used is Leiv Heggstad, Finn Hødnebø and Erik Simensen, Norrøn Ordbok (Oslo: Det Norske Samlaget, 1975).

29 The Norwegian Ingjald Reichborn-Kjennerud noted in his study of old Norse beliefs and folk-medicine that a great number of names of diseases contained the word *troll*. This clearly takes us very close to the use of the Orkney word *trowie*. The Scottish fairies in their green mounds are associated with the dead — sometimes the recently-departed are seen in their number — and the changelings they left behind in human cradles were appropriate to such a world. Also from Reichborn-Kjennerud we have the observation that the Swedish use in the old Borgarting Law of the phrases *sitta ute* and *väcka* ('sit outside, arouse trolls') shows that the older meaning of the word *troll* was 'ghost'. (For a summary of Reichborn-Kjennerud's ideas, see Dag Strömbäck (ed.), *Leading Folklorists of the North* (Oslo-Bergen-Tromsø: Universitetsforlaget, 1971), pp.353-374.)

30 Ernest W. Marwick, *op.cit.* in note 26, p.178.

31 Richard Bergh, *Tro og Trolldom* (Oslo-Bergen-Tromsø: Universitetsforlaget, 1981), p.7.

32 AT 313. Normally in British versions of this tale-type the giant just bursts; the turning to stone at sunrise is a fairly specific Scandinavian element (Alan Bruford, pers.comm).

33 For a number of examples, see Leslie V. Grinsell, *Folklore of Prehistoric Sites in Britain* (Newton Abbot, 1976).

34 For a survey of fairy characteristics, see Katharine M. Briggs, *The Vanishing People* (London, 1978).

35 Duncan J. Robertson in 'Orkney Folk-lore', POAS II (1923-24), after quoting various stories of "the fairy folk proper of our islands", goes on to ask "who can draw a dividing line between fairies and trows", or between trows and several other species, when habits such as that of carrying off mortals are displayed by each.

36 Bede, *A History of the English Church and People* transl. Leo Sherley-Price (Harmondsworth: Penguin, 1955), ch. 30, p.86.

37 For St Bride and Candlemas customs, see F. Marian McNeill, *The Silver Bough*, Vol. 2 (Glasgow, 1959), pp.19-34.

38 Anne Ross, *Pagan Celtic Britain: Studies in Iconography and Tradition* (London, 1967); Guy Ragland Phillips, *Brigantia* (London, 1976).

39 Marija Gimbutas, *The Goddesses and Gods of Old Europe 6500-3500 BC* (London, 1982).

40 For example, the sky-god Zeus of the Achaean Greeks was married to the already present goddess Hera, 'Lady'.

41 See for instance Frank Noel Stagg, *West Norway and its Fjords* (London, 1954), pp.33-34.

42 Peter Tulloch, *A Window on North Ronaldsay* (Kirkwall, 1974) shows a map with Bride's Ness, Bride's Kirk and Bride's Noust.

43 See O.S. Map.

44 O. A. R. Mowat, Ramray, Graemsay (pers.comm.).

45 Hugh Marwick, 'Antiquarian Notes on Rousay', POAS II (1923-24), p.19.

46 John Fraser, 'Antiquities of Sandwick Parish', POAS II (1923-24), p.27. George Marwick of Yesnaby actually saw the ruins of what he describes as

"Bride's Kirk or Briti-Kirk" in Sandwick, and says it had been "a little square building about ten or twelve feet on each side", with a window opening on each side.

47 R. Fotheringhame, Stronsay (pers. comm.).

48 W. J. Watson, *History of the Celtic Place-names of Scotland* (Edinburgh, 1926), p.334.

49 See for instance O. G. S. Crawford, *The Eye Goddess* (London, 1957). For the development of the idea of the moon and sun as eyes of the sky-god, see Raffaele Pettazzoni, *The All-knowing God.*

50 A. D. Hope, *A Midsummer Eve's Dream* (Edinburgh, 1971), p.42. It would also be worth looking into other possible derivations, for instance from a British form Tridwen. A look at the distribution of Triduana sites gives an impression of being in P-Celtic areas, e.g. in Pictish territory such as the counties of Forfar, Aberdeen, Banff, Sutherland and Caithness, and in British territory in Lothian.

51 Hugh Marwick, 'Antiquarian Notes on Papa Westray', POAS III (1924-25), pp.31-7.

52 Hugh Marwick, *Orkney* (London, 1951) quotes a description of Gyro Night given by a native of Papa Westray, who told him that it was held on the night of "the first Tuesday after the first Voar new moon". Marwick notes that Voar, the spring season, was held to begin on the 13th of February. "That date is, of course, Old Candlemas Day, and these Gyro bonfires and torches are thus apparently to be regarded as part of the old Candlemas rites."

53 Walter Traill Dennison, *op.cit.* in note 15, p.96.

54 Raymond Lamb, 'The Black Bridal of Skartan', in *The Orcadian* of 18th September, 1980.

55 Marija Gimbutas, *op.cit.* in note 39, p.211.

56 There are accounts of pork not being eaten in Shetland at Yule, e.g. in John Spence, *Shetland Folklore,* but not at weddings and not with as strong a degree of repulsion as described for Sanday. The Scottish Highland aversion to pork is a strong one (Hugh Ross, pers.comm.).

57 Bente Magnus (pers.comm.).

58 W. J. Watson, *(The History of the Celtic Place-names of Scotland, 1926)* derived the name Orkney from the Celtic *orc,* 'boar', and hence interpreted the old name *Inse Orc* as referring to the islands of a tribe called the Boar people. Kenneth Jackson in *The Problem of the Picts* (1955) prefers the translation 'pig', and the identification of the tribe as 'The Young Pigs', which is of particular interest in the present context. Against that, however, W. B. Lockwood argues for the root to be a pre-Celtic word meaning 'headland' (On the early history and origin of the names Orkney and Shetland', *Namn och Bygd.* (1979), pp.19-35.)

59 Examples of the bones of animals and birds which seem to have been deliberately brought into Orkney tombs are:- sea-eagles and other carrion-eating birds of prey at Isbister, song-birds at Quanterness, dogs at Cuween and at Burray, and deer at the Holm of Papay. See John Hedges, *Tomb of the Eagles* (London, 1984), pp.145-159.

60 For example, in the Irish epic cycle, Cú Chulainn is forbidden to eat dog. Significantly, his name means 'Culand's dog or hound' and at the site of Emain Macha with which he was closely associated, the excavator found in the central sanctuary the head of a dog. See Anne Ross, 'Material Culture, Myth and Folk Memory' in Robert O'Driscoll (ed.) *The Celtic Consciousness* (Portlaoise and Edinburgh, 1982), pp.197-216.

61 R. Henry, quoted in George Low, *A Tour through the Islands of Orkney and Schetland in 1774,* Joseph Anderson (ed.), (Kirkwall, 1879). This and

other descriptions of the customs at the Stone of Odin are surveyed in a paper by Ernest W. Marwick accompanying J. N. Graham Ritchie, 'The Stones of Stenness, Orkney', PSAS 107 (1975-76), pp.1-60.

62 Ker's Naval Log of 1780 (National Library of Scotland, Ms 1083), quoted by Ernest W. Marwick in J. N. Graham Ritchie, *op.cit.*

63 R. Henry, *op.cit.* in note 61.

64 John O'Donovan, quoted in Máire MacNeill, *The Festival of Lughnasa* (Oxford, 1962), p.316.

65 Sir William Wilde, *Beauties of the Boyne and the Blackwater* (1850), quoted in Máire MacNeill, *op.cit.*, p.316.

66 Eugene Conwell, *Preceedings of the Royal Irish Academy* 15 (1879), pp.74-5, quoted in Máire MacNeill, *op.cit.*, pp.316-7.

67 Sir John Sinclair, *The Statistical Account of Scotland* (Edinburgh, 1793), Vol. XII, pp.614-5.

68 For a review of handfast marriages, see A. D. Hope, *op.cit.* in note 50, pp.148-164.

69 Quotation given by Heinrich Wagner, 'Studies in the Origins of the Celts and of Early Celtic Civilisation' (Belfast, 1971), p.38.

70 *ibid.*, p.20.

71 *ibid.*

72 *ibid.*

73 Máire MacNeill, *op.cit.* in note 64.

74 See Heinrich Wagner, *op.cit.* in note 69, and F. Marian McNeill, *The Silver Bough,* Vol. 1 (Glasgow, 1957), p.88-9. John P. Windwick, 'The Ladykirk Stone', POAS 6, pp.55-7, describes an Orkney coronation stone preserved in St Mary's Church, South Ronaldsay.

75 F. Marian McNeill, *op.cit.*, p.89.

76 *ibid.*, p.90.

77 The oath of Odin comes into the Orkney ballad, 'The Play o' de Lathie Odivere', reconstructed from fragments in oral tradition by Walter Traill Dennison. The ballad can be found in Ernest W. Marwick (ed.), *An Anthology of Orkney Verse* (Kirkwall, 1949), pp.54-64.

78 H. R. Ellis Davidson, *Gods and Myths of Northern Europe* (Harmondsworth: Penguin Books, 1964), pp.76-77.

79 These arguments are developed in Heinrich Wagner, *op.cit.* in note 69.

80 Walter Traill Dennison, *op.cit.* in note 15, p.27.

81 Quoted in John Nicolson, *Shetland Incidents and Tales* (Edinburgh, 1931), pp.81-3. See also G. L. Gomme, *Primitive Folk-Moots* (London, 1880), pp.162-163.

82 *ibid.*

83 J. Storer Clouston, *Records of the Earldom of Orkney* (Edinburgh, 1914), p.88, note 1, and p.lxxiv.

84 *ibid.*, p.71. Note also the conclusion of Hibbert in a paper in *Archaeologica Scotica* III on the siting of the Things of Orkney and Shetland: he argued that an older Norse pagan site was chosen, and that the religious element was taken away from the Thing at a later stage, after Christian churches had been established. Hibbert's arguments are quoted and developed by Gomme who uses them to identify a pattern of open-air courts and moot-hills in Scotland. A fascinating article by Evan MacGillivray has just appeared in *The Orcadian* on the subject of 'Orkney's Head Thing at Kirkwall', and I am very interested to note his comment that the Things at Tingwall, Dingishowe and Kirkwall were all on the much older sites of broch-mounds.

85 F. T. Wainwright, 'Picts and Scots' in F. T. Wainwright, *op.cit.* in note 12, p.104.

86 Hugh Marwick, *op.cit.* in note 52, p.198.
87 David Greene, 'The Celtic Languages' in Joseph Raftery, *The Celts* (Cork: The Mercier Press, 1964), pp.15-16 and p.20.
88 *ibid.,* pp.19-20.
89 F. T. Wainwright, *op.cit.* in note 85, pp.105-6.
90 These arguements were drawn together in *The Problem of the Picts,* (Edinburgh and London, 1955) and also cited by Wainwright, and like *The Northern Isles* an essential basis for all subsequent discussion on this period.
91 K. Jackson, 'The Pictish Language' in F. T. Wainwright, *op.cit.* in note 90, p.157.
92 F. T. Wainwright, *op.cit.* in note 85, p.106.
93 J. Jakobsen, *The Place-names of Shetland* (London and Copenhagen, 1936), pp.176-7.
94 Hugh Marwick, *op.cit.* in note 13, pp.251-265.
95 *ibid.,* p.254.
96 Magnus seems to be virtually the only Norse name to have been in steady use into the present.
97 Kaaren Grimstad, 'A Comic Role of the Viking in the Family Sagas', in Firschow, Grimstad, Hasselmo, O'Neil (eds.), *Studies for Einar Haugen* (Janue Linguarum Series Maior LIX, The Hague, Paris), p.249.
98 *ibid.,* pp.250-1.
99 Per Sveaas Andersen, *Samlingen av Norge og kristingen av landet 800-1130* (Bergen-Oslo-Tromsø: Universitstsforlaget, 1977), pp.72-4.
100 Roald Morcken, 'Europas eldste sjømerker?' in *Sjøfartshistorisk Årbok 1969* (Bergen: Foreningen Bergens Sjøfartsmuseum, 1978), pp.7-48. The importance of trade at an early stage in Norway's history has been emphasised by Charlotte Blindheim who points out that the differences between areas and the lack of resources necessitated exchange of goods: "Nature has formed Norway in such a way that the districts *were forced* into contact, since all the resources available must be utilised, for purposes of bartering etc." ('Norwegian Viking Age Archaeology Today' in *Norwegian Archaeological Review* 15:1-2 (1982), p.3).
101 The account of the voyage of Ottar (DE *Othere*) was written by Alfred himself and inserted in a paraphrase of another text. A translation can be found in Gwyn Jones, *The Norse Atlantic Saga* (Oxford 1964), 2nd edition 1986, pp.251-4. See also P. G. Foote and D. M. Wilson, *The Viking Achievement* (London, 1970), pp.40-41.
102 A. P. Smith, *Scandinavian Kings in the British Isles 850-880* (Oxford, 1977), and *Warlords and Holy Men* (London, 1984). It is important to stress here that Smyth's views are the subject of debate, some of it quite robust, but that whatever the outcome as to particular aspects, the central idea of differentiating out the Danish and Norwegian strands of this period is a powerful one which does deserve close attention. It should also be noted that the boundaries between 'Norwegians' and 'Danes' are not identical with the modern nation-state frontiers.
103 F. T. Wainwright, *op.cit.* in note 12, pp.126-130.
104 *ibid.*
105 Smyth in *Warlords and Holy Men* emphasises the likely link between these events.
106 *Orkneyinga Saga,* c.6. Note that in the early raids elsewhere Norwegians rather than Danes are named, and that indeed in the case of the first chronicled 'Danish' raid on England, the ships came from the county of Hordaland in western Norway. This does not conflict with the argument put here that such headline-making activity might not itself be the main

Norwegian use of shipbuilding technology and navigational skills, but rather a smaller-scale *misuse* of them, the larger-scale institutionalised misuse coming later with the Danish attacks and land-taking.

107 Hugh Marwick, *op.cit.* in note 51, p.32.

108 In order to explain genetic disparities between Iceland and Norway — e.g. the greater proportion of red hair in Icelanders and lower proportion of blood group A — it has been suggested that the original settlers of Iceland were not the same genetic mixture as present-day Norwegians. This is likely since the historical evidence is for part of the settlement to have come by way of Celtic areas like Ireland and the Western Isles, with mixed marriages and slavery being factors in the overall composition of the settlers. However, there is no reason to think that the Scandinavian immigration to Orkney was other than direct from Norway, and since Norway itself has had no known major in-migration since the Norse period, it is clearly arguable that the initial Norse settlers in Orkney were of overall similar genetic composition to the present-day Norwegian population. From Table 22 in the present book the higher amounts of blood-group A in Norway and Denmark can be seen, and compared with the figures for Iceland where there is a lower proportion of A but as much of the 'Celtic' group O as in Ireland. (The extent of the Celtic contribution to Icelandic genes is a matter for disagreement but lively debate — see for instance *Norwegian Archaeological Review Vol. 10: 1-2* (1977), pp.60-82 — and what would add some further fuel to the controversy, in the light of the early carbon dates from the Faroes quoted in Chapter 5 of the present book, would be some pre-*Landnámabók* datings from the excavations of Margret Hermannsdottir in the Westmann Islands.) Orkney too is down on blood-group A compared with Norway, but the higher B can be noted, and the contrast made between the Sanday (17% B) and Westray (9% B) figures. The implications of Prof. Derek Roberts' analysis and conclusions of Chapter 4 are so fascinating that it would clearly be interesting to look more closely for other 'pockets' of high B frequency in Europe — and, for that matter, in North Africa. Taking into account factors like genetic drift, it would also be interesting to look closely at figures for Norwegian areas like Sogn, where the dissimilarities between the darker-haired people and their blonder neighbours in Fjordane have long been noted.

109 See for instance Sigrid Kaland, 'Some Economic Aspects of the Orkneys in the Viking Period', p.91: "It is possible that as early as in the Viking period that grain was exported to Norway, where it might have been exchanged for hides, tools and weapons of iron. Norway got grain from England in the 10th century . . . and Orkney exported grain to Iceland in the early medieval period . . ."

110 *ao* in *caora* was originally *ae* (as in the Old Irish spelling *cáera*(, pronounced *xxx i*, hence can readily give the Orkney *keero* (Alan Bruford, pers.comm).

111 Quoted by J. R. C. Hamilton, 'Brochs and Broch-builders', in F. T. Wainwright, *The Northern Isles,* p.64.

112 H. M. Chadwick, *Early Scotland* (Cambridge, 1949), p.113. See also J. R. C. Hamilton, 'Forts, Brochs and Wheel-houses in Northern Scotland', in A. L. Rivet (ed), *The Iron Age in Northern Britain* (Edinburgh, 1966), pp.125-6.

113 John Robertson, *Uppies and Doonies* (Aberdeen, 1967). Subsequent to this Mr Robertson has been finding out about still more aspects of this subject, such as the similarities with the Ashbourne Ball in Derbyshire. In view of the various Celtic traditions that Derbyshire has retained, this comparison has obvious interest.

114 As well as the structure of the treb dykes themselves, which are in some cases older than the growth of peat round them, another hint as to their age comes from the use of the term 'pickie dyke'; see for instance Alexander Fenton, *The Northern Isles, Orkney and Shetland* (Edinburgh, 1978), pp.13-14.

115 J. R. C. Hamilton, *op.cit.* in note 111, p.67.

116 For fuller details of the Gododdin, see for instance Leslie Alcock, *Arthur's Britain* (Penguin, 1971).

117 G. Whittington and J. A. Soulsby, 'A Preliminary Report on an Investigation into *Pit* Place-names', (1968), quoted in W. F. H. Nicolaisen, *Scottish Place-names* (London, 1976). The argument for an Orcadian origin of the Picts has been revived recently in the analysis of their symbol stones made by Anthony Jackson in *The Symbol Stones of Scotland* (Stromness: The Orkney Press, 1984). It could certainly be argued that one effect of the existence of the Roman Empire would have been for small-scale population movements into and out of the lands on the frontier margins: recruitment into auxiliary service or trading opportunities, on the one hand, and retirement or 'going native', on the other. It would indeed have been interesting, as Hamilton points out in a footnote to his chapter on 'Brochs and Broch-builders' in *The Northern Isles,* if a detailed account had only survived of the adventures of the cohort of German Usipii, who after mutinying sailed round the north of Scotland. They were beaten off by the native peoples they encountered, and were eventually intercepted by the Suevi and Frisii and sold for slaves, but Tacitus' reference to them acts as a reminder about the extent to which indirect effects of the Roman Empire could reach out into the surrounding regions.

118 From the unpublished papers of George Marwick of Yesnaby, whose collected folklore was described by Ernest Marwick, *op.cit.* in note 61, as "requiring extensive and critical editing" but "containing a wealth of local traditions."

119 I owe this suggestion to my colleague D. A. MacDonald — *A.B.*

Chapter 8

1 A. Sommerfelt, 'On the Norse form of the name of the Picts and the date of the first Norse raids on Scotland', *Lochlann* 1 (1958), pp.218-22.

2 E. Bakka, 'Scandinavian trade relations with the continent and the British Isles in pre-viking times', *Antikvariskt Arkiv* 40 (1971), pp.37-51.

3 F. T. Wainwright (ed.), *The Northern Isles (Edinburgh: Nelson, 1962).*

4 A. Ritchie, 'Picts and Norsemen in Northern Scotland', *Scottish Archaeological Forum* 6 (1974), pp.23-36.

5 I. A. Crawford, 'War or peace—Viking colonisation in the Northern and Western Isles of Scotland reviewed', in H. Bekker-Nielsen, P. Foote and O. Olsen (eds.), *Proceedings of the Eighth Viking Congress, Århus . . . 1977* (Odense: University Press, 1981), pp.259-70.

6 A. Small 'Norse settlement in Skye', in R. Boyer (ed.), *Les Vikings et leur civilisation,* Bibliothèque arctique et antarctique 5 (Paris: Mouton, 1976), pp.29-37.

7   M. O. Anderson, 'Dalriada and the creation of the kingdom of the Scots', in
    D. Dumville (ed.), *Ireland in early mediaeval Europe* (Cambridge: University
    Press, 1982), pp.106-32.
8   St Findan, 'Vita', in *Monumenta Germaniae Historica. Scriptorum*, xv 1
    (1887), pp.502-6.
9   P. McNeill and R. Nicholson, An Historical Atlas of Scotland c. 400-c. 1600
    (St Andrews: Atlas Committee of the Conference of Scottish Medievalists,
    1975).
10 A. Thorsteinsson, 'The Viking burial place at Pierowall, Westray, Orkney',
    in B. Niclasen (ed.), *Proceedings of the Fifth Viking Congress, Tórshavn
    . . . 1965* (Tórshavn: Føroya Landsstýri, 1968), pp.150-73.
11 R. B. K. Stevenson, 'Christian Sculpture in Norse Shetland',
    Fróðskaparrit, Annales Societatis Scientiarum Færoensis 28-29 (1981),
    pp.283-92.
12 J. Graham-Campbell, 'Bossed penannular brooches: a review of recent
    research', *Medieval Archaeology* 19 (1975), pp.33-47; 'British Antiquity
    1975-6', *The Archaeological Journal* 133 (1976), pp.277-89, and especially
    pp.280-81.
13 J. Graham-Campbell, 'British Antiquity 1974-5', *The Archaeological Journal*
    132 (1975), pp.349-61.
14 D. Whitelock, 'The conversion of the Eastern Danelaw', *Saga-Book of the
    Viking Society* 12:3 (1940), pp.159-76; D. M. Wilson, 'The Vikings'
    relationship with Christianity in Northern England', *Journal of the British
    Archaeological Association,* 3rd series, 30 (1967), pp.37-46; *The Viking Age
    in the Isle of Man* (Odense: University Press, 1974).
15 J. Jóhannesson, *A History of the Old Icelandic Commonwealth,* transl.
    H. Bessason (University of Manitoba Press, 1974), pp.141-3.
16 H. Bekker-Nielsen, 'Skotakollr', *Fróðskaparrit. Annales Societatis
    Scientiarum Færoensis* 18 (1970), pp.145-50; G. Fellows-Jensen,
    Scandinavian personal names in Lincolnshire and Yorkshire (Copenhagen:
    Akademisk Forlag, 1968), p.252.
17 F. Birkeli, 'Hadde Håkon Adalsteinsfostre likevel en bisp Sigfrid hos seg?',
    (Norsk) Historisk Tidsskrift 40 (1961), pp.113-36; 'The earliest missionary
    activities from England to Norway', *Nottingham Mediaeval Studies* 15
    (1971), pp.27-37.
18 F. Birkeli, *Norske steinkors i tidlig middelalder.* Skrifter utg. av det Norske
    Videnskaps-Akademi i Oslo. II, Hist.-filos. Kl., Ny serie 10, 1973.
19 C. Blindheim, 'Trade problems in the Viking Age. Some reflections on
    insular metalwork found in Norwegian graves of the Viking Age', in
    T. Andersson and K. I. Sandred (eds.), *The Vikings: Proceedings of the
    Symposium . . . Uppsala University . . . 1977)* (Stockholm: Almqvist and
    Wiksell, 1978), pp.166-76.
20 C. Weibull, 'De danska och skånska vikingatågen till Västeuropa under 800-
    talet', *Scandia* 43 (1977), pp.40-69.
21 D. M. Wilson and O. Klindt-Jensen, *Viking Art* (London: Allen and Unwin,
    1966), p.101.
22 *ibid.,* pp.116-7.
23 E. Bakka, 'Keltisk stilinnflytelse', *Kulturhistorisk Leksikon for nordisk
    middelalder* 8 (1963), pp.373-5.
24 U. O'Meadhra, *Early Christian, Viking and Romanesque art. Motif-pieces
    from Ireland* (Stockholm: Almqvist and Wiksell, 1979).
25 R. N. Bailey, *Viking Age Sculpture in Northern England* (Glasgow: Collins,
    1980), pp.229-31.
26 P. H. Sawyer, *Kings and Vikings* (London: Methuen, 1982).
27 T. Fanning, 'The Hiberno-Norse pins from the Isle of Man', in C. Fell,

P. Foote, J. Graham-Campbell and R. L. Thomson (eds.) *The Viking Age in the Isle of Man* (London: Viking Society for Northern Research, 1983), pp.27-36.

28 W. B. Lockwood, 'Some traces of Gaelic in Faroese', *Fróðskaparrit. Annales Societatis Scientiarum Færoensis* 25 (1977), pp.9-25; 'Chr. Matras' studies on the Gaelic element in Faroese: conclusions and results', *Scottish Gaelic Studies* 13 (1978), pp.112-26.

29 J. de Vries, *Altnordisches etymologisches Wörterbuch* (Leiden: Brill, 1961), pp.xxi-xxii.

30 W. B. Lockwood, *op. cit.* (1977), pp.21-2; *op. cit.* (1978), p.124.

31 A. B. Ø. Borchgrevink, 'The "seter" areas of rural Norway', *Northern Studies* 9 (1977), pp.3-24.

32 G. Fellows-Jensen, 'Common Gaelic *áirge,* Old Scandinavian *ǽrgi* or *erg?',* *Nomina* 4 (1980), pp.67-74.

33 G. Turville-Petre, *Scaldic Poetry* (Oxford: University Press, 1976), pp.xxi-xxvii.

34 K. von See, *Germanische Verskunst* (Stuttgart: J. B. Metzlersche Verlagsbuchhandlung, 1967), pp.37-41.

35 E. Ó. Sveinsson, *Löng er för,* Studia Islandica 34 (Reykjavík: Menningarsjóður, 1975), pp.173-217.

36 P. Foote, 'Latin rhetoric and Icelandic poetry. Some contacts', *Saga och sed* 50 (1982), pp.107-27 and especially p.111.

37 G. Turville-Petre, *Myth and Religion of the North* (London: Weidenfeld and Nicolson, 1964).

38 G. Turville-Petre, Review in *Saga-book of the Viking Society* 16:2-3 (1963-4), pp.254-7.

39 G. Turville-Petre, *op. cit.* in note 37, p.153.

40 C. J. S. Marstrander, *Bidrag til det norske sprogs historie i Irland. Skrifter udg. av Videnskapsselskapet i Christiania. II, Hist. filos. Kl., 1915, p.69.*

41 K. von See, *Edda, Saga, Skaldendichtung* (Heidelberg: Carl Winter, 1981), pp.84-96, 514-6.

42 E. Ó. Sveinsson, *op. cit.* in note 35, pp.13-116.

43 K. von See, *Skaldendichtung* (München: Artemis Verlag, 1980), pp.86-92.

44 E. Ó. Sveinsson, 'Celtic elements in Icelandic tradition', *Béaloideas 1957* (1959), pp.3-24.

45 N. K. Chadwick, 'Literary tradition in the Old Norse and Celtic world', *Saga-Book of the Viking Society* 14:3 (1955-56), pp.164-99.

46 J. de Vries, 'Germanic and Celtic heroic tradition', *Saga-Book of the Viking Society* 16:1 (1962), pp.22-40.

47 N. K. Chadwick, *op. cit.*

48 A. P. Smyth, *Scandinavian York and Dublin,* I-II (Dublin: Templekieran Press, 1975-9); *Scandinavian Kings in the British Isles 850-880* (Oxford: University Press, 1977).

49 J. Graham-Campbell, *op. cit.* (1976) in note 12, p.286.

50 R. McTurk, Review of Smyth, 1977, *Saga-Book of the Viking Society* 20:3 (1980), pp.231-4.

51 N. Lukman, 'An Irish source and some Icelandic *fornaldarsögur',* *Mediaeval Scandinavia* 10 (1977), pp.41-57.

52 Brian O'Cuív (ed.), *The Impact of the Scandinavian Invasions on the Celtic-speaking Peoples c. 800-1100 A.D.* (Dublin: Institute for Advanced Studies, 1983). The papers were first published in this form in 1975, but originated in a 1959 conference.

53 J. G. P. Friell and W. G. Watson (eds.) *Pictish Studies. Settlement, Burial and Art in Dark Age Northern Britain* (BAR British Series 125, 1984).

54 A. Fenton and Hermann Pálsson (eds.), *The Northern and Western Isles in*

the Viking World. Survival, Continuity and Change (John Donald Publishers Ltd: Edinburgh, 1984).

55 Rosemary Power, '"An óige, an saol agus an bás" *Feis Tighe Chonáin* and "þórr's visit to Útgarða-Loki"', *Béaloideas* 53 (1985), pp.217-94.

Chapter 9

This paper was given as one of the O'Donnell Lectures before the University of Oxford in May 1976. It is now published by kind permission of the Board of English in Oxford, in whom the management of the O'Donnell Lectureship is vested, and the copyright of the article lies with the Board. I should like to thank Mr R. W. McTurk and Dr. Séamas Ó Catháin with whom I have had fruitful discussions on various aspects of my topic. The lecture is printed as it was delivered, with the exception of some minor adjustments and the addition of footnotes. In the footnotes the following abbeviations are used:

ANF   *Arkiv för nordisk filologi* (1889—).
IF   Íslenzk Fornrit (1933—).
KL   *Kulturhistoriskt Lexikon för nordisk medeltid* (1956-78).
ML   R. Th. Christiansen, 'The Migratory Legends', *FF Communications* N:o 175 (vol. LXXI: 1, 1958).
Skj. *Den norsk-islandske Skjaldedigtning*. A I-II, B I-II (1912-15), ed. Finnur Jónsson.

1 Finnbogi Guðmundsson, *Orkneyinga saga* (IF XXXIV, 1965), 81.
2 Echoes from the troubadours are heard for instance in some of Rögnvaldr *kali*'s verses; see e.g. R. Meissner, 'Ermengarde, Vicegräfin von Narbonne, und Jarl Rögnvald', *ANF* 41 (1925), 140-91, and J. de Vries, 'Een skald onder de troubadours', *Verslagen en mededeelingen der Kgl. Vlaamsche Academie voor taal- en letterkunde* (1938), 701-35. Cf. also below, 90.
3 See e.g. C. A. Ralegh Radford, 'Art and Architecture: Celtic and Norse' in F. T. Wainwright (ed.), *The Northern Isles* (1962), 163-87, and works quoted there.
4 Wainwright (1962), 126-40 and works quoted there.
5 See M. Oftedal in *KL,* s.v. *Norn,* and works quoted there.
6 A. T. Cluness, *The Shetland Isles* (1951), 65.
7 Some of this material has appeared in the periodical *Tocher* (1971—).
8 J. Jakobsen, *Etymologisk ordbog over det norrøne sprog på Shetland* I-II (1908-21), *An Etymological Dictionary of the Norn Language in Shetland* I-II (1928-32). A selection of Jakobsen's more important articles has appeared under the title *Greinir og ritgerðir* (1975); this edition also contains a full bibliography of his works.
9 H. Marwick, *The Orkney Norn* (1929). See also other books and papers by the same author, listed in Wainwright (1962), 205-6, and in B. Dickins, 'An Orkney Scholar: Hugh Marwick 1881-1965', *Saga-Book* XVII (1966-9), 15-17.
10 See bibliographies in G. F. Black, *Examples of Printed Folk-Lore Concerning the Orkney & Shetland Islands* (County Folk-Lore III, 1903), ix-xii, and E. W. Marwick, *The Folklore of Orkney and Shetland* (1975), 205-7.
11 K. H. Jackson, 'The Pictish Language', in F. T. Wainwright (ed.), *The Problem of the Picts* (1955), 129-66; cf. also Wainwright (1962), 91-116.

12   IF XXXIV, 289, 114-15.
13   See e.g. D. Mac Ritchie, 'Memories of the Picts', *The Scottish Antiquary* XIV (1900), 121-39; same author, *Finns, Fairies and Picts* (1893); E. Andrews, *Ulster Folklore* (1913), 15-16, 27, 31, 50, 57, 78, 99, 102, 104.
14   See Anne Holtsmark in *KL*, s.v. *Historia Norvegiæ.*
15   G. Storm, *Monumenta Historica Norvegiæ* (1880), 88.
16   Cf. A. T. Lucas, 'Souterrains: The Literary Evidence', *Béaloideas* 39-41, (1971-3), 165-91.
17   S. Thompson, *Motif-Index of Folk-Literature* 1-6 (rev. ed., 1955-8).
18   D. Skeels, *The Romance of Perceval in Prose, A Translation of the Didot Perceval* (1966), 88.
19   E. Vinaver, *The Works of Malory* (1947), I, 161 (Bk. IV, 18), III, 1216-20 (Bk. XX, 21-2).
20   J. Jakobsen, 'Nordiske minder, især sproglige, på Orknøerne', *Svenska landsmål* (1911) [*Festskrift til H. F. Feilberg,* also published elsewhere], 325. The passage translated by me.
21   Wainwright (1962), 102.
22   B. Almqvist, *Norrön niddiktning, Traditionshistoriska studier i versmagi,* 1 *Nid mot furstar* (1965), 152, note 88.
23   *Arv* 21 (1965), 115-35.
24   The reference is in stanza 3b *(Skj.* A I 513, B I 488). The attribution to Hallr Þórarinsson and Rögnvaldr *kali* is not certain, but is accepted as likely by most scholars (cf. Anne Holtsmark in *KL*, s.v. *Háttalykill).*
25   E.g. Finnur Jónsson, *Den oldnorske og oldislandske litteraturs historie* (2nd ed., 1920-4), II 38.
26   For instance in the genres known as *tenson* and *partimen;* see e.g. P. Bec, *Nouvelle anthologie de la lyrique occitane du Moyen Age* (2nd ed., 1972), 140-8).
27   IF XXXIV, 209-11, 215-17, 219.
28   P. M. C. Kermode, *Manx Crosses* (1907).
29   Micheál O Gaoithín said: *Chonaic an seanduine á marú iad agus is ea a bhí sé ag gáirí,* "The old man saw them [his sons] being killed and he laughed". Cf. *Arv* 21, 116. The heroic-laugh motif is also found in a version from Tipperary *(Schools Manuscript 578,* 283 in the Department of Irish Folklore, University College Dublin).
30   *Skj.* B I 498, cf. A I 521.
31   J. Olrik & H. Ræder, *Saxonis Gesta Danorum* (1931-57), 131-4, especially 134.
32   Finnur Jónsson, *Edda Snorra Sturlusonar* (1931), 153-5.
33   Guðbrandr Vigfusson and C. R. Unger, *Flateyjarbók* (1860-8), I 279-83.
34   *Balor with the Evil Eye* (1927), 132-53.
35   *Romance in Iceland* (1934), 138-40.
36   'Keltnesk áhrif á íslenzkar ýkjusögur', *Skírnir* CVI (1932), 114-16; 'Celtic Elements in Icelandic Tradition', *Béaloideas* XXV (1957), 17-18.
37   *Duanaire Finn* Part III (Irish Texts Society XLIII, 1953), XXXIII-IV, LIII-IV.
38   See e.g. T. P. Cross, *Motif-Index of Early Irish Literature* (1952), A162.1.0.1*; E155.1.
39   'An Unsolved Problem in Old Norse-Icelandic Literary History', *Mediaeval Scandinavia* 1 (1968), 129-33.
40   *Skj.* B I 2-3, A I 2-3.
41   See ref. in Einar Ól. Sveinsson (1957), 18, note 37.
42   Some of this material is discussed in A. Bruford, 'Gaelic Folk-tales and Mediaeval Romances', *Béaloideas* XXXIV (1966, also published separately 1969), see references s.v. 'Everlasting Fight' in Index, 284.

43 See Anne Holtsmark, 'Bjarne Kolbeinsson og hans forfatterskap', *Edda* 37 (1937), 1-17.
44 W. Douglas Simpson, *Scottish Castles* (1959), 5; H. Marwick, 'Kolbein Hruga's Castle, Wyre', *Prceedings of the Orkney Antiquarian Society* VI (1928), 9-11.
45 See Anne Holtsmark in *KL*, s.v. *Málsháttakvæði*.
46 *Skj.* B II 140-1, A II 133.
47 Finnur Jónsson, *Ágrip af Nóregs konunga sögum* (Altnordische Saga-Bibliothek 18, 1929), 3-5.
48 Bjarni Aðalbjarnarson, *Haralds saga ins hárfagra* in *Heimskringla* (IF XXVI, 1941), 125-7.
49 *Flateyjarbók* (1860-8), I 582.
50 See e.g. D. Strömbäck, *Sejd* (1935), 198-206, R. I. Page, ' "Lapland Sorcerers" ', *Saga-Book* XVI (1962-5), 215-32, and Marwick (1975), 25-7.
51 Moltke Moe, 'Eventyrlige sagn i vor ældre historie', *Moltke Moes samlede skrifter* (Instituttet for sammenlignende kulturforskning, Serie B, I, VI, IX, 1925-7), II 168-97.
52 Moe (1925-7), II 176-97, especially 176-81, 191-7.
53 There is a reference to Fionn Mac Cumhaill's inordinate love for a dead woman in *Feis tighe Chonáin,* ed. Maud Joynt (Medieval and Modern Irish Series VII, 1936), 14.
54 *Skj.* B II 141 (The edition has *spakk* instead of *sprakk* because of a misprint). Cf. *Skj.* A II 133.
55 *The Vikings and the Viking Wars in Irish and Gaelic Tradition* (1931), 413-16.
56 Sigurður Nordal, *Egils saga Skalla-Grímssonar* (IF II, 1933), 243-4.
57 See Finnbogi Guðmundsson in *KL*, s.v. *Orkneyinga saga.*
58 IF XXXIV, 8-9.
59 See e.g. H. M. & N. K. Chadwick, *The Growth of Literature* I (1932), 92-4; N. K. Chadwick, *The Celts* (1970), 49-50; K. H. Jackson, *The Oldest Irish Tradition: a Window on the Iron Age* (1964), 19-20.
60 *Aided Chonchobuir* in K. Meyer, *The Death-tales of the Ulster Heroes* (Royal Irish Academy, Todd Lecture Series XIV, 1906), 2-21.
61 IF XXXIV, 231-2.
62 On *viðáttuskáldskapr* and its Irish counterpart, see *Norrön niddiktning* (1965), 56 and H. Meroney, 'Studies in Early Irish Satire', *The Journal of Celtic Studies* 1 (1950), 199-226.
63 See references in C. O'Rahilly, *Táin Bó Cúalnge from the Book of Leinster* (1967), xviii.
64 Finnur Jónsson, *Morkinskinna* (Samfund til udgivelse af gammel nordisk litteratur LIII, 1932), 383.
65 Bjarnie Aðalbjarnarson, *Magnússona saga* in *Heimskringla* (IF XXVIII, 1951), 261.
66 L. L. Hammerich, 'Ireland og Kontinentet i middelalderen', *Saga och Sed* (1970), 34. Cf. also Meissner (1925), 149-51.
67 IF XXXIV, 231, note 3.
68 *Skj.* B II 141, A II 133.
69 IF XXXIV, 106.
70 S. Ó Súilleabháin, *A Handbook of Irish Folklore* (1942), 273.
71 Cf. B. Almqvist, 'The Death Forebodings of Saint Óláfr, King of Norway, and Rögnvaldr Brúsason, Earl of Orkney', *Béaloideas* 42-4 (1974-6), especially 24, 29-30, 32.
72 Einar Ól. Sveinsson, *Brennu-Njáls saga* (IF XII, 1954), 446-7, 454-60.
73 Anne Holtsmark, ' "Vefr Darraðar" ', *Maal og minne* (1939), 78.
74 IF XII, 175.

75 Einar Ól. Sveinsson and Matthias Þórðarson, *Eyrbyggja saga* (IF IV, 1935), 140.
76 Holtsmark (1939), 74-96. Cf. also A. J. Goedher, *Irish and Norse Traditions about the Battle of Clontarf* (1938), 78.
77 *The Pirate*, note to Chapter II; cf. Jakobsen (1911) 329-30.
78 See e.g. H. R. Ellis, '"Gjalti": A Study on Battle-Panic in Old Norse Literature', *Comparative Literature Studies* 11 (1944), 21-9; Einar Ól. Sveinsson, 'Visa i Hávamálum og írsk saga', *Skírnir* CXXVI (1952), 168-77.
79 IF XXXIV, 4.
80 R. Meissner, 'Ganga til fréttar', *Zeitschrift des Vereins für Volkskunde* 27 (1917), 1-13.
81 In the introduction to Marwick (1929), xxxiv, the author calls attention to some 'practically identical parallels' between Orkney and Faroese proverbs. He says among other things: '"There are mair ways o' killing a dog or choking him wi' butter" is not far from Fær. "Ilt er at binda hund við smörleyp" . . . "Even the craw thinks her ain bird bonniest" is a clear rendering of Fær. "Kráka tykist best um unga sín".' Both these proverbs occur in Scottish Gaelic and Irish tradition in forms closer to the Orkney than to the Faroese versions (see e.g. T. S. Ó Máille, *Sean-fhocla Chonnacht* I, 1948, nos. 2471, 1975). Since they also occur in England *(The Oxford Dictionary of English Proverbs,* 2nd rev. ed., 1935, 696, 120), it is difficult to say when and how they were disseminated. For a Scottish Gaelic counterpart to a proverb in *Málsháttakvæði,* see Chesnutt (1968), 128 and works quoted there.
82 See especially 'Keltisk och nordisk kultur i möte på Hebriderna', *Folk-liv* VII-VIII (1943-4), 228-52 and 'Nordvästeuropeisk brödkultur i Rígsþula', *Saga och Sed* (1915), 5-19. A bibliography of Å. Campbell's printed works appears in *Arctica, Essays presented to Åke Campbell* (1956), 285-96.
83 See e.g. 'Nordsjøsagn', *Arv* 13 (1957), 1-20; 'Til spørsmålet om forholdet mellem irsk og nordisk tradisjon', *Arv* 8 (1952), 1-41; 'Gaelic and Norse Folklore', *Folk-liv* (1938), 321-35.
84 Inger M. Boberg, *Sagnet om den store Pans død* (1934).
85 Brita Egardt, 'De svenska vattenhästsägnerna och deras ursprung'. *Folkkulture* 4 (1944), 119-66.
86 Dag Strömback, 'Some Notes on the Nix in Older Nordic Tradition', *Medieval Literature and Folklore Studies, Essays in Honor of Francis Lee Utley* (1970), 245-56. Cf. also *KL,* s.v. *Näcken.*
87 The following migratory legends may prove to be especially worthy of close investigation: River Claiming its Due *(ML* 4050), The Visit to the Old Troll — The Handshake *(ML* 5010), The Fairy Hunter *(ML* 5060), Midwife to the Fairies *(ML* 5070), Removing Building Situated above the House of the Fairies *(ML* 5075), The Changeling *(ML* 5085), Married to a Fairy Woman *(ML* 5090). Scottish and Manx versions of legends about children who have died or been murdered before baptism (cf. *ML* 4025) have been treated in an article of mine, 'Norska utburdsägner i västerled', *Norveg* 21 (1978), 109-119, and I suggest there that these legends are of Norwegian origin.
88 D. A. Binchy, *Celtic and Anglo-Saxon Kingship* (The O'Donnell Lectures for 1967-8, 1970), I.
89 Marwick (1929), 187.
90 H. Wagner, *Gaeilge Theilinn* (1959), 274-7; Seán Mac Giollarnáth, 'An Dara Tiachóg as Iorrus Aithneach', *Béaloideas* X (1940), 31. There are further printed Irish versions of this legend in *Béaloideas* V (1935), 132-3: VIII (1938), 158; XI (1941), 102-3; XXVII (1959), 2-5; XXXIII (1965), 52-3; and in S. O' Sullivan, *Folktales of Ireland* (1966), 266-7. There are at least eleven more variants in manuscripts in the archives of the Department of Irish

Folklore, UCD. The Irish versions have been analysed by Séamus Mac Cóil, 'The Witch Sinks Ships', 3rd year students essay 1976 (manuscript in Department of Irish Folklore). Scottish variants occur in: A. Carmichael, *Carmina Gadelica* V (1954), 299-304; J. G. Campbell, *Superstitions of the Highlands of Scotland* (1900), 147; J. L. Campbell, *Tales of Barra Told by the Coddy* (1961), 204-5. Faroese versions are found in J. Jakobsen, *Færøske folkesagn og æventyr* (Samfund til udgivelse af gammel nordisk litteratur XXVII, 1898-1901), 38, 131-2. There are a number of Icelandic versions in Jón Árnason, *Íslenzkar þjóðsögur og ævintýri,* ed. Árni Böðvarsson and Bjarni Vilhjálmsson (1954-61), I, 437; III, 402, 537-8, 586, 610. I am not aware of the existence of this legend in Norway, Denmark or Sweden, and it may be that it is of Irish or Scottish origin.

Chapter 10

1 F. T. Wainwright, *The Northern Isles,* 1962, p.105.
2 K. Jackson, 'The Pictish Language', in F. T. Wainwright, *The Problem of the Picts,* 1955, pp.134-5.
3 P. Sawyer, *The Age of the Vikings,* 1962; *Kings and Vikings,* 1982.
4 K. Jackson, 'The Pictish Language'.
5 A. Rivet and C. Smith, *The Place-names of Roman Britain,* 1979, p.215.
6 A. Ritchie, 'Birsay Around AD 800', *Orkney Heritage,* Vol. 2, 1983.
7 H. Marwick, *Orkney Farm Names,* 1952, pp.205, 215; R. Dodgshon, *Land and Society in Early Scotland,* 1981, pp.77-89; W. Thomson, 'Ouncelands and Pennylands in Orkney and Shetland', *forth.*
8 H. Marwick, *Orkney Farm Names,* p.212.
9 J. Bannerman, *Studies in the History of Dalriada,* 1974, pp.132-146.
10 R. Lamb, 'The Orkney Trebs', in J. Chapman and H. Mytum, *Settlement in North Britain 1000 BC — AD 1000,* p.178.
11 B. Smith, 'What is a Scattald?', in B. Crawford, *Essays in Shetland History,* 1984; W. Thomson, 'Ouncelands and Pennylands in Orkney and Shetland'.
12 N. Fojut, 'Towards a Geography of the Shetland Brochs', *Glasgow Archaeological Journal,* Vol. 9, pp.49-50; B. Smith, 'What is a Scattald?', p.106.
13 St Olaf's Saga (= S. Laing, *Heimskringla*), c.99.
14 St Olaf's Saga, c.99.
15 E. Cowan, 'Caithness in the Sagas', in J. Baldwin, *Caithness: a Cultural Crossroads,* 1982, p.31.
16 E. Cowan, 'Caithness in the Sagas', pp.31-5.
17 Orkneyinga Saga (= A. Taylor, *The Orkneyinga Saga,* 1938), c.11.
18 Orkneyinga Saga, c.12.
19 Orkneyinga Saga, c.8-9.
20 Orkneyinga Saga, c.31.
21 Orkneyinga Saga, c.33.
22 Orkneyinga Saga, c.8.
23 Orkneyinga Saga, c.25.
24 Orkneyinga Saga, c.64-74.
25 Orkneyinga Saga, c.16.
26 Orkneyinga Saga, c.49.
27 J. Anderson, *The Orkneyinga Saga* (1873), 1973, introduction, pp.xxxvi-xliv; B. Crawford, 'The Earls of Orkney and Caithness and their Relations with

Scotland and Norway', unpublished Ph.D thesis, University of St Andrews, 1971; P. Topping, 'Earl Harald Maddadsson, Earl of Orkney and Caithness', *Scottish Historical Review*, Vol. lxii, 1983.

28 H. Lamb, *Climate, History and the Modern World*, 1982, pp.162-7.

29 H. Marwick, *Orkney Farm Names*, pp.229-231.

30 G. Fellows-Jensen, 'Viking Settlement in the Northern and Western Isles: the Place-name Evidence as seen from Denmark and Danelaw', in A. Fenton and H. Pálsson, *The Northern and Western Isles in the Viking World*, 1984, p.161.

31 W. Thomson, 'Ouncelands and Pennylands in Orkney and Shetland.'

32 J. Sephton, *The Saga of King Sverri of Norway*, 1899, c.104.

33 J. Gade, *The Hanseatic Control of Norwegian Commerce during the Late Middle ages*, Leiden, 1951.

34 J. Schreiner, *Pest og Prisfallen i Senmiddelalderen: et Problem i Norsk Historie*, Oslo, 1948.

35 A. Brøgger, *Ancient Emigrants*, 1929, pp.187-8.

36 Lord Henry Sinclair, Mss.rental of 1492, Orkney Archives, D2/7.

37 A. Peterkin, *Rentals of the Ancient Earldom and Bishoprick of Orkney*, 1820.

38 W. Thomson, 'Fifteenth Century Depression in Orkney: the Evidence of Lord Henry Sinclair's Rentals', in B. Crawford, *Essays in Shetland History*, 1984.

39 S. Gissel, 'Agrarian Decline in Scandinavia', *Scand. Journ. Hist.*, Vol.1, 1976; J. Schreiner, *Pest og Prisfallen i Senmiddelalderen.*

40 G. Donaldson, 'Problems of Sovereignty and Law in Orkney and Shetland', in *Miscellany Two* (Stair Society), 1984, pp.19-21, 37-40.

41 B. Crawford, 'The Earls of Orkney and Caithness and their Relations with Scotland and Norway'.

42 R. Saint-Clair, *The Saint-Clairs of the Isles*, Auckland, 1898, pp.138-162.

43 B. Crawford, 'The Earls of Orkney and Caithness and their relations with Scotland and Norway'; B. Crawford, 'Peter's Pence in Scotland', in G. Barrow, *The Scottish Tradition*, 1974; J. Anderson, *The Orkneyinga Saga*, introduction, pp.lxxvi-lxxvii.

44 J. S. Clouston, *Records of the Earldom of Orkney*, 1914, pp.15-18.

45 A. Brøgger, *Ancient Emigrants*, p.184.

46 B. Crawford, 'The Earls of Orkney and Caithness and their Relations with Scotland and Norway'.

47 H. Marwick, *The Orkney Norn*, 1929, p.xxii.

48 H. Marwick, *The Orkney Norn*, pp.xxvi-xxvii; A. Fenton, *The Northern Isles*, 1978, pp.616-622.

49 H. Marwick, *The Orkney Norn*.

50 A. Fenton, *The Northern Isles*.

51 E. Marwick, *The Folklore of Orkney and Shetland*, 1975.

52 F. Wainwright, *The Northern Isles*, pp.190-1.

53 B. Crawford, 'Sir David Sinclair of Sumburgh: Foud of Shetland and Governor of Bergen Castle', in J. Baldwin, *Scandinavian Shetland: an Ongoing Tradition?*, 1978.

54 H. Marwick, *The Orkney Norn*, p.xxv.

55 B. Crawford, 'William Sinclair, Earl of Orkney, and his Family,' in K. Stringer, *Essays on the Nobility of Medieval Scotland*, 1985.

56 W. Thomson, 'Fifteenth Century Depression in Orkney: the Evidence of Lord Henry Sinclair's Rentals'.

57 P. Anderson, *Robert Stewart, Earl of Orkney, Lord of Shetland*, 1982.

58 J. S. Clouston, *History of Orkney*, 1932, p.294.

59 J. S. Clouston, *Records of the Earldom of Orkney*, 1914, p.283.

60 P. Anderson, *Robert Stewart, Earl of Orkney, Lord of Shetland.*
61 A. Peterkin, *Notes on Orkney and Zetland,* 1822, pp.62-5.
62 P. Anderson, *Robert Stewart, Earl of Orkney, Lord of Shetland,* pp.165-186.
63 J. S. Clouston, *History of Orkney,* p.329.
64 G. Donaldson, 'Problems of Sovereignty and Law in Orkney and Shetland'.
65 H. Marwick, *Merchant-Lairds of Long Ago,* 1939 (2 vols.).
66 W. Thomson, *Kelp-making in Orkney,* 1983.
67 W. Thomson, *The Little General and the Rousay Crofters,* 1981, pp.30-41.

Chapter 11

1   Robert S. Barclay, *The Population of Orkney 1755-1961* (Kirkwall, 1965), pp. 8,10.
2   Orkney Library. *Pundlar Process,* Memorial and Abstract of the Proof, 1 May 1758, p.42; Additional Memorial for James Douglas, Earl of Morton, 13 November 1758 p.34.
3   H. Marwick, *Merchant Lairds of Long Ago* (Kirkwall, 1936, 1939). W. P. L. Thomson, *Kelp-making in Orkney* (Stromness, 1982). Alistair J. Durie, Linen Spinning in the North of Scotland 1746-1773, *Northern Scotland,* Vol. 2, No. 1 (1974-5), pp.20, 30, 33.
4   R. P. Fereday, *Orkney Feuds and the '45* (Kirkwall, 1980), pp.47-53.
5   R. P. Fereday, William Balfour after the '45, His Relations with the Earl of Morton and Sir Lawrence Dundas, *Orkney Heritage,* Vol. 1 (1981), pp.27-30.
6   Joseph Forster, *Members of Parliament, Scotland 1357-1882* (1882).
7   Sir Charles Elphinstone Adam, *View of the Political State of Scotland in the last Century* (1887). Orkney Archives, D13/4/19, Members Elected 1730-1811. Scottish Record Office, GD. 51/1/198/3, J. Balfour to Henry Dundas, 18 October 1795. Irene Rosie, *Thomas Balfour, M.P. for Orkney and Shetland 1835-37* (Kirkwall, 1978) pp.16, 18.
8   Peter Anderson, *Robert Stewart, Earl of Orkney, Lord of Shetland* (Edinburgh, 1982), pp.33-35.
9   O.L. Roland St Clair, *Orcadian Families,* Typescript genealogies compiled before the First World War. J. Smith, *The Church in Orkney* (Kirkwall, 1907).
10 O.L. *Pundlar Process,* State of the Process, 12 November 1757, p.223, William Honyman's evidence given in 1753.
11 R. P. Fereday *op. cit.* (1980), Chapters 1, 2 and 10.
12 B. H. Hossack, *Kirkwall in the Orkneys* (1900), p.218.
13 Edmund H. Burrows, *The Moodies of Melsetter* (Cape Town 1954), pp.23-24.
14 R. P. Fereday *op. cit.,* (1981) pp.42-52.
15 Hossack mentions all these Balfours. Orkney Archives contain a mass of further information in the well-catalogued Balfour Papers.
16 Based on the list in J. Mooney's *Kirkwall Charters* (1950) with the addition of John Riddoch, who is mentioned as Provost in the Kirkwall Burgh Council Minutes for 1764-1776. The following Minute Book is missing.
17 Ian MacInnes, The Alexander Graham Case, The Royal Burgh of Kirkwall and the Unfree Traders of Stromness, *Orkney Heritage* (1981), p.108. J. Storer Clouston, *A History of Orkney* (Kirkwall, 1932), p.343.

18 B. H. Hossack pp.155-6. William Traill, *A Genealogical Account of the Traills of Orkney* (Kirkwall, 1883). Thomas W. Traill, *Genealogical Sketches* (1902).
19 John Henderson, *Caithness Family History* (Edinburgh, 1884), pp.239-240.
20 James T. Calder, *History of Caithness* (Wick, 1861), 2nd edition 1887), p.250-254. O.A. D2/9/2, Bond repayable Candlemas 1820.
21 Corinne J. Coghill, *George Traill, M.P. for Orkney and Shetland 1830-1835* (Kirkwall, 1980).
22 W. P. L. Thomson, *The Little General and the Rousay Crofters* (Edinburgh 1981) pp.11-14.
23 Memorial tablet on the north side of the tower arch in the parish church of St Stephen by Saltash, Cornwall.
24 Peter Anderson *op. cit.* pp.32, 131, 132.
25 B. H. Hossack, p.281.
26 G. E. C. *Complete Baronetage.* Vol. IV, 1665-1707 (1904), p.355.
27 R. P. Fereday (1980), Chapters 3 to 10 and pp.125-7; (1981), p.48.
28 Orkney Church Records, No. 9, 4/7, Kirkwall Presbytery (1716-38), p.214 November 1716.
29 Sir John Barrow, *The Mutiny and Piratical Seizure of H.M S. Bounty* (1831), Folio Society edition 1977) pp.65, 135, 259.
30 North Riding Record Office, Zetland (Dundas) Archive, ZNK/X/1/2/83, John Pringle to Sir Lawrence Dundas, 5 August 1766.
31 P. N. Sutherland Graeme, *Pateas Amicis, The Story of the House of Graemeshall in Orkney* (Kirkwall 1936), p.40.
32 O.A. D13/4/19, Minutes of the Michaelmas Head Court at Kirkwall, 11 November 1760.
33 B. H. Hossack, p.176.
34 S.R.O. GD. 150/2513, Supplication, 2 March 1715. D. Defoe, *An Account of the Conduct and Proceedings of the Late John Gow . . .* (1725, reprinted Kirkwall, 1890, and Edinburgh, 1980), p.33-35.
35 E. W. Marwick, *The Folklore of Orkney and Shetland* (1975), pp.156-8.
36 O.A. D2/5/7 Honyman v Halyburton, 4 January 1762.
37 J. Storer Clouston, *History of Orkney* (1932) pp.368-9.
38 The Scottish Nation, *Bibliographical History of the People of Scotland,* P.489. Peace's Orkney and Shetland Almanac (1907), p.143.
39 O.A. D2/23/6, Abstract of the Minute of Sale, 26 October 1827.
40 Hugh Marwick, The Baikies of Tankerness, *Orkney Miscellany* Vol. 4 (1957) pp.27-47 O.A. D2/4/13 Marriage Contract (1785).
41 P. N. Sutherland Graeme, George Eunson — Orkney's 18th Century Firebrand, *Orkney Miscellany* Vol. 4 (1957) pp.1-16. J. Forster, *op. cit.,* (1882), p.19.
42 Hugh Marwick, The Feas of Clestran, *Proceedings of the Orkney Antiquarian Society* Vol. XI (1932-3), pp.31-38. D. Defoe, *op. cit.,* pp.35-53.
43 R. P. Fereday (1980) *passim.* Orkney Sheriff Court Records, SC 11/5/31.
44 O.A. D2/6/2 Thomas Balfour of Elwick's Account Current with David Balfour W.S. Item under 4 August 1784.
45 Joseph Forster (1882), p.207. Memorial Tablet in north aisle of nave of St Magnus Cathedral, Kirkwall. *Peace's Orkney and Shetland Almanac* (1906). J. G. Lockhart, *The Life of Sir Walter Scott,* Chapter VII. E. W. Marwick's article on the Laings in *The Orcadian* 30 November 1967.
46 Orkney Church Records, No. 9 Kirkwall Presbytery (1716-38) p.428, 4 June 1736.
47 O.A. D2/9/16 Thomas Balfour to Mrs Balfour, 12 January 1778. D2/17/3, Thomas Balfour appointed factor (after 26 October) 1778. D2/15/6,

Inventory of lands disponed by David Covingtrie, 26 October 1778. D2/10/2, Disposition and Assignation, 11 May 1784.

48 B. H. Hossack, pp.138-9. Jane Ross, *Orkney and the Earls of Morton, 1643-1707* (Kirkwall, 1977), pp 18-23.
49 Orkney Sheriff Court Records, SC 11/5/33, Petition for the Burgh of Kirkwall, 1705.
50 Hugh Marwick, *Merchant Lairds of Long Ago* (Kirkwall) 1936, 1939 p.6.
51 O.S.C.R. SC 11/5/30, draft letter David Traill of Sabay (to Robert Douglas?) c. 1722 referring to the election of 1702. B. H. Hossack, p.139.
52 Sir Charles Elphinstone Adam, *View of the Political State of Scotland in the last Century* (1887), comments on Orkney Freeholders in 1788.
53 B. H. Hossack, p.351.
54 S.R.O. CE/8/9, p.71, letter from Excise Office, Edinburgh, 25 August 1807. B. H. Hossack p.352.
55 O.L., *Orkney Law Papers* 1821-33, No. 8, Defences for Charles Spence against Mr George Richan, 16 February and 2 March 1831.
56 G. Barry, *History of the Orkney Islands* (1805) pp. 377-8. W. P. L. Thomson, *Kelp-Making in Orkney* (1983) pp.48-49, 101-102. P.R.O. London, H.O. 50/43, Petition dated Kirkwall, 4 June 1798.
57 Holden Furber, *Henry Dundas, First Viscount Melville 1742-1811 Political Manager of Scotland, Administrator of British India* (1931). Alexander Murdoch, *The People Above. Politics and Administration in Mid-Eighteenth Century Scotland* (Edinburgh, 1980), pp.128-131, 133, 136-7.
58 Roland St Clair, *Orcadian Families* pp.1192-3.
59 Joan Heddle, *The Family of Heddle, of Cletts and Melsetter* Typescript in Orkney Archives.
60 P.R.O. London, H.O. 50/43 Abercromby to Henry Dundas 23 July 1798.
61 O.A. D2/17/13 Details of marriage and children.
62 *The Statistical Account of Scotland 1791-1799,* edited by Sir John Sinclair, Volume XIX, *Orkney and Shetland* (1978), p.179.
63 O.A. D2/4/12 Ligonier to Thomas Balfour, 27 September 1775.
64 O.A. D2/6/2, Thomas Balfour's Account, 4 August 1784, shows that half the price of Sound was borrowed from J. Balfour.
65 J. Burke, *History of the Commoners of Great Britain and Ireland,* Vol. III, p.136.
66 W. P. L. Thomson, *The Little General and the Rousay Crofters* (Edinburgh, 1981), pp.8-10.
67 C. E. S. Walls, An 18th Century Orkney Litigation, *P.O.A.S.,* Vol. X (1931-2) pp.59-69. Hugh Marwick, *Merchant Lairds of Long Ago* (1936, 1939), pp.4, 8, 24-6, 96-7, 103.
68 R. P. Fereday, *op. cit.* (1980), pp.25-6.
69 *ibid.,* pp.29-30.
70 Orkney Church Records No. 1, 1/1. Synod of Orkney and Caithness Minutes, p.151, 6 July 1717. *Ibid.,* No. 9, 4/7, Kirkwall Presbytery Records, pp.36-7, 7 May, 4 June 1718.
71 John Smith, *Church in Orkney* (1907), pp.76-7.
72 *Ibid.,* pp.190-1, 272-3, 215-6.
73 Ambula Coram Deo, The Journal of Bishop Geddes for the year 1790, edited by Rev. William James Anderson, *The Innes Review,* Vol. VI, No. II, 1955. Bishop Geddes declined Sutherland's invitation to dinner.
74 A Day in Burray, *The Orcadian,* 27 July, 1889. Orkney tradition recalled by Professor Ronald Miller, Stromness, in 1982.
75 Local tradition remembered by Peter Leith, Appiehouse, Stenness in 1973. Scarth was fined in his youth for immorality, see Kirkwall Kirk Session Minutes, 10 July 1820.

76 Tradition related by the last Traill of Holland to John Mooney, Cromwell Cottage, Kirkwall, and passed on to the author by Miss Embla Mooney in 1981.
77 B. H. Hossack, pp.268-9.
78 H. Marwick, The Feas of Clestran, *P.O.A.S.,* Vol. XI (1932-3) p.36.
79 *Glasgow Courant,* No. 46, 18-25 August 1746, page 2 col. 1.
80 O.A. D15/Box 1/Bundle 6/item 1. Mr John Dickenson was a schoolmaster in Westray until early 1733, when he moved to teach in Stromness. Orkney Church Records No. 9, 4/8, Presbytery of Kirkwall (1738-81), p.20, 3 October 1739, indicates that M. Mackenzie left KGS in 1739.
81 Orkney Library, *Pundlar Process,* page 167, evidence of Thomas Balfour, merchant in Kirkwall.
82 *Northern Notes and Queries or the Scottish Antiquary,* Vol. IV, No. 15, 1889, p.125. The lairds were assisted by the 'Dons' i.e. families reputed to be descended from survivors of the Spanish Armada wreck.
83 O.A. D2/18/13, William Balfour, Edinburgh, to Mrs Balfour Younger of Trenaby, Westray, 31 July 1759.
84 Fasti Academiae Marischallanae Aberdonensis . . . 1593-1866 Edited by P. J. Anderson, *New Spalding Club,* Aberdeen, 1889-1898, Vol. II, 337, 338. O.A. D2/23/14, David Balfour, Edinburgh, to Mrs Balfour of Trenaby, 10 and 21 March 1774.
85 O.A. D2/9/4, Bill to the Mr Balfours, Academy, Harrow on the Hill, March to May 1795.
86 O.A. D2/23/6 Draft letters rebuking Edward, 1796. D2/9/7, Mary Balfour, Edinburgh to Mrs Manson Junior, Kirkwall, 12 April 1795.
87 O.A. D2/7/13, Letters from Mary and Ann Balfour. For the relatives in Flanders see D2/21/11, Mr Jean Balfour Ghent to David Balfour, Shapinsay, 2 December 1860 and Letterbook 48 pp.902-3.
88 *Edinburgh Magazine and Literary Miscellany,* June 1819, pp.485-6.

Chapter 13

1 Corporal John Downie, who settled in the town after the Napoleonic Wars, left a legacy for educating needy children. In 1887 this was amalgamated with two other legacies and called 'Downie's Mortification'. Finstown received its name from an Irish soldier called David Phin who settled there about the year 1822. Phin, who had fought at the battle of Waterloo, first of all set up a school in Harray, and subsequently built a cottage in Firth where he opened a public-house which became known as 'Phin's' — the present-day Pomona Inn in Finstown.

2 Robert Rendall in 'Orkney Crofter', *Country Sonnets* (1947).

List of Figures

page

Fig. 1. Skara Brae 21

Fig. 2. Plans of selected Orcadian chambered tombs 22

Fig. 3. Liddle house 24

Fig. 4. Grain earth house 26

Fig. 5. Interior of Bu Broch. 1 Vestibule; 2 Peripheral Rooms; 3 Kitchen Service Area; 4 Hearth and Cooking Tank; 5 Cupboard; 6 Storage Compartments 27

Fig. 6. The Pictish symbol stone from the Brough of Birsay 29

Fig. 7. The Pictish house at Buckquoy 30

Fig. 8. A Viking grave at the Broch of Gurness 32

Fig. 9. Ard share fron Neolithic/Early Bronze Age Isbister (a) and an Early Iron Age 'mattock' from Bu (b). (scale 1:4) 33

Fig. 10. Leaf-shaped (a) and barbed and tanged (b) arrowheads from Unstan. (1:1) 34

Fig. 11. Top and bottom rotary querns (a and b), saddle quern and rubber (c), trough quern (d), mortar (e), pestle, grinder and pounder (f-h). All from the Broch of Gurness. (a-e 1:15; f-h 1:4) 35

Fig. 12. Neolithic pots from Isbister (a and b), an Early Iron Age one from Bu (c), a Pictish one from Howe (d), and a pot lid from Gurness (e). (1:5) 37

Fig. 13. Early Iron Age crucible from Bu (a) (3:4) and mould for casting Pictish ring-headed pins from Gurness (b) (1:1) 39

Fig. 14. Bone implements and a needle from the Broch of Gurness (a-d) and spindle whorls and a loom weight from Pictish/Viking Saevar Howe (e-g), (1:2) 40

Fig. 15. Gold discs and amber beads of the Early Bronze Age from the Knowes of Trotty (a), jet button, ring and bone beads from Neolithic/Early Bronze Age Isbister (b-d), bronze Viking and Pictish ring-headed pins and an Early Iron age globular-headed one from the Broch of Gurness (e-g), and three bone pins from Pictish/Viking Saevar Howe (h). (1:2) 41

Fig. 16. Bronze penannular brooch (a), tortoise brooch (b), and rings (c-g) from the Broch of Gurness. (1:2) 42

Fig. 17. An Early Iron Age long-handled comb from Bu (a) and a composite one from Pictish/Viking Saevar Howe (b). (1:2) 43

Fig. 18. Stone gaming board from Pictish/Viking Buckquoy (a) (1:3) and a bone die from Gurness (b) (1:2) 44

Fig. 19. Polished stone mace head and axe from Neolithic/Early Bronze Age Isbister (a and b), Early Bronze Age dagger from Flanders Moss, Wasbister (c), and a sword pommel (d) and guard (e) from the brochs of Lingro and Gurness. (1:2) 46

Fig. 20. Unidimensional variation in prehistoric Orkney and comparative British male crania 57

Fig. 21. Multivariate evaluation of ten cranial measurements for early Orkney samples and some comparative series. (Left = males; right = females). Canonical axes 1 and 2. 58

Fig. 22. Multivariate evaluation of non-metric cranial traits in Orkney Norse and some comparative samples 60

Fig. 23. Plot of O against B frequencies (of the ABO blood-group system) for a number of Scottish regions and surnames, together with 'old Orkney' and 'Scots' surnames 62

Fig. 24. (a). Average crude birth rate, 1971 and 1972. The rate gives the number of births per 1,000 population. Births data are corrected for usual residence of mother. *Source of data:* Registrar General (Scotland), Annual Reports 1971 and 1972. (After Jones, 1975) 67

Fig. 24. (b). The 20-34 age group as a percentage of the over-50 age group, 1971. *Source of data:* 1971 Census of Scotland, County Reports 68

Fig. 25. Proportions (shaded areas of circles) in 1861 of marriages in which both partners were born in the same Orkney parish. (After Boyce *et al.*, 1973) 69

Fig. 26. Distribution of distances between residences at time of marriage of husbands and wives marrying on Sanday between 1855 and 1965. (50-mile circles marked from the south end of Sanday) 71

Fig. 27. Proportions (shaded areas of circles) of grey, intermediate, dark- and light-blue eyes (Martin categories 12, 14-16) for Orkney and other areas of Britain. (After Boyce *et al.*, 1973) 74

Fig. 28. Genetic distances of regional Orkney samples (using combined serological data) 78

Fig. 29. Variation in the Orkney and Scottish frequencies for cardiovascular and ischaemic heart disease 83

Fig. 30. Variation in British and other European breast, stomach, oesophagus and prostate cancer rates 85

Fig. 31. Genetic distance analysis shows that the Orkney population stands rather apart from the eight others 103

Fig. 32. Genetic relationship of Orkney to the eight populations 105

Fig. 33. The four main types of fingerprint pattern 108

Fig. 34. Genetic distance plot based on gene frequencies for six blood group and four serum protein and enzyme systems 110

Fig. 35. Dermatoglyphic distance (males) based on the frequencies of four fingerprint patterns (Fig.1). [Data source: Harvey & Suter (1983)] 112

Fig. 36. Dermatoglyphic distance (females) 112

Fig. 37. Hair colour variation. [Data source: Suter (1979), Harvey & Suter (unpubl.), Pálsson & Schwidetzky (1975)] 114

Fig. 38. Eye colour variation. [Data source: Harvey & Suter (unpubl.), Muir (1977), Pálsson & Schwidetzky (1975)] 115

Fig. 39. Distribution of ages at death in Birsay, in ten-year intervals (males) 126

Fig. 40. Distribution of ages at death in Birsay, in ten-year intervals (females) 127

Fig. 41.

Fig. 42. Orkney in relation to north-west Europe 136

Fig. 43. Some 18th-century lairds' houses 229

Fig. 44. The Holm of Papay (Papa) — was it Findan's desert island? 282

330

List of Photographs

Cover: Lobster Fishing *(Keith Allardyce)*

between pages 2 and 3:
1 (a) West Shore, Stromness *(R. S. Moore)*
   (b) The Harray Loch *(R. S. Moore)*
2 (a) Yesnaby *(R. S. Moore)*
   (b) Sandwick, South Ronaldsay *(R. S. Moore)*
3 (a) Making Orkney Cheese: Mrs Jamesina Laird of Hozen, Dounby *(Chick Chalmers)*
   (b) Drying cuithes: James Wilson, Stromness *(Chick Chalmers)*
4 Harvest of corn *(drawing by Sylvia Wishart)*

between pages 10 and 11:
5 (a) House at Skara Brae *(Mike Brooks)*
   (b) Knap of Howar, Papa Westray *(R. Baikie)*
6 (a) Maeshowe *(Mike Brooks)*
   (b) The Tomb of the Eagles, Isbister *(Mike Brooks)*

between pages 26 and 27:
7 (a) The Ring of Brodgar *(Mike Brooks)*
   (b) Bronze Age house, Liddle *(Mike Brooks)*
8 (a) Interior, Bu Broch, *(North of Scotland Archaeological Services)*
   (b) Broch of Gurness from the air *(Phoenix Photos)*

between pages 50 and 51:
9 (a) Brough of Birsay from the air *(Royal Commission of Ancient Monuments for Scotland)*
   (b) St Magnus Church, Egilsay *(Ernest W. Marwick)*
10 (a) Yarpha, Orphir *(W. Hourston)*
   (b) Cutting the crop, Rendall *(R. Baikie)*
11 (a) Quoys, Graemsay, with Hoy High lighthouse in the background *(W. Hourston)*
   (b) The Flaws family of Wyre, who operate the Rousay, Egilsay and Wyre ferry service *(G. Flaws)*
12 (a) Harvest time: the North Ronaldsay sculptor Ian Scott works on the family farm at Antabreck *(Arthur Kinloch)*

331

x

between pages 122 and 123:
13 (a) A Stromness fisherman and his wife *(J. Ellison)*
14 (a) Stromness lifeboat crew, c. 1930 *(W. Hourston)*
   (b) The Housegarth Band *(S. Davies)*

between pages 138 and 139:
15 Printer and song-writer Allie Windwick at one of the old
   linotype machines formerly used by *The Orcadian (Chick
   Chalmers)*
16 Three people with a great knowledge of traditional Orkney
   life and events: (above) Willie Thomson of Neven, North
   Ronaldsay *(Chick Chalmers),* (below left) Mrs Margaret
   Ann Clouston *(H. T. L. Russell),* (below right) Peter
   Leith Snr. of Appiehouse, Stenness.

between pages 170 and 171:
17 Four Westraymen *(G. Burgher)*
18 (a) Poet and niece: George Mackay Brown and Judith
   (Paddy Hughes)
   (b) The poet Ann Scott-Moncrieff
   (c) Mrs Johina Leith, writer on traditional island life
   (d) Margaret Tait, film-maker *(Ernest Shearer)*

between pages 178 and 179 (colour):
C1 Willie Marwick, Stromness, who witnessed the scuttling of
   the German Fleet in Scapa Flow in 1919 *(Bob Michelson)*
C2 Bill Velzian, Stromness, Orkney chair maker *(Nicol Firth)*
C3 Mrs Helen Philcox, Stromness, spinning *(Nicol Firth)*
C4 At an Orkney wedding: the bride, groom and Master of the
   Household who prepares the traditional bride's cog for
   the guests to drink. Willie Laughton was the Master of
   the Household at the wedding of Joy and John Tait of
   Holm *(Charles Tait)*

between pages 186 and 187:
19 (a) the writer Bessie Skea ('Countrywoman')
   (b) the writer Christina M. Costie (centre), with her sister
   Bessie (left) and brother Hubert (right) *(J. Sinclair)*

20 (a) Elizabeth Miller, proprietrix of *The Orcadian (J. Miller)*
   (b) Ola M. Gorie pioneered Orkney silverware *(S. Chirgwin)*
   (c) Jean Campbell, community drama producer, took part in
   many plays
   (d) Ingirid Jolly, singer and musician *(S. Burgher)*

between pages 202 and 203:
21 Lord Birsay *(Chick Chalmers)*
22 (a) the writer Ernest W. Marwick and his wife Janette *(Chick Chalmers)*
   (b) John D. Mackay, Headmaster of Sanday School

between pages 218 and 219:
23 (a) Captain Robert Sutherland, Head of the Sea School at Stromness
   (b) A veteran of the Cape Horn run in the days of sail: Captain David Peace with relatives
24 (a) Throwing up the Ba' at the Market Cross, Kirkwall *(Phoenix Photos)*
   (b) Two well-known figures in Orkney affairs: former MP Jo Grimond and former Islands Councillor Alex. T. Annal *(Ian Gow)*

between pages 226 and 227:
25 (a) The house of Clestrain, Orphir, where John Rae was born *(Tom Kent)*
   (b) The old house of Cursetter, Firth *(Tom Kent)*
26 (a) Westness House, Rousay *(Tom Kent)*
   (b) Melsetter House in the island of Hoy *(Jonathan M. Gibson)*
27 Four members of the Moodie family of Melsetter: above left is Captain James Moodie RN, the 7th laird, above right the 9th laird, Major James Moodie
28 (a) A country corner: by the Brig o' Waithe, Stenness *(W. Hourston)*
   (b) In the town: the Double Houses, Stromness *(W. Hourston)*

between pages 234 and 235:
29 (a) Malcolm Laing, historian and brother of Samuel, the translator of *Heimskringla*
   (b) The Arctic explorer John Rae
   (c) William Balfour Baikie, explorer of the Niger River
   (d) His father, Captain John Baikie RN, who served in the Napoleonic Wars
30 Four figures from the 'Golden Age' of Orkney scholarship: (a) Duncan J. Robertson, (b) John Mooney *(J. Sinclair)*, (c) J. Storer Clouston, (d) Hugh Marwick *(painting by Stanley Cursiter, photographed by W. Hourston)*.

between pages 250 and 251:
31 (a) Walter Traill Dennison, writer and folklorist
   (b) Robert Rendall, poet and naturalist *(painting by Ian MacInnes, photographed by S. Chirgwin)*
   (c) William Groundwater, poet and naturalist *(W. Marr)*
   (d) Evan MacGillivray, writer and scholar
32 (a) Ex-Provost George S. Robertson of Stromness *(W. Hourston)*
   (b) Making a Ba': Jim Harrison of Kirkwall *(The Tree Studio)*
   (c) Islands Council Convener Edwin Eunson *(S. Chirgwin)*
   (d) An Orkney seafarer: John Hourie *(painting by Sylvia Dennison, photographed by S. Chirgwin)*

between pages 258 and 259:
33 Orcadians of today: quarry workers *(Chick Chalmers)*
34 At the Show 1 *(S. Burgher)*
35 At the Show 2 *(S. Burgher)*
36 A young Orcadian *(L. Burgher)*

334

Acknowledgements for Photographs

Keith Allardyce—cover; R. S. Moore, Kirkwall—1(a), 1(b), 2(a), 2(b); Chick Chalmers, Edinburgh—3(a), 3(b), 15, 16(a), 21, 22(a), 33; Susie Gilbertson, Kirkwall—4; Mike Brooks, Edinburgh—5(a), 6(a), 6(b), 7(a), 7(b); R. Baikie, Rendall—5(b), 10(b); NOSAS—8(a); Phoenix Photos—8(b), 24(a); RCAMS—9(a); Orkney County Library—9(b), 10(a), 11(a), 14(a), 25(a), 26(a), 28(a), 32(a); Margaret Flaws, Wyre 11(b); Arthur Kinloch, Glasgow—12; Stromness Museum—13, 20(c), 29(b); S. Davies—14b; Mrs I. Wick, St Rognvald House, Kirkwall—16(b); Peter Leith, Stenness—16(c), 18(c); G. Burgher—17; Judith Dixon—18(a); Michael Scott-Moncrieff—18(b); Bob Michelson, Hamburg—C1; Mr and Mrs J. Tait, Holm—C4; J. R. K. Foubister, Tankerness, Miss J. Isbister, Holm, and Margaret Davidson, Mintlaw—19(b); J. Miller—20(a); S. Burgher—20(d), 34, 35; Sanday School—22(b); Eoin Scott, Redland—23(b); National Galleries of Scotland—29(a); Carrick House Collection—29(d); Lodge Kirkwall Kilwinning—29(c); Elizabeth Gore-Langton—30(a); Rev. Harald Mooney—30(b); Cmdr Erlend Clouston—30(c); Tankerness House Museum—31(a); Stromness Academy—31(b); William Groundwater, Kirkwall—31(c); Ingegerd MacGillivray, Stockholm—31(d); John Robertson, Kirkwall—32(b); L. Burgher—36.

The editors also wish to express their thanks for assistance to Mr Bryce Wilson; Mrs R. Rosie, Hornersquoy, Kirkwall; Mr and Mrs J. D. Eunson, Hornersquoy, Kirkwall; Mr Archie Bevan, Stromness Academy; Mr Rowan McCallum, Orkney Islands Council; Mr and Mrs Roderick Thorne, Sanday; Mr David Bain, Kirkwall; Mrs Diana Reynolds, RCAMS; Mr and Mrs Stuart Lindsay, Inverness; and to the staffs of Orkney County Library and Archives, Tankerness House Museum, Stromess Museum, *The Orcadian* and BBC Radio Orkney.

Acknowledgements for Photographs

List of Tables

Page

Table 1. Some demographic information on Orcadians, past and present. *Data from Hedges (1982) 56

Table 2. Stature* in Norse and recent Orkney male samples, compared with some Scottish and Scandinavian groups 61

Table 3. Stature distribution by name in Deerness males (% and average) 64

Table 4. Overall stature in Deerness males and females, relative to Orkney/Scots names 64

Table 5 Variation in physique: Deerness, Westray and the U.K. 65

Table 6. Hair colour (%) for Orkney, Scotland and Iceland 72

Table 7. Variation in hair colour between islands 72

Table 8. Comparison of reduced (pooled) categories of eye colour for Orkney and northern Britain 73

Table 9. Eye-colour variation: Orkney and Shetland school children (M + F) 73

Table 10. Frequency (%) for Orkney and some comparative samples. Both sexes are combined unless specified (European data from Harvey and Suter, 1983) 75

Table 11. Some Orkney blood group frequencies in relation to surnames (using data of Allan and Lewes) 77

Table 12. IgG (Gm) frequencies (in %) for regional Scottish and Northern Isles samples (Izatt, 1973) 79

Table 13. The incidence of indophenol oxidase variants in some European samples 80

Table 14. Some 'colour blindness' frequencies — Northern Britain (in %) 81

Table 15. Regional variation in 'colour blindness' for Orkney. (N = number in sample) 81

Table 16. Non-taster frequencies for Orkney and some other British samples (%) 82 82

Table 17. Deaths from malignant tumours in all Orkney (1967-1971) and in Deerness and the South Isles (1865-1965) 84

Table 18. Relative frequencies of mortality from malignant tumours and vascular diseases in relation to old Orkney and other surnames... 86

Table 19. Age composition of deaths from tuberculosis* in Orkney prior to 1915 (restricted sample). *Mainly pulmonary 87

Table 20. Phenotype numbers and frequencies, and gene and haplotype frequencies, in the Orkney sample 94-96

Table 21. HLA Antigen and gene frequencies 98

Table 22. Gene and haplotypes frequencies (%) of blood groups and serum proteins for Orkney, Shetland and other areas. (These frequencies, which are based on data in the corresponding table in R. J. Berry and J. L. Johnston, *The Natural History of Shetland,* are for illustration only and apart from the column of overall Orkney figures are not the data used in the distance analyses described in the text) 99

337

Table 23. Genetic distances from Orkney (7-9 loci) $\times$ 10^4 100
Table 24. Genetic distances from Orkney (13 loci) $\times$ 10^4 102
Table 25. Details of the physical anthropological study of Faroe Islanders conducted by the British Museum (Natural History) in association with Odense University, Denmark 1977-79 109
Table 26. Genetic distances—ranked from Orkney 109
Table 27. Dermatoglyphic distances—ranked from Orkney 113
Table 28. Measures of central tendency of ages at death: Modal Class, Mean and Median, deaths above age four years 129

Index

Abkhazia 132
ABO blood-group system 63, 76-78, 93
Agricultural Revolution 223, 269
Ágrip 200
Albania 154
Aleutian Islands 132
Alfred the Great 164
amber 25, 42
amphora 52
Anderson, Joseph 152
Aneirin 169
Angus (county) 169
antibodies 90-91
Aphrodite 143
Arabia 138
armlets 44
Armorica 159
arrowheads 34, 45
Arthur, King 169
Askeberg, Fritz 163, 164
Athelstan 178
Atlakviða 195
Atlamál 195
auger 38
Australia 3
awls 38
axe heads 45
Ayre, Brough of 45

Ba' 168
Baikie family 236
Balfour, Colonel Thomas 230, 239-40
Balfour, David 230, 252-3
Balfour, John 227, 228, 230
Balfour, William 228, 230
Balfour family 228-30
Bali 2
Balor 183
Barry, Rev. George 121, 249
Barra 173
barrows 51
Bateson, Gregory 2
beads 44
Beaker Folk 25
beakers 55
Beaker period 55
Bear Stone 55
Beaquoy 24

Beddoe, John 70
Bergen 216, 219
Bergh, Richard 146
Bernard of Kamsto 157
Berriedale 47, 275
Berry, R. J. 4, 131
Berwick 124
Bessie Millie 173
birch 47, 275-7
Birkeli 178
Birsay 1, 12, 25, 29, 30, 31, 32, 146
Birsay, Broch of 29, 31
Birsay, Lord 4
Bjarni Kolbeinsson, Bishop 199, 200, 205
Bjorn Hítdœlakappi 163
Black Death 144, 217, 218
Blackhammer 23
Black Sea 158
Black Stones of Iona 155
Blindheim, Charlotte 178, 179
blubber 34
Boardhouse, Loch of 146
Bookan-type tombs 23
bones 49, 55, 59, 152
borg 28
Borwick, Broch of 170
Bothwell, Bishop Adam 220, 227
Böðvarr 201
Bragi Boddason 182, 197
Brand, Rev. J. 246-7
brachycephalics 55
Breedakirk 149
Breetaness 149
Bridesness 149
Brigantes 148
Brigit 148
Britain 143, 159
Brittany 159
brochs 26, 27, 28, 49, 125, 151, 160, 168, 211
bronze 38, 43
Bronze Age 24, 25, 33, 34, 38, 42, 55, 107, 154, 155, 160, 161, 168
Brodgar, Ring of 23, 25, 52
Brown, George Mackay 6, 8, 174
Bruntland 170
Brusason, Earl Rognvald 10

brushwood knots 203, 204
Brydekirk 148
Brythonic (languages) 159, 162, 168, 191
Brøgger, A. W. 7, 9
Bu 26, 27, 28, 33, 36, 38, 49, 50
Buchan 177
Buckquoy 12, 30, 31, 32, 49, 50
Bugge, Alexander 165
burials 25, 28, 31, 32
burnt mounds 24
Burray 45
Burrian 45

Caithness 51, 121, 133, 137, 160
Campston 157
Canada 3, 119
Candlemas 150
Cannigall 162
Cantick Head 162
caora 167
Capper, D.P. 9
Carbisdale, Battle of 125, 168
Catterick 169
cattle 48, 50
cauldron 36
ceall (cill) 161
ceathair 159
cells 89
Celtic, Continental 159
Celtic, Insular 159, 162
Celts 9, 158
centenarians 119
ceremonial complexes 23
Chadwick, H. M. 167, 168, 202
Chadwick, Nora K. 186, 202
chambered tombs 21
chert 34, 36, 38
Childe, Gordon 14, 42, 44, 45, 125
Christianity 30, 31, 32, 107, 140, 148
Christiansen, Reidar Th. 171, 190, 201, 206
chromosomes 89-90
cists 28, 31, 55
Clestran (Clestrain) 235
Clickhimin 167
climate 47, 214, 269, 275
cloak-fastener 180
Clontarf, Battle of 137, 168, 204, 213
Clouston, J. Storer 12, 137, 138, 139, 165, 258, 259
Clouston, Mrs Margaret Ann 119
Cluness, A. T. 119
cockles 48
cod 49

Coldoch 168
colour vision deficiency ('colour blindness') 80-81
combs 45
Conall Cernach 202
Concobhar Mac Nessa 202
Connaught 202
Copenhagen 156
copper 38, 42
corn 151
Cornwall 159
courts 157
Cowie, J. R. 118, 119, 132
crab shells 49
Crawford, I. A. 175
crofts 1
Croy, Johnie 155
Cú Chulainn 194, 203
Culdees 161
Cumbrian (language) 159
Cursiter, Stanley 5
Custer, General George 3
Cutt, William Towrie 3
Cuween Hill 23

daggers 45
dances 135
Dalriada 211
'Danes' 166
Darraðarljód 204
davach 12, 211
Davis Straits 123
Deerness 54, 55, 56, 59
Deira 169
Deirdre 138
Denmark 108
Dennison, Walter Traill 142, 150, 156
desoxyribose nucleic acid (DNA) 89-90
Dicuil 107
diseases 131
distance analysis (see genetic distance)
divorce 153
Donaldson, Gordon 4
Drever, Ezekiel 2
dróttkvætt 182
Dublin 165
Duffy blood-group system 77
Dumfries 148, 154
Dundas, Henry 227
Dundas, Sir Lawrence 226, 228, 230
Dunrossness 211
Dwarfie Stane 23

eagles 52
East Giron 170

East Kilbride 148
Ecuador 132
Eday 125, 149
Eday, Calf of 26
Edda-poem 156, 183, 194, 195
Edinburgh 169
Edmonston, A. 118
egg cell 89
Egill Skalla-Grímsson 163, 201
Egilsay 10, 17
Egypt 138
Einar the Hebridean 107
Eirik Blood-axe 212, 213
Eithne 212
England 147, 160, 164
enzyme 91
Etkin, Edward 157
Eunson, Edwin 4
Europe 158
Everlasting Fight 197, 198
Evie 28, 30, 32
evil eye 173
eye colour 70, 114-5
Eyjar 188

Færeyinga Saga 107
fair 153, 154, 155
fairies 145, 147, 173-4
Falcon Stone 155
farm-names 150, 215
Faroes 76, 107-117, 131, 173, 174, 181, 182, 207, 222
Faroese language 181-2
Fea family 236-7
Fea, James 121, 271
February 150, 157
Fenton, Alexander 15, 219, 265
Fereday, R. P. 162
fertility 155
Fetlar 172
Fife 169, 177
Findan (see St Findan)
fingerprints 75-6, 108
Finland 77
Finn Arnisson 21
Fin Mac Cumhaill 183, 194
Finnmark 146
Fir Bolg 183
Firth 26
fish 133
fishing 3, 134-5
Fjalquoy 133
fjellsamer 146
Fjölsvinnsmál 184
flagstones 133

Flateyjarbók 197, 200
flax 50
flint 34, 36, 38
Florvåg, Battle of 144, 214
Flotta 124
Fojut, Noel 49
Fomorians 167, 183
Forbes clan 155
fornaldarsögur 184, 194, 198, 199
Fornyrðadrápa 199, 200, 201, 204
Forth 168
Foula 172
Four Couple Reel 135
Frakokk Moddansdóttir 191
Franklin 3
Fraser (Frysell), Alexander 157
Fraser (Frysell), Nicoll 157
Frew, Water of 168

Gaelic (language) 162
Galloway 148
Garson, J. 55
genes 89-93
genetic distance 97-105, 108
genetic drift 93, 109
genotype 91
Gesta Danorum 184, 197
glass 44
Glastonbury 178
Glims Moss 47
Gododdin 169
Goidelic (language) 159, 160, 162, 168
gold 25, 42, 51
goose 50
Gormflaith (see Hvarflöd)
Goudie, Gilbert 9
Gow, John 235
Graeme (Graham) family 234
Graemsay 149
Grain 26
grain exports 167, 217
Graunt, John 120
Gray, John 70
Gray, Thomas 137
Greek mythology 143
Greene, David 159
Greenland 119, 217
Gregory, Pope 148
Grelod 212
Grimstad, Kaaren 163, 164
Groa 212
Groat, Dr 152, 153
Grógaldr 184
Grooved Ware culture 15, 20, 21, 50
    pottery 23

growth studies 62
Gulathing Law 164
Gunn, John 8
Gurness 28, 30, 32, 45, 52
gýgr 150
gyro 150

Håkon the Good 212
Hákon Haraldsson 178
Hákon Pálsson 191
Hálogland 164
Hallr þorarinsson 195
Hamburg-Bremen 178
Hamilton, J. R. C. 167, 168
handfast marriage 154, 155
Hanseatic League 216, 217
haplotype 92
Harald Fairhair (Finehair), Haraldr hárfagri 9, 139, 164, 166, 189, 199, 200, 201
Harald Hardråde 164
Haraldr Gormsson 194
Haraldr Hákonarsson 191
Haraldr Maddaðarson (Harald Maddadsson) 191, 196, 214
Harray 23, 24, 25, 42, 45
Háttalykill 195, 196, 197, 198, 203, 204, 205
Hávamál 156
Hay clan 155
hazel 47, 275-7
head-hunting 168, 202
heather ale 195, 198
Hebrides (Western Isles) 107, 140, 192, 211, 212
Heðinn Hjarrandason 197
Heimdallr 183
Heimskringla 200, 203, 204, 237, 252
Helgi Hundingsbani 194
hen 50
Henry, Rev. R. 152
Henshall, Audrey 23
heritors 225
hermits 107
herring fishing 269
Highlands 151, 169
Hildr 185, 196, 197, 198
hillforts, vitrified 160
Hirdmanstein 157
Historia Norvegiae 9, 11, 16, 192
Hjaðningavíg 197
Högni 197
Holm of Papa Westray (Holm of Papa, Holm of Papay) 23, 139
Honyman, Robert 235

Honyman, William 227, 235
horse 48, 49, 51
Howe 28
Howmae 26
Hoy 23, 47, 185, 197
Hudson's Bay Company 119, 269-70, 271
huldrefolk 147, 173
Human Leucocyte Antigen (HLA) system 91
Hvarflöd Melkolmsdóttir 191, 196

Iberian peninsula 158
Iceland 76, 77, 107, 111, 121, 172, 207, 217, 222
impignoration 13, 218
Indo-European (language) 159
influenza 130, 133
Iona 155, 177
Iran 155
Ireland 77, 107, 143, 147, 155, 159, 160, 173, 174, 176, 207
iron 36, 38, 43, 51
Iron Age 11, 12, 26, 27, 28, 34, 36, 152, 154, 155, 160, 161, 168
Isbister 23, 33, 59, 152
Ishihara charts 80
Ívarr ljómi 197

Jackson, Anthony 16
Jackson, Kenneth 160, 191
Jakobsen, Jakob 11, 158, 160, 161, 162, 168, 189, 193
January 157
Jarlshof 167
Jerusalem 203
jet 42
Jettanas 146-7
jette 146
Johannes 178
Johnston, R. T. 2
Jón, Bishop 199
jötun 146

Kalahari 3
Kamsto (Campston) 157
Kanu 154
Karasjok 146
Kattegat 165, 166
Kautokeino 146
Kell blood-group system 77
kelp industry 122, 223, 224, 226
Ker 152
kil 161
Kilbride 148

Kirbister 10
Kirkbride 148
Kirkwall 152, 168, 225, 227
Knap of Howar 15, 20, 21, 48
Knucker Hill 162
Knugdale 162
Kolbeinn *hrúga* 199

Labraid Loingseach 167
Lag an Aonaigh (Laganeeny) 153
Laing, Malcolm 237
Laing, Samuel 237, 251-2
Lamb, Gregor 63
Lamb, Raymond 28, 31, 151
Lammas Fair 155
lamps 34
Lancers 135
Landnámabók 107
landvaettir 193, 194
Lapps 146
Leith family 139
leprosy 87
Lerwick 119
Lesliedale Moss 47
leucocytes (white cells) 91
Liddle 24, 25, 33, 47
Liddle Bog 47
Liddle Farm 47
Liestøl, Knut 190
light 150
Lingro 28
Links of Noltland 20
Linn, Loch 162
linne 162
Ljot (Ljótr *niðingr)* 191, 212
Lockwood, W. B. 180, 181
Loons, The 45
Lot, King 169
Lothian 168, 169, 170
Low, Rev. George 137, 248
Lug 183
Lugnasad 155, 156
lunulae 42
Lutheran blood-group system 77
lygisögur 184
Lyness 124-5

MacGillivray, Evan 261, 263
Mackay, John D. 4, 15, 263
Mackenzie, Bishop Murdo 235
Mackenzie, Murdoch 235-6, 243, 247
Mackintosh, W. R. 254-5, 262
Maddaðr Melmarason 191
Maelmuire 191
Maeshowe (Maes Howe) 21, 23, 52

Malcolm II 212
Man, Isle of 178, 192, 211, 212, 222
Manson, T. M. Y. 144
Märchen 170
mark 216
marriage 152, 153, 155
Marstrander, C. J. S. 165
Marwick, George 170
Marwick, Ernest W. 4, 143, 145, 146, 219, 261, 262
Marwick, Hugh 9, 11, 12, 15, 150, 158, 160, 161, 162, 168, 187, 211, 216, 219, 259, 260
mattocks 34
Matras, Chr. 180, 181
mean 128
Meath, County 153
Mecklenburgh 178
median 128
Meil, Willie 143
Melbrikta (Maelbrighde) 202
Melkolmr 191
Melsetter 228, 245
mermaids 142-4, 156
metal 34
metallurgy 25
meur-steen 156
Midhowe 28, 38
Miller, Ronald 125
MNS blood-group system 97
Moddan 191
mode 128
Montrose, Marquis of 125
Mollusca Orcadensia 1
Moodie, Captain Benjamin 228
Moodie, Captain James 228
Moodie, Captain James RN 228
moon 148
Mooney, John 258
Moray 191, 202
Morcken, Roald 164
Morkinskinna 203, 204
Morris, Chris 31
mortality pattern 125
Morton, Earls of 222, 226, 246
Muir, Edwin 5
Muirchertach 183
multiple sclerosis 19, 82
Munch, P.A. 10
mutation 92

Napoleonic Wars 270
Narbonne 196
natural selection 92-3, 132
Nechtan 149

necklaces 42
Neolithic period 12, 20-23, 33, 34, 42, 45, 48, 49, 51, 52, 55, 59, 148, 209
Nerthus 149
Newark Bay 55, 56
New Orkney Book, The 3, 263
New Zealand 3
Nicoll 157
Nidaros 218
Njals saga 204
Njörðr 149
'Nor Wast' 209
Norðreyjar 188
North Ronaldsay 26, 122, 125, 137, 149, 162
North Uist 175, 176
Northern Isles, The 10, 158
Northumbria 150, 169, 177
Norway 7, 31, 107, 140, 142, 146, 151, 164
Noust of Bigging 149
nucleotide 89
nucleus 89
nykra-vatn 173

oath 154, 155, 156
odal (udal) land tenure 137, 215, 220
Odin (Óðinn) 156, 183
Odin, Stone of 152, 154, 156, 157
O'Donovan, John 153
ogam inscriptions 29, 30
Óláfr Tryggvason 197
Old Europe 149, 151
'Old Europeans' 148
Orkneyinga Saga 53, 120, 139, 166, 187, 191, 201, 202, 205, 214
Orkney Shore 1
Ottar of Hálogaland 164
otters 47
Otterswick Bay 47, 151
Oxtro, Broch of 31

P-Celtic 159, 160, 161
Panum, P. L. 131, 132
Papa Stronsay 149
Papa Westray (Papay, Papey) 150, 166
Papae 9, 10, 149, 191, 192
Parochial Survey of Ireland 138
Pearson, Karl 130
peat deposits 47
pedwar 159
Peller 120
pennyland 216

Peterkin, Alexander 250
Peterkirk 151
Pentland Firth 29, 175
Peti 9, 192
Péttar 175
Péttlandsfjörðr 175
Petrie, George 14, 151, 156, 157, 254
Phaedrus 138
phenotype 91
Picti 44
Pictish period 36, 38, 43, 50
Pictland 150
Picts 8, 10, 11, 29, 30, 140, 166, 168, 169, 175, 192, 193, 210
Pierowall 32, 45, 167
pigment 44
pigs 48, 50, 151-2
pit-names 169
place-name studies 158-162, 168
Plato 138
polkas 135
pollen analysis 47, 48, 275
pork 150-1
Porsangerfjord 146
Portugal 52
pottery 21, 23, 25, 27, 36, 51
press gang 118
promontory forts 30
proteins 89-92
PTC 81-2
pumice 42
Pundlar Process 226, 236, 237, 260

Q-Celtic 159, 160, 161
Quadrilles 135
Quandale 25, 132
Quanterness 23, 26, 42, 59
quarry 133
Queen Victoria (dance) 135
Queenafjold 25
quern, rotary 36
quernstones 36
Quoyboon, Stone of 146
Quoyness 23, 55
quoys 215
Quoyscottie 25, 33

Rackwick 123
radiocarbon dating 32, 107
Rae, John 3
Ragnarr *loðbrok* (Ragnar Lodbrok) 165, 194
Ragnarsdrápa 197
Rath Dubh 154

razos 184
Reformation 220
Reid, R. W. 55
Rendall, Robert 1, 2, 7
Renfrew, Colin 15, 125
Rennibister 26
rentals 217
Rheinau 176
Rhine gold 195
riddarasögur 184
righ 170
Righ Knowe 170
Rigr 183
Rígsþula 183
ring 156
Ritchie, Anna 12, 30
Rinyo 20
Robertson, Duncan J. 147, 193
Robertson, ex-Provost George 119
Robertson, John 168
Rognvald, Earl (Rögnvaldr kali) 120, 184, 195, 196, 203
Rognvald of Møre 9
Rögnvaldr Eysteinsson 189
Romans 27, 52, 160, 168, 169, 170
Rousay 20, 23, 25, 28, 45, 125, 132-5, 139, 146, 147, 149, 193, 194, 207
run-rig 215

Saevar Howe 30, 31, 38, 49, 50
Sagen 171
saithe 49
Sami people 147
Sanday 4, 23, 47, 70, 77, 142, 143, 144, 151, 167, 216
Sandwick 47, 149, 168
Saxo Grammaticus 184, 197, 198
Scandinavia 36
Scapa 162
Scapa Flow 270
scattald 211
School, Sea 3
schottisches 135
Scockness, Loch of 146
Scotland 147, 159
sea-eagles 152
seal legends 172, 206
Scott, Sir Walter 145, 147, 204, 228, 230, 237, 246
seed 48
'Scottification' 161, 189, 218
Seurlus 201
Shapinsay 162, 230
sheep 48, 50

Shetland 24, 36, 59, 76, 107, 108, 118-9, 124, 131, 140, 143, 144, 158, 160, 162
sidhichean 145, 173
Sigmund Brestisson 107
Sigmundr öngull 203
Sigurd, Earl 137, 202, 212
Sigurðr the Dragon-Slayer 183, 194
Sigurðr Jórsalafari 203, 204
silver 31, 43
Sinclair, Lord Henry 219, 220
Sinclair, Sir James 220
Sjaelland 165
sjókona
Skaill, Bay of 47, 168
Skaill, Loch of 47
Skagerrak 165
Skara Brae 15, 20, 21, 42, 44, 45, 48, 49, 52, 89
Skartan, Knowe of 151
skotakollr 178
Skye 176
slaves 176
slewchan stones 170
Smyth, Alfred P. 165, 185
Snigreabhad 173
Snjófriðr (Snaefriðr) 199, 200, 201
Snorri Sturluson 193, 197, 203
soil 269
South Ronaldsay 23
Spain 52, 143
St Andrews (parish) 157, 162, 218
St Ola (parish) 28, 122
St Boniface 150
Brendan 181
Bride 148, 150
Ciaran 154
Columba 155
Findan 176, 279-283
Magnus 55, 188, 204, 213
Olaf 188
Patrick 181
Rognvald 55
Sunniva 149
Tredwell (Triduana) 149, 150
standing stones 23, 147
steatite (soapstone) 36
stefna 157
Stenness 21, 23, 152, 153, 157
Stenness, Standing Stones of 23, 52, 152
Stenwick 2
Stewart, Earl Patrick 220, 221, 222, 268
Stewart, Earl Robert 220, 221, 268
Stewart family 233-4

Stewart period 143
stones
    clan stones 155-6
    coronation stones 155
    holed stones 156
    oath-stones 154, 155, 156
    symbol stones 29, 45
Stormay 17
Straither, Burn of 162
Strip the Willow 135
Strömbäck, Dag 190, 206
Stromness 3, 162, 270
Suðreyjar 188
Summerdale, Battle of 220
surnames 60-64
Sutherland 124, 160
Sverre 214

Tacitus 149
Tailtiu (Teltown) 153, 154
Tara 155
taking the profit 173
Tarbh na Leòid 173
Taversoe Tuick 23, 42
temples 148
tenure, land 1
Thor 186
Thoth 138
Thrave 168
Three Fragments 185
Thurnam, John 55
Tiree 167, 173
tir-unga 211
tombs 52
Tomison, Governor William 3
tools 33, 36, 38
torcs 42
Torf Einar 166
Torwoodlee 168
townslands 215
Trafalgar 118
treb duke 28, 52, 168
tredan 149
treens 211
Trenaby 228, 230, 231
trolldómr 145
trollkerling 145
trolls 144-7, 173
Tromsø 164
troubadours 184
trows 144-7, 173
Tuatha Dé Danann 183
Tudor, J. R. 253-4
tunmal 215

tunvollr 215
Turville-Petre, E.O.G. 182
Twinyes 162
twyn 162
tylosis 82
Tyng 157
'Tyng and Stein' 157

Unst 119
Unstan tomb 23
Ustand ware culture 15, 20, 21, 51
urisland 12, 211
USSR 132
uvette 145
Uyeasound 119

Verran 170
Vikings 7, 8, 9, 28, 31, 43, 52, 107,
    139, 163, 166, 176, 192, 210
villages 28, 45
Votadini 168, 169
Voystown 170

Wagner, Heinrich 155
Wainwright, F. T. 10, 11, 14, 15, 158,
    160, 162, 165, 175, 176, 190,
    193, 210, 218
Wales 147, 151, 154, 159, 160, 169
Wallace, Rev. James 120, 246-7
Walls 124, 162
Wapenstein 157
Wasbister 149
water-horse 173
Watson, W. J. 149
Welsh (language) 162
Western Isles (Hebrides) 160
Westness 32, 45, 231
Westray 1, 20, 26, 32, 45, 65, 79, 124,
    162, 167
whaling 119
Wideford Hill 23
William, Bishop 120
William the Lion 214
willow 47
witchcraft 173, 207
Wood, Dr William 151
Yarso, Knowe of 23
Yeats, W. B. 138
Yell 172
Yesnaby 47, 149
Yetna-steen 146

þorfinnr Sigurðarson 187